LIVERPOOL'S HISTORIC WATERFRONT

The World's first mercantile dock system

Merseyside County Museums
Royal Commission on Historical Monuments

LIVERPOOL'S HISTORIC WATERFRONT
THE WORLD'S FIRST MERCANTILE DOCK SYSTEM

Nancy Ritchie-Noakes

RCHM SUPPLEMENTARY SERIES: 7

London   Her Majesty's Stationery Office

ISBN 0 11 701188 6

Design by Barrie Jones, ASTD

Printed in the UK for HMSO
Dd 736272   C30   8/84

Contents

List of illustrations

Abbreviations

HSLC	Historic Society of Lancashire and Cheshire
Liv CL	Liverpool City Libraries
Liv DPL	Liverpool Daily Post and Echo
MCM	Merseyside County Museums
MDHC	Mersey Docks and Harbour Company
PHS	Pejobscot Historical Society, Maine, USA
RCHM	Royal Commission on Historical Monuments (England)
(Troughton, 1810)	T. Troughton, *History of Liverpool*, 1810
Univ. Liv	University of Liverpool
WAG	Walker Art Gallery

Forewords

The Royal Commission on Historical Monuments welcomed the opportunity of being involved with the study of the Liverpool South Docks and in the preparation of a book about them. A new departure in a number of ways, our contribution marks the first time that the Commission has become involved in a major study of large scale industrial installations; further, the industrial North West is an area that the Commission has previously chosen largely to ignore. This work is also in part a documentary study of structures that have vanished rather than a report on extant buildings. This marks an interesting development in the Commission's relationship with historic buildings, especially as all here are 'late' and do not derive their interest from great antiquity.

Such, however, is easily explained by the national significance of the site and of the structures that it bore and now preserves. The Commission's Warrant requires it '... to make an inventory ... of the Monuments and Constructions ... illustrative of the contemporary culture, civilisation and conditions of life of the people of England'. The Albert Dock Warehouses are among the most spectacular remains from the heroic age of 19th-century technology; equally important, the port of Liverpool was once the daily scene of the working lives of twenty thousand people and the goal of countless seamen. Our involvement needs no justification.

This outcome represents a triumph for our policy of co-operation with other bodies, and I rejoice to contribute to this tripartite foreword. The Commission's staff have been involved with the work of the Docklands History Survey from its inception to this publication based upon it, but ours is the privilege to join in the achievement of Mrs Ritchie-Noakes and her colleagues. Probably none of the supporting organizations could, alone, have undertaken so quickly the exhaustive survey, the massive documentary research and the preparation of the book. We would welcome similar opportunities elsewhere.

The Rt Hon The Lord Adeane, PC, GCB, GCVO
Chairman, Royal Commission on Historical Monuments (England)

When the County Council made a commitment in 1980 to create the Merseyside Maritime Museum in the Albert and Canning Dock area the first important step was taken to restore life to an important part of Merseyside and Liverpool's historic dockland. We realized then that in creating new uses for Liverpool's South Docks much important evidence of the world's first enclosed dock system and of the lives of those who worked there would be lost unless a professional survey was made of the history of the docks, buildings, equipment and the documentary evidence which survived. With the cooperation of the Manpower Services Commission and the Merseyside Development Corporation a survey was begun by the County Museums Department to make sure that a record of the history of this area was retained. The preparation of this book has been greatly assisted by the work of that project. I would like to add my congratulations and thanks to Nancy Ritchie-Noakes, the author of this book who also directed the County Museums' survey of the Liverpool South Docks. My thanks are also due to the Royal Commission on Historical Monuments (England) and to Her Majesty's Stationery Office for their part in making this publication possible.
Cllr James Stuart-Cole, DL
Chairman, Merseyside County Council

Merseyside Development Corporation was set up in March, 1981 to regenerate in every sense the disused docklands of Merseyside. Parliament subsequently approved our acquisition of the South Docks Estate. This had been the heart of Liverpool's prosperity in the 19th century and our objective is to make it a living part of the city again. We are finding new uses for old buildings, land and docks. In doing so it is essential that we properly value our industrial and architectural heritage whilst introducing new enterprise and investment and fostering a resurgence of interest in the city's waterfront.

The Development Corporation gladly funded this analysis and appraisal of its estate by the County Museums Department and is delighted with this important volume. It provides new insights into the development of the dock system and will become an authoritative guide to historical information as well as a source of enjoyment to many readers.
Leslie C. Young, CBE, DL
Chairman, Merseyside Development Corporation

Author's preface and acknowledgments

Most chroniclers of the history of Liverpool have acknowledged the crucial contribution to the growth of the city made by the development of the port. Few of these authors, however, have detailed the construction and operation of the individual components of the dock system or examined their role in port expansion. The present study concentrates on these components and limits itself to an introductory examination of the building and working of the group of docks at the southern end of the system on the Liverpool shore. The South Docks, as they came to be known, evolved from the first dock built early in the 18th century at the mouth of a tidal inlet called the Pool to a three-mile-long stretch of interconnected docks, basins and graving docks by the third quarter of the 19th century. Early in the 20th century many were remodelled so as to accommodate bigger, modern ships, although ultimately to no avail. The Mersey Docks and Harbour Company closed the redundant and outmoded South Docks to commercial shipping in 1972. In 1980 Merseyside County Council opened the first phase of Merseyside Maritime Museum in the Canning Dock area and in the next year most of the rest of the South Docks were vested in Merseyside Development Corporation. Many of the new uses sought for the old docks necessitate redevelopment which should be improved by the ready availability of a digest of the docks' histories. The preparation of such a digest, which it is hoped will also be useful in other ways, is the main purpose of this book.

Its production was inspired by the work of three people: Richard Foster, Director of Merseyside County Museums, John Ritchie, Director of Development, Merseyside Development Corporation and Linda Moss Little, author of *Liverpool's South Docks*. It was mostly realized with the help of three people: my academic editors Nicholas Cooper and Keith Falconer of the Royal Commission on Historical Monuments (England), and Linda Moss Little of the Merseyside Docklands History Survey. While some few passages throughout are by one or another of these people, the whole of the chapter on Dock Architecture is by Nicholas Cooper. The rest of what I and the book owe these individuals is too great and diverse to describe here; it must suffice to record my profound thanks for guidance, invaluable criticism and forbearance. Likewise, it is not possible to detail the contributions made by all of the many other people whose help so much improved my own inadequate work. The following list of names and organizations shows the breadth of the generous and gratifying support received.

Adrian Allan, University Archives, Liverpool
Athenaeum Library, Liverpool
K. Ball, Director, Intertek Machine Technology Ltd, Liverpool
J. E. S. Benton, Reprographic Unit, Liverpool City Council
Anthony Blacklay, B Arch, Dip Arch Cons, RIBA
Dr R. A. Buchanan, Director, Centre for the Study of the History of Technology, University of Bath
C. J. Burns, Assistant Surveyor to Bridgewater Estates plc
Andy Cameron, Public Relations Dept, The Mersey Docks and Harbour Co
Jonathan Coad, MA, FSA, Inspector of Ancient Monuments, DOE
W. J. Crompton, Head of Division of Industrial Archaeology, The City of Liverpool College of Higher Education
Cubitts Northern, Bromborough, Merseyside
W. G. Curtin & Partners, Liverpool
R. W. A. Dallas of the Photogrammetric Unit of the Institute of Advanced Architectural Studies, University of York
Dr P. N. Davies, Head of Department of Economic History, University of Liverpool
C. Ellmers, The Museum of London
R. Stuart Fell, RIBA
R. S. Fitzgerald, Keeper of Industrial Archaeology, Leeds Museum of Science and Industry
F. V. Flanagan, Engineer's Dept, The Mersey Docks and Harbour Co
J. D. Fryer, M Sc, C Eng, M I Mech E, Senior Lecturer Mech Eng Dept, Sunderland Polytechnic
Thos & Jas Harrison Ltd
A. Hayman, former Manager Bridgewater Department, Manchester Ship Canal Co
Elaine J. Howarth, Senior Management Surveyor, Merseyside Development Corporation
Mrs Freda Howens, Reprographic Unit, Liverpool City Council
J. C. James, MSM Dept, The Mersey Docks and Harbour Co

Barrie Jones, DIP TD (LIV), ASTD, Designer,
    Merseyside County Museums
Dr R. J. B. Knight, Deputy Head of Printed Books and
    Manuscripts Dept, National Maritime Museum
The staff of the Municipal Research and Record Office
    Departments, Liverpool City Libraries
McTay Construction Ltd, Civil Engineering Division,
    Bromborough, Merseyside
Dr Sheila Marriner, University of Liverpool
The Mersey Docks and Harbour Company
T. M. Osborne, Merseyside Development Corporation
Tony Perry, ABIPP, Royal Commission on Historical
    Monuments (England)
J. Gordon Read, MA, DAA, Keeper of Archives,
    Merseyside County Museums
Mrs I. H. Rothwell, Merseyside Development Corporation
R. J. Rumbold, Merseyside Development Corporation
J. E. D. Saner, C Eng, F I C E, M I Mech E, S B St J, Senior
    Works Engineer, Mersey Docks and Harbour Co
Edward Sargeant, RIBA
Helen Simpson, BA, DAA, Assistant Keeper of Archives,
    Merseyside County Museums
Michael Stammers, Curator,
    Merseyside Maritime Museum
Walker Art Gallery, Liverpool
Ward, Ashcroft and Parkman, Liverpool
David Williams, Estate Manager,
    The Mersey Docks and Harbour Co
Peter Williams, ABIPP, Royal Commission on Historical
    Monuments (England)
G. A. Winckles, Merseyside Development Corporation.

Much of the research on which this publication is based
was collected by members of the Merseyside Docklands
History Survey which was funded by the Manpower
Services Commission and Merseyside Development
Corporation and sponsored by the Museums Department
of Merseyside County Council from June 1981 until June
1983. Ably directed by Erica Jones, the research assistants
who helped were: David Cropper, Paul Derby, Geoffrey
Gavan, Stephen Edwards, Evelyn Bruen-Knowles,
Andrew Parsons, Gwendoline Roberts, David Samuels,
Mark Tanner, Mary Webster and Rosalind Woodhouse.
    The modern architectural drawings in the book are by
Ken Worrall, DIP Arch (Oxford), RIBA and the maps and
diagrams by Geoff Phillips, BA (HONS).

The main source of information about the Mersey
docks is the Mersey Docks and Harbour Board Collection
deposited with the Keeper of Archives, Merseyside
County Museums, William Brown Street, Liverpool.
Much of this collection is listed and available for
consultation. In view of this, footnotes in the succeeding
text have been limited to references which are quotations
(direct and indirect), which are outside the main body of
source material or which are particularly difficult to find
within the Dock Board Collection except by use of a
detailed reference. The factual material contained in the
text has been taken mostly from the minutes of the Dock
Committee and its various sub-committees, from the Dock
Engineer's Reports, from Worked-up Papers, from Bills
and Acts and from records of disbursements. These are
detailed in the Bibliography. Also available for
consultation is the Merseyside Docklands History
Survey subject catalogue which consists largely of
transcriptions of Dock Board documents, microfilmed
drawings, archive and modern record photographs and a
number of research papers prepared by members of the
Survey team. A guide to the Docklands History Survey
is available from the Keeper of Archives, Merseyside
County Museums.

When someone tackles the subjects of Liverpool's
North Docks, the Birkenhead Docks and the comparative
histories of other British ports, the story of the South
Docks will need to be re-written. J. B. Priestley's
description of Liverpool docks applies equally to their
physical attributes and to this first attempt at a general
description and interpretation of their history: 'It was hard
to believe that by taking ship here you might eventually
reach a place of sharp outlines.' The journey must be
risked.

Editorial note

Measurements

The units employed in this book are imperial – ie inches, feet, yards and miles for linear measurement, pounds, hundredweight and tons for weight, and acres or squares of linear measurements for area. These units are adopted because they were those used in the design and construction of the docks and their fittings, and are those given in the documentary sources from which much of the information is taken. Furthermore, by reproducing the original measurements their logic as standards is apparent – eg 25-ton cranes, 60ft dock entrances – whereas the metric equivalent would frequently appear arbitrary.

LINEAR MEASUREMENT
1 inch = 25.4mm
1 foot (12 inches) = 304.8mm
1 yard (3 feet; 36 inches) = 914.4mm
1 mile (1760 yards) = 1.6km

AREA MEASUREMENT
1 acre = 0.4ha

WEIGHTS
1 pound (lb) = 453.6 grams
1 hundredweight (cwt; 112lbs) = 50.8 kilograms
1 ton (20cwt; 2240lbs) = 1016.1 kilograms

Tidal Datum in the Liverpool Docks

The datum for the depth of the docks in Liverpool is taken as the depth of the sill of the Old Dock, and is referred to throughout this book, where it occurs, as ODS. This lies at 25ft below high water of ordinary spring tides, $11\frac{1}{2}$ft below high water at neaps.

Abbreviations

DCM	Dock Committee Minutes
DER	Dock Engineer's Reports
LOR	Liverpool Overhead Railway
LRO	Liverpool Record Office
LTB	Liverpool Town Books
LWONT	Low Water Ordinary Neap Tide
MCM	Merseyside County Museums
MDC	Merseyside Development Corporation
MDHB	Merseyside Docks and Harbour Board
MDHS	Merseyside Docklands History Survey
ODS	Old Dock Sill
WALCON	West African Lines Conference
WUP	Worked-up Paper

THE DEVELOPMENT OF THE PORT OF LIVERPOOL

1   Entrance to Queen's Dock, c1800, looking east from the entrance basin.

Liverpool and Northwest England

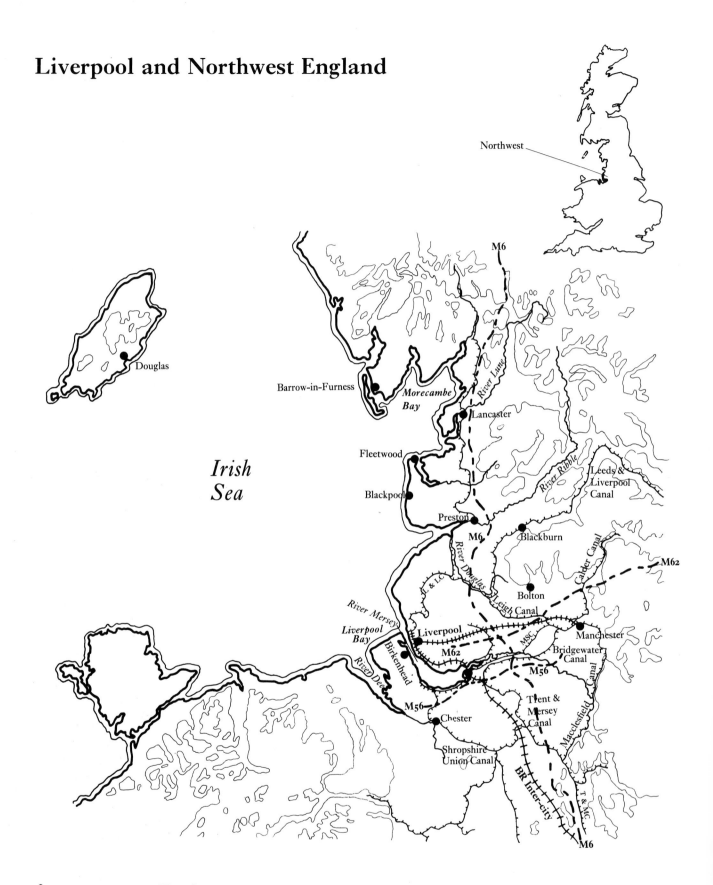

Northwest

Douglas

Irish
Sea

Barrow-in-Furness

*Morecambe
Bay*

Lancaster

River Lune

M6

Fleetwood

Blackpool

Preston

M6

River Ribble

Leeds &
Liverpool
Canal

Blackburn

Calder Canal

M62

River Douglas

Bolton

J & LC

Leigh Canal

River Mersey

*Liverpool
Bay*

Liverpool

Birkenhead

M62

MSC

Manchester

Bridgewater
Canal

M56

River Dee

M56

Chester

Trent &
Mersey
Canal

Macclesfield Canal

Shropshire
Union Canal

BR Inter-city

T & MC

M6

The historical background

In 1710 the Corporation of Liverpool undertook the building of the world's first enclosed, commercial, maritime dock. By the end of the 18th century, when no rival port had built more than a single dock for itself, Liverpool possessed a complete dock system. The success of the experiment saw the transformation, within two hundred years, of a small town beside a tidal creek into a metropolis.

The River Mersey offers to shipping both advantages and difficulties. It has a tidal range of over thirty feet, strong winds and swift currents. In the seaward approaches to the estuary, between the mouth of the Dee and the Lancashire shore to the north, are over 20,000 acres of sandbanks that dry out at low tide. In the estuary itself the shoals and the navigation channels shift constantly, and the tide race is often strong. Before the building of any dock, the height of the tides enabled ships of deep draught to reach the town quay and the slight shelter offered by the Pool, the tidal inlet to the south. On the other hand the only ships that could safely lie close to the town were those that could take the ground at low water, while ships floating at all states of the tide, far out into the Mersey, were exposed to the weather, to the hazards of the river, and to many difficulties in the discharge of their cargoes. By the late 17th century, ocean going ships in substantial numbers were sailing to Liverpool, and were increasingly finding the facilities of the primitive port inadequate to receive them.

The population of Liverpool grew from a few hundred in the late middle ages to some six thousand by 1700. When Defoe visited the town in about 1680, he was able to describe it as '. . . a large, handsome, well built and increasing or thriving town'.[1] On his second visit in 1690 he wrote that it was '. . . much bigger than at my first seeing it and, by the report of the inhabitants, more than twice as big as it was twenty years before that'.[2] Most of this increase in population (in which Liverpool shared with the country immediately round about) was due to immigration from the neighbouring counties of Lancashire and Cheshire, yet when in 1699 the Burgesses petitioned for parish status they spoke of a flight of merchants from the London plague of 1665 as a cause of Liverpool's growth.[3] Some support for their contention is given by an account of 1667 of '. . . one Mr Smith, a great sugar baker in London . . . [who was] to bring a trade of at least

£40,000 a year from the Barbadoes which formerly this town never knew'.[4] The convenience of the port for the American trade was already apparent.

In 1688 Liverpool acquired a purpose-built Custom House. Long dependent on the ancient Port of Chester for customs collection, by 1699 its trade had so far outstripped that of Chester that it was established as a head port in its own right. Imports of tobacco had grown from nothing in 1665 to 1.75 million pounds by the end of the century; of sugar from 700cwt to 11,600cwt. Exports of salt grew in the same period from 6,000 bushels to 300,000. It must have been increasingly difficult to see how further expansion of trade was possible within the limitations of the existing port, and by 1700 means were being actively sought of alleviating its drawbacks, of turning to advantage such physical assets as it enjoyed, and of increasing the accommodation offered to shipping.

The radical solution that was reached, the building of a dock within the confines of the Pool, was unprecedented in the context of a commercial port. The principle of a wet dock, that is to say of a basin fitted with gates in order to impound water in which vessels could float at all states of the tide, was not an entirely novel one when the Corporation began the work. A wet dock had been built by the Navy at Deptford early in the 16th century, and similar naval docks were built at Portsmouth and at Plymouth by the end of the following century to receive ships for refitting or prior to dry docking. Two London predecessors, the 1½-acre Blackwall Dock of c1660 and the 10-acre Howland Great Dock at Rotherhithe opened in 1699 (which could accommodate 120 of the largest merchant ships of the day) were both built as lying-up and as refitting basins and had no quays for the landing of cargo. The dock at Liverpool was, by contrast, from the outset an integral part of the port's trading facilities and deep enough to accommodate fully laden vessels.

Dock building in Liverpool in the 18th century barely kept up with the demands of trade, as the provision of each new dock fed commercial pressures for yet further accommodation. When the first dock (later known as the Old Dock) was newly completed the tonnage of shipping inwards was 18,800, and 18,400 outward. Before Salthouse Dock was opened in 1752, the tonnage inward and outward had grown to 29,100 and 31,800. When George's Dock opened in 1771 the figures stood at 59,700 and

The Mersey Docks in 1972

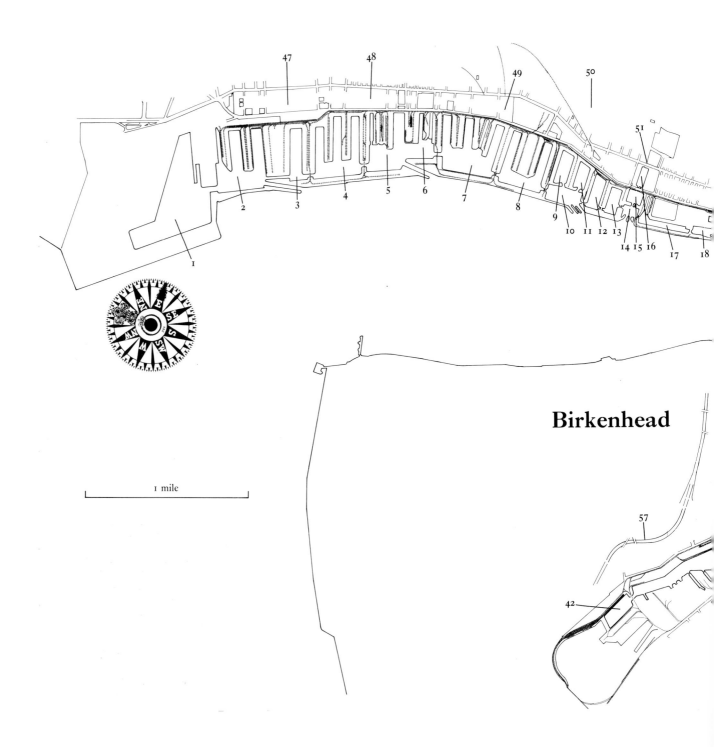

Birkenhead

1 mile

Liverpool

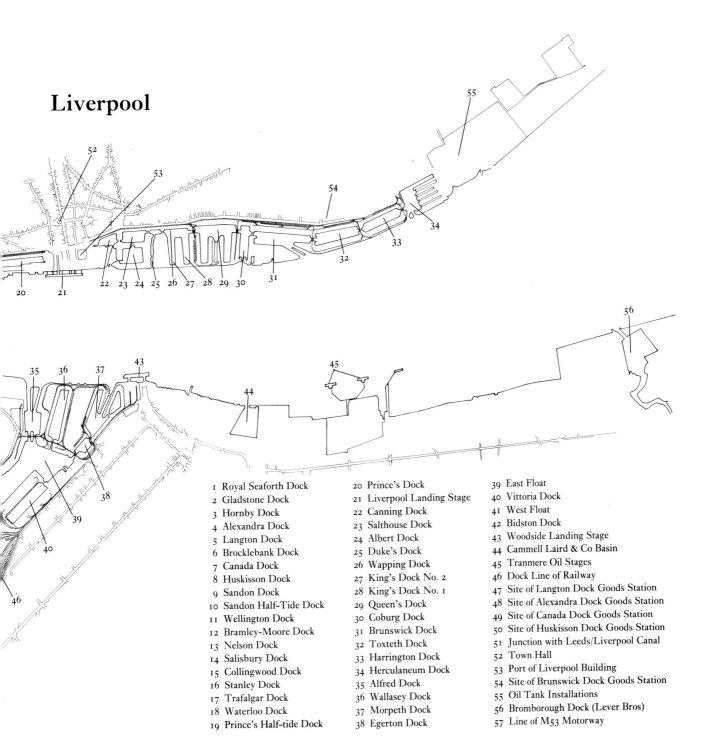

1 Royal Seaforth Dock	20 Prince's Dock	39 East Float
2 Gladstone Dock	21 Liverpool Landing Stage	40 Vittoria Dock
3 Hornby Dock	22 Canning Dock	41 West Float
4 Alexandra Dock	23 Salthouse Dock	42 Bidston Dock
5 Langton Dock	24 Albert Dock	43 Woodside Landing Stage
6 Brocklebank Dock	25 Duke's Dock	44 Cammell Laird & Co Basin
7 Canada Dock	26 Wapping Dock	45 Tranmere Oil Stages
8 Huskisson Dock	27 King's Dock No. 2	46 Dock Line of Railway
9 Sandon Dock	28 King's Dock No. 1	47 Site of Langton Dock Goods Station
10 Sandon Half-Tide Dock	29 Queen's Dock	48 Site of Alexandra Dock Goods Station
11 Wellington Dock	30 Coburg Dock	49 Site of Canada Dock Goods Station
12 Bramley-Moore Dock	31 Brunswick Dock	50 Site of Huskisson Dock Goods Station
13 Nelson Dock	32 Toxteth Dock	51 Junction with Leeds/Liverpool Canal
14 Salisbury Dock	33 Harrington Dock	52 Town Hall
15 Collingwood Dock	34 Herculaneum Dock	53 Port of Liverpool Building
16 Stanley Dock	35 Alfred Dock	54 Site of Brunswick Dock Goods Station
17 Trafalgar Dock	36 Wallasey Dock	55 Oil Tank Installations
18 Waterloo Dock	37 Morpeth Dock	56 Bromborough Dock (Lever Bros)
19 Prince's Half-tide Dock	38 Egerton Dock	57 Line of M53 Motorway

73,400. By around 1800 the combined tonnage of shipping entering and leaving the port was around 400,000.

An important element in this increase had been the growth of the coasting trade and of transhipment. While the tonnage of shipping entering Liverpool had increased by 23 per cent between 1709 and 1716, the tonnage outward grew by 50 per cent in the same period. In the 18th century the port already traded with the whole of the known world save for the Far East. It played a great part in the development of the three-cornered trade: trade goods and salt to Africa, slaves to the Americas, and tobacco and sugar home. Imports of tobacco stood at 2 million pounds in 1715 and at 6.1 million in 1750; of sugar at 30,000cwt and 100,000cwt. By 1800 the United States, then the second largest market outside Europe for British produce, accounted for five-sixths of Liverpool's exports. In addition, a large Mediterranean traffic had grown up in fruit and wine, a Baltic trade in timber and naval stores, and the Irish and coastwise trades remained important. The complexities of the trading patterns that evolved may be illustrated by the import of glass beads from Italy and of East India goods shipped under bond from London, for re-export to Africa.

Two factors that contributed greatly to the success of Liverpool's docks in the 18th century were their closeness, both physically and administratively, to the town. Physically the docks lay immediately adjacent to the town centre: the Old Dock quays were five minutes' walk from the Town Hall, and subsequent docks were built on ground reclaimed from the foreshore between the town and the river. (In this, Liverpool formed a contrast to the City of Bristol, which in 1712 had promoted a similar enclosed dock at Sea Mills. The distance of the Bristol dock from the commercial centre of the City was fatal to its success.)

Administratively, the Trustees of the Liverpool Docks were the Corporation of the town, and the community of interest between the borough and the port was guaranteed by the identity of those concerned with the government of the one and the promotion of the other. Furthermore, the Corporation owned the potential sites for dock development and controlled their reclamation and use. By the end of the 17th century the Corporation estate extended from the boundary of Toxteth Park northward to the Pool, covering an area of nearly 1,000 acres, and a series of legal actions confirmed the borough's rights over the foreshore. It was here that the 18th century docks were built, the nucleus of the south docks which are the subject of this study.

The development in the 18th century of improved landward communications opened up the port to the produce of the hinterland, and created fresh markets for its imports. Improvement of waterborne transport preceded substantially better roads. The Mersey was made navigable to Warrington in the 1690s. A series of speculative Acts passed in the 1720s for further improvements proved abortive, but in 1732 the River Weaver was made navigable and in 1736 the Mersey and Irwell Navigation was opened from Warrington to Hunt's Bank, Manchester. The Douglas Navigation was completed in 1742, the Sankey Canal in 1757, and in 1774 the Leeds and Liverpool Canal was opened to Wigan. Two years later the Bridgewater Canal created a route to the Midlands. Many of these improvements were actively promoted by the Corporation. The Corporation contributed towards the parliamentary expenses of the Sankey Brook Act, and the Trustees of the Docks lent the services of their dock engineer, Henry Berry, in its construction. Subsequently Berry undertook improvements to the Weaver Navigation. These waterways opened up first of all the country immediately round about, and then more distant markets, making available the coal of Lancashire, the salt of Cheshire, the coal and iron of South Yorkshire, the textiles of Manchester and the West Riding, the pottery of Staffordshire and the hardware of Birmingham. Liverpool alone of ports on the western seaboard enjoyed links with such a rich manufacturing district and so great a range of outlets for its imports.

Local roads were suffering from over-use even in the 17th century. Coal carts were causing severe damage to the streets of the town in 1667, and carriers might be fined if they did not use the Pool Bridge, over the neck of the Pool, to avoid the town centre on their way to the quay.[6] Yet it was much later before arterial roads were substantially improved. The principal roads from the east remained bad west of Warrington until after 1750. Until after 1760 there was no regular wagon trade to Manchester. Waterborne transport remained of far greater importance than carriage by land, until the building of railways in the next century.

By the beginning of the 19th century, the population of Liverpool was almost twelve times as great as it had been a century before, and prosperity had transformed both the appearance of the town and the quality of society. The town had acquired distinguished public buildings, a replanned commercial centre, fine residential streets and squares, and public parks. Its gigantic warehouses, the largest in Britain, were a similar sign of its wealth. The cultural standards of an elite had done much to alter the character of the town. Liverpool had become a place of prospective fortune, attracting such entrepreneurs as John Swire, George Holt, the Brocklebanks and the Booths, the Ismays, the Inmans and Thomas and James Harrison. The newcomers provided an influx of talent and, with the experience of the established men, maintained the engineering expertise, the commercial enterprise, the administrative efficiency and the practical experience necessary to the port's continued expansion. In the 19th century Liverpool possessed a wealth of talent unrivalled in any other port at the time.

Whereas in the previous century there had been little fundamental change in the way in which the docks were used, apart from the volume of trade and in the numbers of ships entering the port, the 19th century saw radical developments which made for still more rapid growth in the port. The great increase in the size of ships that came from building in iron and steel, required improvements to the port's approaches, the almost complete reconstruction of smaller, older docks, and the introduction of powered handling to load and unload the vast cargoes that such ships could carry. The introduction of steam to the ocean routes meant that ships could sail on regular schedules, no longer dependent on the weather; this and the greater capital cost of such steamers, also called for mechanized cargo-handling to effect a speedy turn-round, and modifications to dock entrances so that ships need not wait idly in the river until high tide before they could enter the docks. Above all, the trade of the port grew still faster than before, requiring yet more dock provision and greater lengths of quay. Traffic inwards in 1825 had been 1.2 million tons; in 1865 it was 4.7 million tons; by 1900 it had risen to 12.4 million.

Parallel to the impact of iron and steam on the development of deep-sea vessels was the improvement of land communication offered by the railways. The Liverpool and Manchester Railway was opened in 1830. Seven years later, Liverpool was linked to Birmingham and so to London by the Grand Junction Railway (later to be the London and North Western); by 1840 the town of Birkenhead, across the Mersey and linked to Liverpool since 1815 by steam ferries, had developed still more direct connections with the Midlands by the Birkenhead and Chester Railway, later a part of the Great Western. The Lancashire and Yorkshire Railway and the Cheshire Lines Committee were to provide further connections with the great manufacturing districts to the east. In the 1830s a complex of local lines was also developing, most of them tributary to the Liverpool and Manchester but some, such as the St Helens and Runcorn Gap, providing an independent alternative to it.

Not unnaturally, with the prospect of such rapid growth, dock building began to attract private promoters. In the 18th century, assisted largely by the Corporation's ownership of much of the potential space for dock development, all docks had been provided by the Liverpool Dock Trustees with the exception of the Duke's Dock of 1773 (built as the terminus for the Bridgewater Canal) and a very few small basins which will be noted in their place. In the 19th century, private developers promoted more substantial docks. As early as 1833 the St Helens and Runcorn Gap Railway built a coal dock near Widnes, while the London and North Western Railway developed a group of docks at Garston from 1853. In the late 1830s a group of merchants and shipowners promoted the first Harrington Dock, at the south end of the then existing Liverpool group and a few years later a very much greater enterprise was the promotion of docks at Birkenhead on the opposite shore of the Mersey.

The Birkenhead site was a natural one to choose for dock building – a shallow valley extending back from the Mersey, enabling docks to be excavated from the land and offering when complete a large enclosed area of water. An Act of Parliament was obtained in 1844, and in 1847 the engineer J. M. Rendel had completed two docks, Morpeth and Egerton. Subsequent development, however, was attended by engineering and financial failures which culminated in the vesting of the Birkenhead and the Liverpool docks under a single authority, the Mersey Docks and Harbour Board. This had been formed in 1858 following concern that the Liverpool Dock Trustees were increasingly unrepresentative of the broad range of dock users. Thereafter, the only major challenge to the Board's monopoly of docks on the Mersey was the opening of the Manchester Ship Canal in 1894. Built with the express intention of bypassing the port of Liverpool, this was virtually a 36-mile-long dock, entered at Eastham, a little up river from Birkenhead, with numerous berthing points along its length and 7 terminal docks at Manchester.

The decline of the port in the 20th century had a great variety of causes, some internal to it and some external. The pace of expansion was already slowing before the 1914–18 War and the ensuing slump made conditions difficult for the manufacturers who were the shipowners' customers. The further decline in recent decades of the traditional manufacturing districts in the hinterland, and a shift of trading from the Atlantic routes to East Coast ports convenient to a growing European traffic, left Liverpool over-provided with berths.

At the same time, the growing size of ocean-going ships found many of the docks and their approaches too small.

The amortisation policies of the Board were planned over too long a time scale to allow for the adequate replacement of obsolete installations. A further disincentive to change was the apparently inexhaustible supply of dock labour, which left the Board reluctant to embark on expensive modernization of cargo-handling appliances. The effects of such policies were accentuated by two World Wars, during which the docks and their equipment suffered severely from lack of maintenance and from over-use, as well as from actual damage in the Second World War. Control of shipping has increasingly passed out of the hands of Liverpool men and of Liverpool companies with an interest in maintaining traffic in the port. Since 1945, the City of Liverpool which was once such a magnet for men of talent, ambition and culture has suffered from an exodus of population, from a

reputation for industrial unrest and from inner-city social problems. By 1971 a radical reconstruction of the administrative and financial structure of the port was found necessary, and the powers of the Mersey Docks and Harbour Board were transferred to a newly formed Mersey Docks and Harbour Company. In 1981 the South Docks were amongst the lands vested in Merseyside Development Corporation which is charged with the regeneration of docklands no longer needed for merchant shipping.

1 Defoe, *A Tour through the Whole Island of Great Britain*, Penguin ed, 1971, 541.
2 Ib 542.
3 Picton, 1873, 1, 126.
4 Ib 129.

2   Charles Okill's plan of The Pool (reconstructed from deeds, 1828).

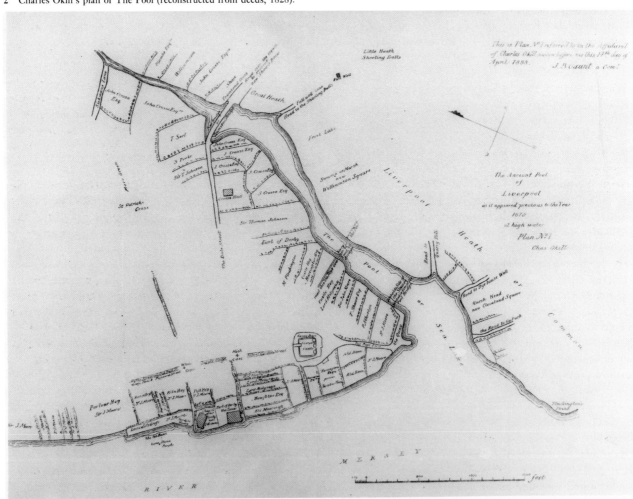

The evolution of the Mersey dock system

While the growth in the numbers of ships using the port created an apparently relentless demand for ever more and larger docks, the disposition and form of these docks were determined by other factors. The most immediately striking feature of the layout of the Liverpool docks is that they form a narrow strip, some 7 miles long and seldom more than a $\frac{1}{2}$ mile wide, along the eastern edge of the River Mersey. The origin of the port was in a riverside quay and in a small, tidal inlet that lay just to the south of the town. The subsequent growth of the docks was constrained by the presence of high ground that prevented the excavation of docks on land, and forced dock development on to the foreshore where for two hundred years the only method of dock construction available was by excavation from made ground within the tidal margins of the river. The limitations of the site were made more acute by the first docks being situated at the narrowest part of the Mersey, where the shore shelves quite steeply to a depth at which dock construction by reclamation was impossible. The long, narrow ribbon of the Liverpool docks was the unavoidable result.

When, after a century of dock development in Liverpool, the engineer Thomas Telford was surveying for the first Birkenhead dock scheme, he remarked that the existing docks had been built on the wrong side of the Mersey.[1] From a topographical point of view he was right, but he ignored the facts of geography. The growing wealth of the region and the rapid growth of Liverpool itself made the continued expansion of the docks there inevitable. Each new dock was generally built beyond the last, northward and southward from the original nucleus, sometimes leap-frogging sites that would only be developed years later. The development of larger ships increasingly determined that the newest, deepest docks would be built closer to the open sea to the north. Nevertheless the southern docks remained adequate for many ships trading to the Mediterranean and to the shallow ports of West Africa and South America and until their closure in 1972 continued to give berths to vessels of considerable size.

While the development of the dock system was determined by commercial pressures and by the constraints of topography, the forms of docks were in large part the result of the gradual introduction of more sophisticated dock and entrance design that improved the port's efficiency. The principle of the Old Dock – the original dock of 1710 – was used in all subsequent Liverpool docks for almost a century, and comprised a wet dock entered from a 'dry' basin. The wet dock itself had gates which were only opened for an hour or two at either side of high tide to allow ships in or out, and thus preserved the water level within the dock. The dry basin had a broader entrance from the river, and no gates, and dried out when the tide receded. The function of the dry basin was to afford to ships a sheltered approach to the narrower entrance into the dock itself, and also to give a berth to any vessel that did not need to float at all times. The Old Dock, Salthouse and George's Docks which were built off the Old Dock's dry basin, and King's and Queen's Docks were all built according to this principle. Its defects, however, were summed up by the engineer William Jessop in 1800, when he asked:

'*Why with so great a flow of tide as there is at Liverpool were the bottoms of the docks and the sills of the gates laid so much above low water that ships drawing more than 10 or 12 feet cannot enter the docks at neap tides; or admitting the depth of the docks to be right, why in the original design were they not provided with intermediate basins or locks to correct the deficiency?*'[2]

The problem was to become acute as ships grew in size, and if its solution was deferred, it was probably partly out of a lack of resolution and of expertise on the part of the Dock Committee and partly, too, out of a shortage of funds. The 1811 Dock Act gave the Trustees specific powers to build half-tide basins, but Clarence Dock, designed by Hartley and opened in 1830, was the first to be entered by such a basin, initiating another development in the growth of the dock system. The principle of a half-tide basin is that by possessing an outer lock gate and a lower sill than the wet dock to which it gives access, it is itself a wet dock which ships can enter for a time on either side of the flood, and thus be better placed to enter the inner dock or the river when the state of the tide allows.

Once introduced, half-tide basins were normally constructed for all of the new docks built between 1830 and 1879 when the first locked entrance was built at Langton. Half-tide basins served the dual purposes of docks and locks, but they were a compromise in which each function impaired the effectiveness of the other. They became outmoded in the latter part of the 19th century when cargo-handling patterns changed, calling for features which were functionally discrete.

The half-tide dock also represented an attempt to extend the deep water available to ships. Inside the dock system the water level could be raised artificially by means of impounding engines. These, by pumping water into the basin and into the dock itself, could maintain the water level at an artificially high level (normally that of spring highs) and thus make the docks usable by vessels of greater draught than could otherwise have passed between them. Impounding was first introduced in Liverpool at the Sandon Half-tide Dock (in the northern group) in around 1885; it was introduced in the South Docks with an installation at Coburg Dock in 1890, and proved a considerable success.

In 1824, Jesse Hartley, the Dock Engineer appointed in that year, had expressed the germ of much later development in the docks when he wrote:

'I would construct an entrance basin of adequate capacity for the convenience of four docks . . . accessible from one dock to the others by means of a continuous line of connection along the river quay, to be separated however from each other as occasion may require . . . Any one of these docks might be restricted to the exclusive use of vessels impelled by steam . . . .'[3]

Hartley realized the advantages of reducing the number of river entrances into the dock system, and of increasing simultaneously the degree of internal communication between the docks. These advantages were several. Ships unloading in one dock could move to another without having to pass into the Mersey *en route*; minimizing the number of river entrances made it possible to build long, continuous lines of river wall that, it was hoped, would train the river current and help to prevent the build-up of silt in the navigation channels (it was calculated that each cubic yard of water contained 29cu ins of sand and mud in suspension);[4] minimizing contact with tidal water made it easier to maintain water levels in the dock system. The system of intercommunication was applied earlier in the northern group than in the south; by the mid-1830s the docks from George's Basin to Clarence were all interconnected. The building of Wapping Dock in the southern group in the 1850s provided the opportunity to link the entire line down to Brunswick. The reduction of river entrances took place piecemeal, and in the southern group never produced such a clear, unbroken line of river wall as it did in the north despite the continued presence

of the Pluckington Bank. This long bar of silt between Albert and Herculaneum Docks presented a continual obstacle to shipping and resisted all attempts permanently to remove it whether by scour or by dredging. Nevertheless, Queen's Dock lost its separate entrance in 1905, and Coburg in 1907. At their close, the only river entrances into the south docks were by the Canning Half-tide Basin at the northern end and by the Brunswick and Herculaneum entrances at the south. Only these last two took ocean-going ships of any size.

The earlier Liverpool docks were all more-or-less rectangular basins, affording relatively short lengths of quay in proportion to their water area. For as long as docks were often used for laying-up ships as well as for discharging and taking on cargo, this arrangement suited such a dual function: the earliest views of the docks show them crowded with vessels far out from the quay. But the growth of trade in the port required, above all, an increase in the available length of quay, while the larger ships of later years did not require to lie up in enclosed water when out of commission. Increases in the cost and speed of ships made speedy turn-round essential, and this was impossible in a crowded dock. The solution was the introduction of the branch dock layout, whereby a number of relatively narrow docks, affording long quay room on both sides, open like fingers off a broader dock (a vestibule) whose primary function is to enable ships to manoeuvre between the dock entrance and the branch docks. Normally approached by a simple lock, the vestibule assumes much of the function of a half-tide dock in enabling vessels to approach their loading and unloading berths.

The first Liverpool docks to be built on the branch dock pattern were Langton Dock (1879) and Alexandra (1880) in the north, confirmation of the increasing tendency for innovation to be concentrated at the seaward end of the port. In the southern group, King's and Queen's Docks were rebuilt around 1905 with branch docks, and with their completion the development and modernization of the southern group of docks was almost at an end.

Discussion so far has concentrated upon the physical development of the dock system, on the principal innovations by which the port was enabled to accommodate the successive pressures of ship numbers and of ship size. Parallel to these developments, however, were changes in the ways in which the docks were used.

While it was only in the 19th century that docks were built that were designated from the first for specific trades, a degree of *de facto* specialization was well established by

Comparative ship dimensions

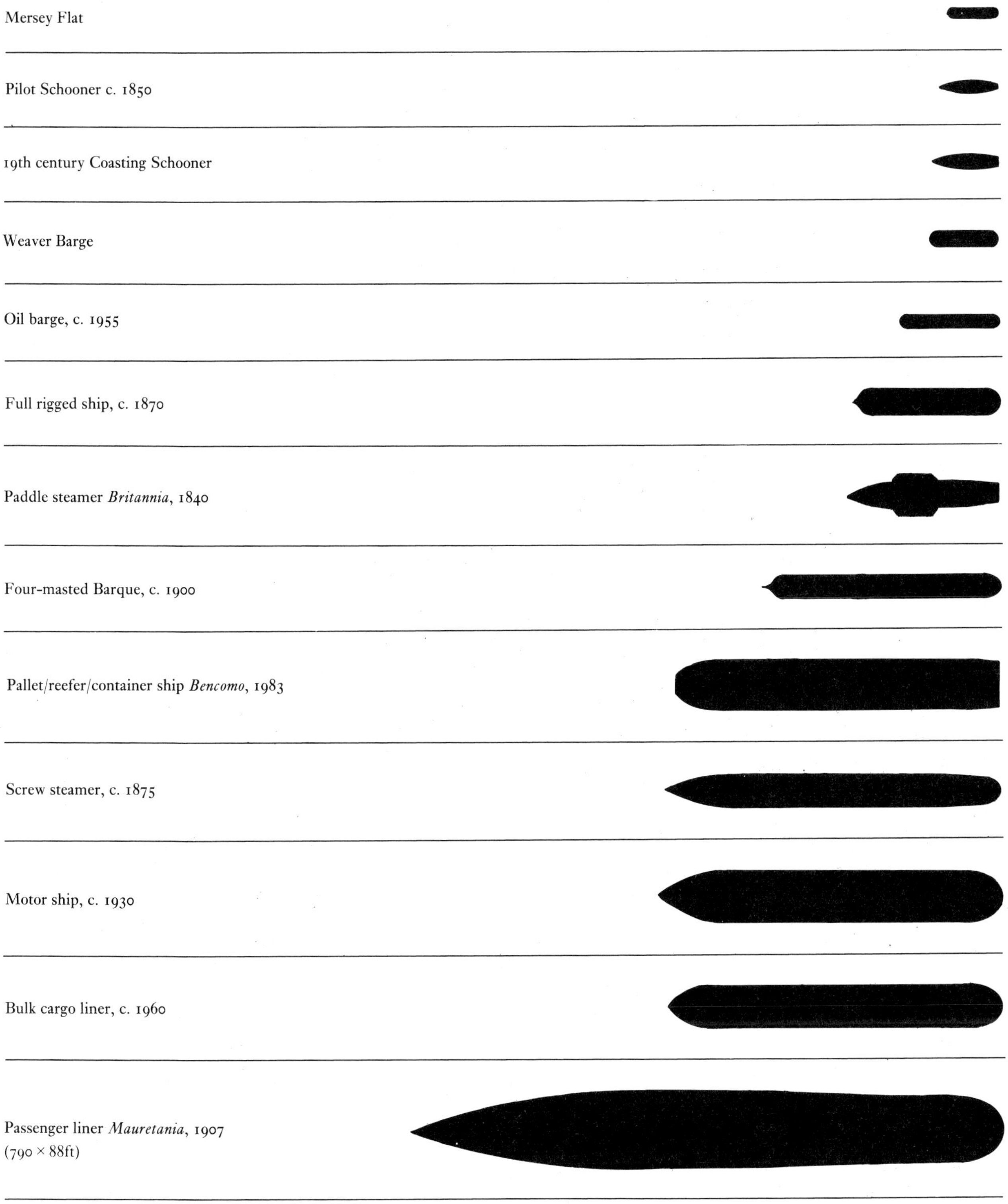

Mersey Flat

Pilot Schooner c. 1850

19th century Coasting Schooner

Weaver Barge

Oil barge, c. 1955

Full rigged ship, c. 1870

Paddle steamer *Britannia*, 1840

Four-masted Barque, c. 1900

Pallet/reefer/container ship *Bencomo*, 1983

Screw steamer, c. 1875

Motor ship, c. 1930

Bulk cargo liner, c. 1960

Passenger liner *Mauretania*, 1907
(790 × 88ft)

the late 18th century. Salt and coal traders, and the smaller coasting ships and those trading to the Mediterranean, had come to be concentrated in the Old Dock, in Salthouse Dock and in George's Dock Passage; George's Dock was to be dominated by traders to West Africa, to North America and the West Indies. The Duke's Dock, built as the Liverpool terminus for the Bridgewater Canal, became the transfer point between inland and ocean-going traders. Sugar, spices, tea, herrings, cotton and corn were forwarded inland from Liverpool for distribution; raw materials were transformed inland into finished products which then returned to Liverpool for re-export. Manchester Dock, occupied almost exclusively by the flats working the Rivers Mersey and Irwell, was used from its opening in 1785 by the coal trade.

King's Dock was quickly adopted by the tobacco trade, and the Corporation built a special tobacco warehouse near the dock's north-east corner. Inclined quays were built at Queen's Dock to facilitate the unloading of timber ships, and its wharves were kept free of buildings to make room for balks. Other important cargoes from the North Atlantic, from North America and the West Indies, included whale products from the Greenland fishery, cotton and sugar. From the Mediterranean came wine and fruit.

Apart from the inland carriers' and river craft docks, the first specialized docks to be built were Clarence Dock, opened in 1830, and Brunswick in 1832, the one for particular ships and the other for particular cargo. Clarence Dock was built a little apart from other docks, following Hartley's suggestion in 1824, in order to isolate steamers which were still thought to be a fire risk. Brunswick Dock was built for the timber trade. The seasonal nature of the trade, and its specialized handling requirements, made a purpose-built dock especially desirable. In order to facilitate the inland distribution of timber cargoes, Brunswick Dock was connected in 1835 by a branch line of railway to the Liverpool & Manchester Co, Park Lane goods station at Wapping. The concentration of timber vessels from the Baltic, West Africa and the Americas did not, however, exclude other trades, and Brunswick was also extensively used for the transhipment of other cargoes, the more so when the opening within the next twenty years of Huskisson and Canada Docks as further, specialized timber docks, drew the timber importers away from Brunswick to the modern facilities.

With the growing number of steamers, further specialized provision became necessary. A constructional tendency in the mid-century was the provision of very wide entrance locks to take the beamy paddle-steamers; the 70ft Coburg river entrance of 1856 and the 100ft Canada entrance of 1857 were not again equalled until the rebuilding of the Brunswick river entrance with 80ft and 100ft locks after the turn of the century. A further requirement of steamers was coal, and in 1857 Bramley-Moore Dock was provided with a high-level coal railway linked to the Lancashire & Yorkshire Co lines for loading both bunker and cargo coal: the development of ocean-going steam-ships made increasingly necessary the establishment of coal reserves at distant ports. Coaling in the southern group became concentrated at Herculaneum Dock, where two 25-ton coaling cranes and a variety of specialized coal-handling apparatus were installed in the 1890s. Herculaneum Dock also became the first to possess purpose-built oil stores, excavated from the sandstone cliff to the east of the branch dock in 1881.

One development which left more of a mark on the landward installations of the port than on its dock layout was the introduction of the closed dock system. In the 18th century the quays were open to the town, and the opportunities for pilferage were enormous. Customs collection was also very difficult. Before any of the quays were enclosed, there were in the vicinity of the docks a number of warehouses under Crown lock in which dutiable goods could be lodged. The inadequacy of this arrangement was highlighted by the Commissioner of Customs and Excise's decision in 1805 not to extend the provisions of the 1803 Warehousing Act to Liverpool, because of lack of secure stores. The first and simplest reaction to the problem was the erection of barrier walls between the docks and the public streets. Prince's Dock was the first to be so enclosed, although a short stretch of wall had earlier been built across the south end of the King's Dock tobacco warehouse. A more sophisticated solution was that exemplified by the Albert Dock development where each stack of warehouses was in a secure area and the whole complex was also enclosed. From the 1840s, an increasing number of the older docks, and all new ones, were provided with walls and secure, policed entrance gates, many of which are notable examples of Jesse Hartley's distinctive treatment of masonry.

The 19th-century growth of the port must have seemed at times a somewhat *ad hoc* development, a matter of meeting by expedients each new demand as it arose, by docks now in the north, now in the south, now in Birkenhead, each one soon proving inadequate to accommodate the pressures it was intended to meet. In fact dock development was guided by certain underlying principles that have already been indicated: the constraints of the site, developments in the optimum form of docks, increasing specialization and the development of the closed dock system. But whereas, before the late 19th century, growth had in general been by new construction, thereafter, as pressure for further development began to slacken somewhat and as the older docks became increasingly inadequate for the size of modern vessels, the emphasis began to change from one of expansion by new construction to development by reconstruction.

Though by the late 19th century the tonnage of shipping entering the port was second only to that of London, and the average size of vessels using the port twice London's (reflecting the predominance in Liverpool of modern, ocean-going steamers over a coasting trade that was declining from railway competition), the service offered by the port came in for increasing criticism. Despite the fact that the profits of the port went solely to pay for its maintenance and improvement and to service the debt incurred in the building of the docks, a commentator in 1885 wrote that

'... the rates have been complained of as unusually heavy. This result can only be due to the large amount of dredging required for maintaining the depth in the docks; the number of entrances which have to be kept in repair owing to the small size of many of the docks; the costly accessories of the sluices and landing stage; the high price of land for extension in close proximity to Liverpool; and more especially the limited use of modern appliances for the rapid discharge of cargoes and for their economical transit.'[5]

A massive programme of work was initiated by Parliamentary Acts of 1891, 1893 and 1898, involving the substantial reconstruction of the Canada, Huskisson and Sandon Docks in the north, all of them approaching fifty years old, and also of King's, Queen's and Brunswick Docks in the south which were even older. Dockside facilities were modernized as well. Single and double storey transit sheds with hydraulic and electric roof cranes were erected on nearly all the quays, replacing the tobacco warehouse and the proliferation of assorted sheds which had been built in succession since the end of the 18th century. At Brunswick Dock, the half-tide entrance was closed and a new double lock entrance was built further south. The principle of the angled entrance facing up river, first adopted for the Langton entrance in 1879, was applied to Brunswick; its position was chosen in the mistaken belief that it would avoid the Pluckington Bank.

These reconstructions were the last major works in the South Docks. In 1906 powers were obtained to permit the construction of what were to become the Gladstone system at the northern end of the Liverpool estate and the Victoria Dock in the East Float at Birkenhead. The latter was opened in 1909, but nothing of the Gladstone development was completed before the First World War save a huge graving dock, 1050ft long and 120ft wide – large enough to take transatlantic liners.

From 1914 to the end of the Second World War, the future was so uncertain that planning and decision-making became almost impossible, progressive growth all but ceased, and a coherent pattern of development is hard to trace. The net commercial tonnage entering the port in 1914 was just over 19,000,000 (a figure that itself represents no vast increase over the previous ten years). By 1917 it had fallen to 15,680,000; by 1918 to 11,687,000. It picked up slowly during the 1920s, dropped again during the early 1930s, rose from 1936 but was then once again severely affected by war. Work on the Gladstone Dock system began again in 1922 and when it was complete in 1927 it comprised a wet dock and two branches with a river entrance 1,070ft long and 130ft wide. The Gladstone river entrance now serves also for the modern Royal Seaforth Dock. Other inter-war developments were the opening of Bidston Dock at Birkenhead, and some rebuilding at Clarence Half-tide and Trafalgar Docks in the northern group.

During the Second World War, the virtual closure of the Port of London and of other East Coast ports caused the diversion of a great deal of traffic to Liverpool. The port was severely strained by the arrival of 1,285 convoys consisting of up to 50 ships at once, while more than 4,700,000 troops passed through the port. Resources were further stretched by the problems of accommodating and of moving goods through docks damaged by enemy action: over 90 acres of dock sheds and warehouses were totally destroyed and another 90 acres put out of commission.

Dock improvement schemes after the war comprised new entrance locks to the west Waterloo Dock, and to Canada and Langton locks. The former was designed primarily to meet the requirements of the Irish Sea passenger ships and the coastwise trade. The latter, a major operation which included the widening of the Canada–Brocklebank passage and the remodelling of the whole area around the old Canada Basin, provided a locked entrance to the north shore and replaced the old Canada lock which had faced the prevailing wind and the flood tide. Expensive as this reconstruction was, it failed to generate any useful financial return. There was never any question of substantial improvements in the South Docks, which had been under-used for many years and by the 1960s were becoming too great a financial liability for the Dock Company to bear. The deep water required by modern ships was only available at the northern end of the Dock Estate near the mouth of the estuary. In 1972 the South Docks were closed to commercial shipping.

By contrast, the same year saw the opening of the Royal Seaforth Dock, north of Gladstone Dock. (The land here, and powers to enclose it, had been acquired as long ago as 1906, over sixty years before work began on the 500-acre site.) The building of the Seaforth Dock and the closure of the South Docks were both prompted by changes in the nature of ships' cargoes since the Second World War, and the replacement of a great deal of the older tramp and mixed cargo trade by dry cargo bulk carriers which operated on regular routes with homogeneous loads. The Royal Seaforth Dock has little in common with earlier docks in the port. It is a huge, polygonal basin of 85 acres, surrounded by ten specialized berths including grain, timber and container terminals, roll-on roll-off facilities, and accommodation for general cargo.

Over two and a half centuries of the port's history, the landscape of the docks and the facilities they provided have changed constantly, and the port has incorporated examples of many different forms of cargo and ship handling. It is this diversity and the constant evolution of these facilities, from the original building of the Old Dock as the first enclosed commercial dock in the world, that makes the history of the Liverpool docks of more than local interest. In the chapters that follow, many of these provisions are described in detail.

But even though there are pages in which ships themselves are barely mentioned, they must never be forgotten in what follows. Their presence was ultimately the only reason for the docks' existence, and their disappearance the only reason for the South Docks' decline. The development of the port was inevitably linked to the evolution of ships: from such ships as *The Brothers* of 1787, a frigate-built ship of 325 tons for the African trade; to the transatlantic sailing packet *James Munroe* of 1818, 424 tons; to Holt's screw steamer *Agamemnon*, 1865, of 2,280 tons; to Harrison's *Novelist*, 1940, 6,133 tons; and to the Australian *Remuera*, the first container ship to enter the Royal Seaforth Dock, of over 40,000 tons. Such developments demonstrate as clearly as possible the necessity for constant change in the port, and it is this that the following chapters set out to describe.

1 Mountfield, 1965, 38. Also McIntyre, 1972
2 W. Jessop to Chairman of Dock Committee, 14.iv.1800; DCM 1.v.1800
3 DCM 24.xi.1824
4 Rennie, J., *British & Foreign Harbours*, 1854, 214
5 Vernon-Harcourt, L. F., *Harbours & Docks*, 1885, 512

3   Light float moored in Herculaneum Dock at the MDHB Buoy Store, *c*1920.

Quayside fixtures in the South Docks

4 (*top left*) Iron bollard, *c*1855, Salthouse Dock.

5 (*left*) Pitch boiler, 1810, by Phoenix Foundry, Liverpool.

6 (*bottom left*) Granite bollard, *c*1845, Canning Graving Dock No. 2

7 (*above*) Ships' and barges' iron bollards at Duke's Dock river entrance.

8 (*below*) Granite bollard, *c*1855, excavated from Salthouse—Duke's passage.

The Pool was the ancient haven of Liverpool. There are no contemporary maps that show it before the Old Dock was formed within it, but its outline has been traced in great detail from early deeds, and its character as a broad, shallow creek seems clear. The Liverpool shoreline in the 16th and 17th centuries lay far back from the present river wall which defines the extent of the later docks built out into the Mersey. The medieval shoreline ran along New Quay, Strand Street (names which preserve the memory of it) and to the south along Wapping. Between Strand Street and Wapping lay the mouth of the Pool, a tidal inlet from the Mersey fed by a stream that ran off the Mosslake Fields beneath a bridge (the Townsend Bridge) at Dale Street, down where the Old Haymarket is now, down the line of Whitechapel and Paradise Street, and began to broaden out into the Pool itself where Paradise Street begins to approach Hanover Street. The lie of the land preserves the line, even though the stream itself was culverted long ago.

The shallow Pool could on its own have afforded little

9 The Pool of Liverpool showing position of Old Dock and subsequent reclamation (Charles Okill, 1828).

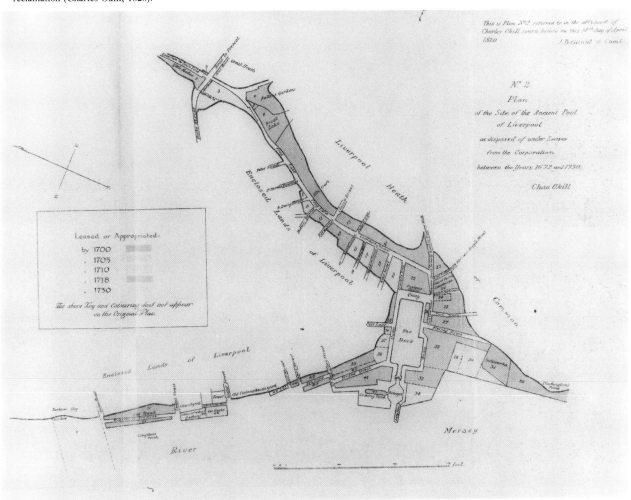

shelter from the sea before the building of breakwaters. That some sort of mole existed at the mouth of the haven in the 16th century is evident from a reference of 1560 to its destruction in a storm.[1] The Town Council voted money for its reconstruction, and the Mayor called upon every household in the neighbourhood of the Pool to contribute a labourer *gratis* to undertake the work. Thus on Monday every house in Water Street sent a man to do digging and ditching, and on Tuesday the houses in Castle Street; on Wednesday men came from Dale Street, on Thursday from Juggler Street, and so on until all was finished in the next year. A new haven is mentioned in that year, perhaps formed by a realignment as well as by the rebuilding of the breakwater.

The problem of the depth of water may have been ameliorated by sluices, first recorded in 1635, and probably roughly on the line of King Street where the stream widened into the Pool. These sluices may have been used to hold back water in order to scour a channel at low tide. At intervals throughout the century the Corporation spent money to maintain the approaches to the harbour and the old quay, and in 1665 they built a new quay, probably on the Mersey itself. At least from the latter part of the 17th century there was constant encroachment on to the foreshore from occupiers of adjacent land, and leases of Corporation property frequently included a clause which required lessees to embank or to wall in the Pool lands. In 1667 Sir Edward Moore wrote in his *Rental*, an inventory of his Liverpool property with advice to his son on how to manage it, that his closes backing on to the Pool

'... *may be the greatest concern you have in England; for if the Pool be made navigable, the shipping must lie all along the closes, and the trade will be all in them for the whole town ... I do not question but to see this brought to a head in my time.*'[2]

Sir Edward did not see his predictions realized, but he was not alone in anticipating the development of the Pool. When the first proposals for a dock were put forward, early in the 18th century, there is no doubt that years of discussion had predisposed opinion to favour a scheme for the regularization and improvement of the facilities provided for Liverpool ships using the Pool.

1 Stewart-Brown, 1930, 89
2 Fergusson-Irvine, ed. *Sir Edward Moore: Liverpool in King Charles the Second's Time*, 1899, 104

Since there is evidence that the idea of an enclosed or embanked dock of some kind had been current since the late 17th century, it is probably impossible to attribute the notion to any one individual. In January, 1708, one of the town's MPs, Sir Thomas Johnson, approached George Sorocold (the engineer and millwright who may have been responsible for the Howland wet dock at Rotherhithe) with a view to producing such a scheme for Liverpool. In November of that year the Town Council formally requested Johnson and the other Member for the town, Richard Norris, 'to treat with and agree for a proper person to come to this town and view the ground and draw a plan of the intended dock'.[1] Both men were prominent tobacco merchants and, being involved in what at the time was Liverpool's most valuable import trade, were sensitive to the urgent need for better port facilities. In the event, the man they commissioned was not Sorocold but Thomas Steers. In 1709, the first Dock Act was passed, in May 1710 Steers was instructed to proceed with the work, and in the summer of 1715 the dock was partially opened for shipping.

The preamble to the Act set out the advantages of the Dock: the benefits to trade, to Liverpool as a nursery of seamen, and to the Navy in time of war. Opposition came chiefly from the Cheshire cheese merchants whose vessels anchored in the Sloyne, near the Cheshire shore of the Mersey, and at Frodsham on the Weaver and who would have to pay harbour dues towards a dock that they would never use. Their objections were over-ruled: only naval vessels and those sheltering from storms were to be exempt. The Act authorized the Trustees to borrow £6,000, a sum which would prove quite inadequate but which seems to have been based on Sorocold's original scheme for a kind of canal rather than on the bolder proposals of Thomas Steers.

The novelty of Steers' dock lay in its being formed by building within the tidal area of the Pool rather than by excavating on land (as had been Sorocold's plan). This first dock became a prototype for most of the subsequent Liverpool docks which were built on land reclaimed at some time from the Mersey. Although the water area of the Pool was probably already substantially diminished by progressive reclamation of the foreshore, the site of the Old Dock would still have been a difficult one to work. No records of the building of the dock survive, but

something must have been done to keep the water out of the workings which were attacked on the east by the stream of the upper Pool and on the west by the tide water of the Mersey.

The Old Dock was roughly rectangular, aligned east-west, with some $3\frac{1}{2}$ acres of water area and a tidal ('dry' in local parlance) entrance basin. Excavation on Canning Place (the present site of the Old Dock) has revealed a yellow sandstone coping above a brick wall which was curved on the face and stepped at the rear. The stone may have come from St James' Mount or Brownlow Hill, but it is also possible that Steers may have re-used stone from the ruined Castle as his 1708 estimates took account of this source. The walls were apparently not very substantial: shipbuilders are said to have pulled down sections of wall when they wished to launch their vessels into the dock.[2]

Precise dates for the construction of the $1\frac{1}{2}$-acre, octagonal, tidal entrance basin and the graving dock off its north side are not recorded, but an entrance basin of some description may well have been built at the same time as the Old Dock. In 1714 the Corporation ordered the land around the new dock to be leased and the money so raised to be applied to the completion of the works. The same year a graving dock was built by Alderman Norris and his partners who apparently held it until the site was needed around 1740 for the construction of the Dry Dock (later Canning). In 1718 Steers was ordered to draw up plans for the enlargement of the Old Dock,[3] but no definite response to this is recorded. In Chadwick's map of 1725 a timber pier or landing stage is shown projecting into the river on the south side of the entrance to the dock and the Bucks' view of 1728 also shows it but of much greater length.

The first graving dock having been absorbed in the enlargement of the Dry Dock, the Corporation built the second graving dock in about 1746 'at the north end of the new pier'[4] on the site which was subsequently utilized to form George's Dock Passage. The third graving dock was built some ten years later near the west side of the entrance to the new Salthouse Dock; this last was the one which became known as No 1 Graving Dock. Graving Docks Nos 2 and 3, on the west side of the Dry Dock, were built between 1765 and 1769. The first graving docks built by the Dock Trustees were those at Brunswick Dock

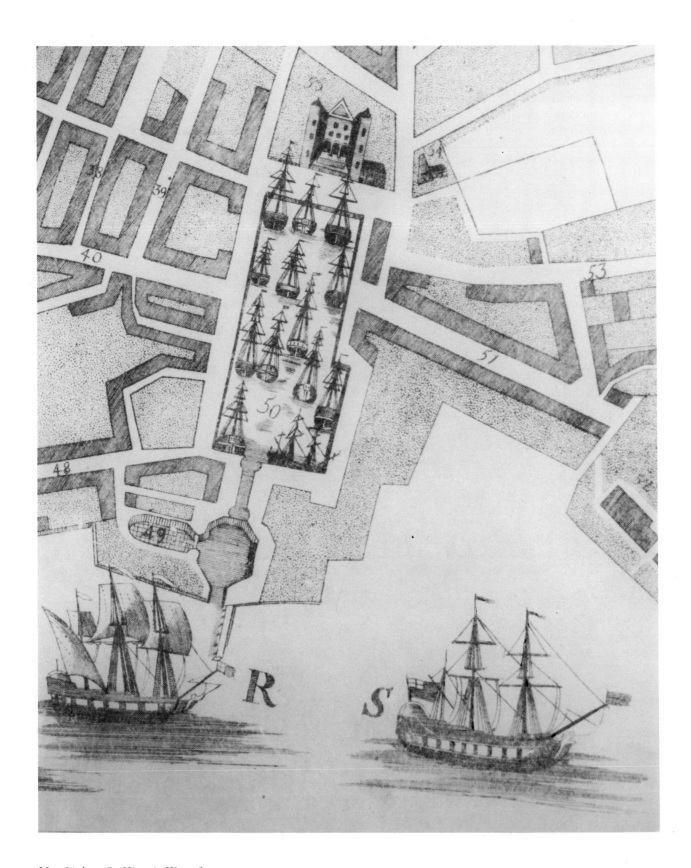

in the 1830s, and all of the earlier ones had to be purchased at various times from the Corporation. Nos 1, 2 and 3 were not acquired until needed in 1841 for the development of the Albert Dock site.

Other amenities in addition to graving docks were still needed, and a Council resolution listed these as including:

'... *an addition ... for light ships to lie in while refitting ... and a pier in the open harbour on the north side of the entrance ... for ships when ready to sail from this port to lie within till a fair wind happens, and which very often are prevented when within the wet dock (i.e. the inner dock) by other ships lying before at the entrance and are all pressing to get out before them*'.[5]

The Dock Act of 1737 accordingly sanctioned the enlargement of the entrance basin and the construction of a pier as well as the building of a new wet dock. The contract for the pier (that is the north-west wall of what is today Canning Dock) was given to Edward Litherland who was to build it of stone from Brownlow Hill. Parts of

the Canning Dock walls still visible in 1983 probably date from this reconstruction of the first entrance basin, and the use of stone here suggests that experience had shown that brick was not an ideal material for dock walls before an effective hydraulic cement had been developed. The sandstone masonry visible on the inner faces of the Canning Graving Docks (formerly Nos 2 and 3) probably dates from Hartley's reconstruction in the 1840s.

By the early 19th century the problems of the Old Dock were becoming acute. It was argued that it was too small, and that it could handle neither very many nor very large ships. Furthermore John Rennie, in a report on the port of Liverpool in 1810,[6] claimed that the quays were unacceptably narrow, and that the dock site could not be bettered as the location for a New Custom House and market. (Baines suggested, in retrospect, that the dock had become so filled with sewage as to have been a nuisance).[7] These agitations led to the Liverpool Dock Act of 1811 which give powers to fill the Old Dock. Nevertheless, it stayed open for another 15 years, largely due to opposition

10 (*opposite*) J. Chadwick's plan of Old Dock, 1725.

11 A view of the Custom House from Traffords Wyent, *c*1770.

P.P.Burdett del.   E.Rooker sculp.

. *A View of the Custom House. Taken from Traffords Wyent.*

to its closure from, amongst others, the Liverpool Shipowners' Association. Some opponents maintained that the dock was well suited to small coasting ships that would have difficulty in finding berths among the ocean-going vessels elsewhere, while owners of warehouses in the vicinity were concerned at the relocation of trade. The Act's opponents did not have much sympathy for the overcrowded excise men or for the market proposed for part of the site: it was complained that hardy seamen would have to resign their favourite berths to fish wives, rabbit catchers and sellers of turnips and tripe. There were further complications over the Old Dock's closure due to disagreement between the Corporation and the Dock Trustees, the former of whom owned the western part and the latter the eastern. Agreement was finally reached in June 1826 only after an extraordinary proposal in April of that year to build a dividing wall across the dock on the line of the property boundary. Once the Old Dock was filled up the eastern end of the site reverted to the Corporation, and the first stone of John Foster junior's new Custom House was laid in 1828. In retrospect the decision to close the Old Dock can be seen as inevitable: not only was it (as urged at the time) too small to be of real use, but because it had been built within the old Pool it lay back from the Liverpool shoreline of the River Mersey, beyond which in a long line from north to south all subsequent docks were to be built. Increasingly the Old Dock would have become cut off from the sea. The Dry Dock, however, was not closed by the 1811 Act, but was converted into a wet dock and re-named Canning Dock (see p41). The level of the sill of the Old Dock however remained as the datum for dock sills throughout the Liverpool Docks for a further century, and is referred to as ODS. A marker was established on the riverward side of Canning Island in 1845.

Operation

The principal promoters of the first Liverpool Dock Act, Sir Thomas Johnson and Richard Norris, had been tobacco merchants, but Liverpool ships of the 18th century traded with all parts of the world save for the Far East where trade was the monopoly of the East India Company. While there was only one wet dock, all trades were intermingled and there must at times have been considerable congestion arising out of this variety of merchandise, of ship sizes and of turn-round times, out of seasonal fluctuations in trade, and in time of war out of the numbers of ships arriving together under convoy or waiting to sail under embargo. Nevertheless, in part due to the Dock's very success, Liverpool's trade was growing both on its own and at the expense of its rivals. In 1784 a commentator noted:

'We have within the last six weeks 210 vessels reported besides the coasting trade. We have under our care a great accumulation of East India goods for the African and other exports, besides coffee and other goods ... We have at present several cargoes of tobacco ... which is not a tenth part of what may be expected to arrive from Virginia, Maryland, etc. ... There are many hundreds of merchants, particularly the Irish, Scotch and coasting trades who subscribe to the usefulness of the Dock ...'[8]

An index of the usefulness of the Dock was the increase in customs business. Liverpool opened its first custom house in 1680, near the river end of Water Street at the corner of Goree, and its dependency on Chester as a customs port was severed in 1699. In 1717 trade had grown so that a new custom house was needed. This was designed by Thomas Ripley, builder of the London Custom House (1718–21), and was completed in 1722. In the following year the limits of the port and legal quays of Liverpool were redefined and the Collector's jurisdiction considerably extended. Burdett's view of 1773 shows the Old Dock with the Custom House flanked by warehouses, some of which survived to be described by Picton more than a century later as '... old warehouses ... with their quaint curved gables and large projecting penthouses [that] remind one of the quays of Amsterdam'. The warehouse adjoining the Custom House is probably that identified by Rideout as the King's warehouse of 1744 and he mentions that a further warehouse was annexed for customs use in 1767, while an early 19th-century examination of deeds of 1719–20 shows that at least one of the warehouses close to the dock was owned by Richard Norris.

1 LTB 7.xi.1708
2 LRO Corporation Records 15.v.1752. Also Burstall, A. R., *Shipbuilding in Liverpool*, Sea Breezes, 1st series, vol 20, 194
3 Peet, 1930, 179
4 LRO Returns relating to Liverpool Town dues, etc, 1857, 35
5 Touzeau, 1910, I, 444
6 DCM 22.i.1810
7 Baines, 1867, I, 365
8 Jarvis, 1954, 118

Salthouse Dock

The 1737 Dock Act that had provided for the enlargement of the Dry Dock also sanctioned the building of a wet dock to the south of it. The location of the new dock was determined by the need for it to open off the reconstructed entrance basin to the Old Dock, and by the wish for it to serve John Blackburne's salt works which had been sited in Salthouse Lane, off Hurst Street, since at least 1705. For many years the new dock was called simply South Dock, and it was only in the 1780s when it was no longer the only dock south of the Old Dock that the name Salthouse Dock became established.

The layout of Salthouse Dock was largely determined by its constricted site. The 4½-acre dock measured 150yds, 110yds, 80yds and 295yds along the north, east, south and west quays respectively, with the longest side forming part of the pier between dock and river. It was at the end of this pier that No 1 Graving Dock was built around 1756, but it is not known whether or not this feature formed part of Steers' original scheme.[1] In fact, since Steers died in 1750 aged about eighty and with the new dock still incomplete, it is likely that much of the responsibility for construction was left to Steers' clerk of works and successor, Henry Berry.[2] As plans for the early docks seem often to have been altered in execution, Berry's contribution to the eventual configuration of Salthouse Dock probably equalled that of Steers.

In 1738 the Corporation gave £1,000 and just over 7 acres of land to the Trustees for the purposes of building the new dock. The progress of construction was slow, hampered perhaps by the site's deep sand and muddy gravel or perhaps by shortage of funds. Masonry tenders were invited in 1738 and by 1739 work had started on the necessary alterations to the adjacent Dry Dock. In 1749 the shipbuilders around the dock were given 6 months' notice to conclude their activities there, and in 1750 Steers was asked to report on whether the jetty head at the north-west corner should be leased or reserved for public use.[3] The dock was opened to shipping in 1753, but it was not finished until 1754 when the Corporation advanced £1,000 to the Trustees 'to enable them to complete the new dock, they having no funds for that purpose, or power to borrow any'.

The early references to buildings proposed to be erected on the Salthouse Dock quays by the Trustees are ambiguous or unsubstantiated; in the late 18th and early 19th centuries there were several proposals for building warehouses or erecting arcades,[4] but if any of these reached fruition no details of their construction have survived. Tenants, however, erected a variety of structures, some of which were then rented back to the Trustees for use as workshops and dock yards. The very short leases, typically three to seven years, granted to all tenants (including the Trustees) did not encourage substantial building.

Salthouse Dock.

12 Salthouse Dock, surrounded by transit sheds, c1900.

There was criticism from about 1800 of the dock's small size and of its tendency to silt up, landward access was congested until the filling-in of the Old Dock in 1826, and the widening of the west quay in 1825 had only partly relieved the overcrowding. Remedies proposed in reports by Jessop in 1800[5] and Foster in 1805[6] came to nothing and no significant improvements were effected until the dock was remodelled, and the Canning Half-tide Basin created, in the course of Albert Dock works. In November 1841 the Canning and Salthouse Docks were run dry, stanks were constructed to keep the water out and work commenced on deepening Salthouse Dock, rebuilding its walls and providing a second entrance. The excavation was undertaken by Messrs Bower & Murray who removed most of the material by wagon to Beacon's Gutter; the construction costs in the financial year 1841–42 amounted to £20,600. In October 1842 the dock re-opened for shipping with an iron cantilever swing bridge over the new entrance by the Haigh Foundry.

A decade later, in conjunction with the Wapping Improvements, the east quay was re-aligned parallel to the new road between the Custom House and the Crosbie Street railway terminus, adding a further acre of water, and the south quay was pierced by a new entrance to Wapping Basin. The ships re-admitted to the enlarged dock in January 1855 now had access to the rest of the southern docks as far as Queen's Dock. Within a century of its original construction Salthouse Dock had been nearly doubled in size; originally with only one entrance 34ft wide, it latterly was provided with three passages – two 45ft wide and one 50ft wide. No further major structural changes were undertaken, though substantial repairs were needed in 1912 when a part of the south end of the west quay wall, one of the oldest in the port, fell forward into the dock taking part of the shed above with it.

A shed 45ft wide and running almost the whole length of the east side of the dock was built in 1844; ten years later this was in the way of the works for the new Wapping Dock, and it was removed to Canning Dock. Open transit sheds were built along the north and west sides of the dock during the late '40s and early '50s, and parts of these were enclosed in 1859. In 1855 a closed shed on the east quay replaced the shed which had been removed to Canning Dock, and one of its gable ends has been retained as a landmark on the Inner Ring Road. The last major building to be put up on the Salthouse quays was a transit shed at the south end of the west side of the dock, in 1912.

Operation

Many of Liverpool's larger shipyards in the 18th century, whose predecessors had been forced out of their previous locations on the margins of the Pool through the construction of the Old Dock, came later to be established

13 Salthouse Dock in 1890 from the north, with Duke of Bridgewater's 1783 warehouse in the middle distance.

on the strand between Salthouse Dock and the Mersey. Here, among many others, were John Okill who in 1739 laid down the first Liverpool-built ship for the Royal Navy, the 44-gun ship *Hastings*. Other shipbuilders in the area who won naval contracts in the 18th century were John Sutton, and Roger and John Fisher. There were numerous builders of merchant ships, notable among them the Edward Graysons (father and son), Samuel Pearson, William Walley, James Rathbone who set out as a timber merchant but who entered the ship-building business through his opposition to the slave trade that was being carried on in ships built of his timber, and Peter Baker who by contrast traded in a large way with West Africa – including trading in slaves.

Liverpool's salt trade expanded greatly in the 18th century, assisted enormously by the making of the River

14   Detail of John Eyes' plan of 1768 with Salthouse Dock identified as South Dock

15   Salthouse Dock seen from roof of Albert Warehouses, 1907.

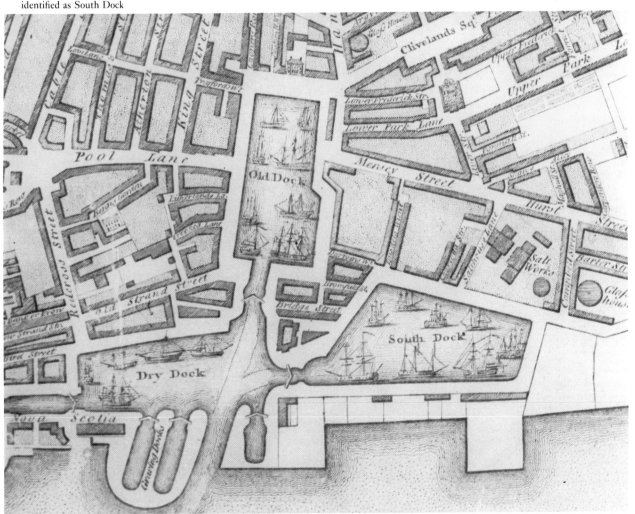

Weaver fully navigable from the Cheshire salt fields in the 1730s. While 15,000 tons were carried on the Weaver in 1732, the amount had doubled twenty years later. The trade was further encouraged by the construction of the Sankey Brook Navigation (St Helens Canal) in the 1750s, opening up the coalfields around Parr and St Helens. The two leading promoters of the canal were salt manufacturers, John Ashton of the salt works at Dungeon and John Blackburne junior, while Liverpool Corporation gave permission for its dock engineer, Henry Berry, to spend two days a week on the project. For most of the century there were regular sailings from Salthouse Dock for London and Bristol, for Scotland where salt was used to pickle herrings and to Ireland where it was used to cure pork. The growth of the Liverpool salt trade in the 19th century, however, largely occurred elsewhere in the Port. Blackburne's salt works was moved up stream to Garston Creek in 1793 when the smoke and fumes from the salt pans were no longer tolerable in what had become a densely populated area.

Trade with Ireland, however, continued throughout the life of the dock. Besides stone, hides, coal, yarn, foodstuffs, especially potatoes, and beer (Guinness was imported from 1824, latterly in the Company's own vessels), there was considerable passenger trade. Even in the 20th century many small vessels, mostly schooners and ketches, sailed between Liverpool and the ports on the north-east coast of Ireland.

'Only men of nerve and experience could trade regularly to such difficult ports as Kilkeel and Annalong, situated on the rockbound Down coast with Carlingford lough the sole refuge in bad weather .... Potato cargoes to Liverpool, with coal homeward to Down, were often the owners' private ventures. In addition; all the vessels carried "stone" cargoes, a few loaded in Kilkeel though most were exported from Annalong. The "stones" were Mourne granite setts and kerbs, quickly loaded down wooden shutes ... They were bad cargoes in rough weather and we rarely carried more than a hundred tons, for a schooner with a kerb cargo sailed as if in a strait-jacket and, in a seaway, she had a most uncomfortable roll, the dead weight in the bottom of her half-filled hold acting like a pendulum. . . .'[7]

In the 18th century a regular trade in cheese and other Cheshire dairy products developed to London and in the first decade of the 19th century there was increasing emphasis on coasting trade as the opening of larger wet docks elsewhere in the port attracted away the larger vessels. The Mediterranean trade, however, also continued to flourish throughout the period with the import of such commodities as wine, fruit, olive oil and sulphur, and by the early 1840s, berths were appropriated to vessels trading to Lisbon and Constantinople.

With the opening of the Albert Dock in 1846, there came a great change in the way the Salthouse Dock was used. Part of the change was due to the reconstruction of the dock itself, part was due to the building of the new Canning Half-tide entrance basin, while the greatest was due to the building of the warehouses around the Albert Dock. Lying parallel to Albert Dock and linked to it by a new entrance, Salthouse Dock became the loading dock for Albert. By the mid-1850s the pattern was well established of big ocean-going ships discharging into the Albert Dock warehouses and then moving to Salthouse for loading.

The ocean-going ships leaving Salthouse in the 1850s included those of the Black Ball Line to Australia, whose famous wooden sailing vessel, *Marco Polo* with 900 passengers on board made a record run of 68 days (faster than the best steamer's run, by a week) from Liverpool to St Phillip's Head in 1852. A preference for loading in Salthouse is clearly shown in the Pier Master's Log Books and is substantiated by a statement in 1860 from the warehouse superintendent of Albert Dock, that ships would not use the (newer) Wapping Warehouse for want of privilege of loading in Salthouse Dock. In the latter part of the 19th century, Salthouse continued to be used by large vessels, but its dependence on Albert Dock diminished as sailing ships were superseded by steamships too large for that dock. By the end of the century, however, such vessels had also outgrown Salthouse and the character of the dock returned to something like what it had been before the 1840s reconstruction. Once more it was the coasters and the Irish trade that tended to make their home in Salthouse Dock, together with (from 1912) the Royal Naval Reserve.

1 Evidence of LTB & 1754 is conflicting
2 LTB 7.xi.1750
3 LTB 3.i.1750
4 DCM 30.vi.1799; DCM 13.vi.1826
5 DCM 1.v.1800
6 DCM 30.vii.1805
7 England, 1981, 52–3

George's Dock was constructed under the terms of the 1761 Dock Act and in response to continual pressure for more dock space. The site of the new dock was occupied by a number of long-established users of the foreshore, especially shipbuilders, who had previously contested the Corporation's claims to ownership of this land.[1] However, the 1761 Act established the Corporation's right to the foreshore, and the Corporation subsequently granted to the Trustees some 14 acres for dock construction at the ends of James Street and Chapel Street.

George's Dock and Basin were probably designed by Henry Berry, who had succeeded Steers as dock engineer in 1750. The construction started in June 1762, but was interrupted in October by a violent storm which destroyed all of the wall so far completed. John Eyes' 1765 Survey of Liverpool shows the site and outline of the intended dock, but it is not clear whether his lines, featuring a series of embrasures along the river wall, are meant to represent actual engineering works, such as Berry's St Helens Canal lock chambers. The structures described by Eyes were not built in any case, and the 3-acre dock eventually completed in 1771 was rectangular and lying parallel to the river. It had a tidal ('dry') entrance basin at the north end and a lock-like passage (made from the 1746 graving dock) at the south end where it was connected to the existing Dry Dock.

In 1768 the Corporation paid John Hope twelve guineas for copying and altering the plans of a set of warehouses intended to be built between Water Street and Moor Street,[2] but no warehouses were erected until 1793 when the first Goree warehouses were built on the east side of George's Dock. According to Troughton,[3] these comprised seventeen large warehouses, many of them thirteen storeys high, but they were completely destroyed by fire in 1802. On the night of the Goree fire, it was only the chance of a westerly wind, away from the ships, and a high tide enabling vessels to be moved clear that prevented the blazing warehouses from setting the ships in the dock alight. As it was, the value of the goods destroyed was over £250,000 and the value of the buildings themselves was another £44,000. Although the Goree fire was frequently cited over the next few decades as an argument against building warehouses alongside docks, the Corporation resolved in 1807 to erect warehouses on George's Dock west quay and replaced in 1810 the Goree

warehouses on the east. The second Goree warehouses, which were brick, six storeys high, with a street-level stone arcade, stood until destroyed by bombing in 1941 (they are described further on p139).

George's Dock was enlarged slightly by John Foster between 1810 and 1815; Foster consulted Rennie over the design of a caisson for building the seaward foundations.[4] When the walls were reported to be in an extremely dilapidated state in 1822 he instigated a further rebuilding programme. The first excavation contracts were let to Joseph Jones and John Perry, and the masonry contract to William McConochie, after the original contractor, Timothy Grindrod, had been found to be involved in a materials fraud that also touched Foster himself. The work was completed under the direction of the newly-appointed Jesse Hartley.

George's Dock.

16   George's Dock, c1890.

The new masonry was to be founded on oak or beech piles, and built behind an iron cofferdam formed of iron piles on a system patented by Peter Ewart. Machinery and all materials (including an iron railway for moving them) were provided by the Trustees, presumably in order to guarantee their quality.[5] In 1824 a transit shed was built on the new east quay, with iron columns and a slate roof on fir trusses. When opened in 1825, the reconstructed dock was some thirty per cent larger in area than its predecessor, with a west pier that extended forty yards further into the river.

More reconstruction took place in the late 19th century. In 1871 the entrance basin was closed, in order to improve the approaches from the town to the ferry landing stages on the river, and from then on the only access to George's Dock was by a 40ft passage from Canning Dock. A continuing decline in the use made of the dock thereafter, and the need for a proper esplanade and for still better access to the Mersey ferries, led finally to the closure of the Dock in 1900 and to that of the ferry basin in 1904. The site is now occupied by the principal buildings of the Pier Head: the Port of Liverpool Building, the Royal Liver Building, the Cunard Building and the George's Dock Tunnel Building which houses the ventilating machinery for the Mersey tunnel, but remains of George's Dock wall are still visible in the lower basement of the Cunard Building.

Operation

In the 18th century George's Dock was dominated by traders to West Africa, North America and the West Indies, and the area surrounding the dock, all reclaimed from the foreshore after 1750, was soon densely occupied too. The west quay was the site of a number of timber yards while up to the 1780s shipbuilders clung tenaciously to the east quay. To the west of George's Dock Passage lay the neighbourhood known as Nova Scotia, where, amongst the offices of the Dublin and Isle of Man packets and the Manchester flats were tar warehouses, coal merchants, blockmakers, public houses and the dwellings of river pilots and boatmen. To the south-west of the dock was Mann Island, a somewhat insalubrious part of the waterfront lined with warehouses and public houses.

Despite the enlargement of George's Dock in the 1820s,

17   A view of the original Goree Warehouses (Troughton).

18   Cunard liner *Aquitania* at Liverpool Landing Stage between 30 May
and August, 1914.

the ocean-going ships were increasingly supplanted by the coastal and Mediterranean shipping typical of the later years of all the early docks. In the 19th century, Mediterranean traders from George's Dock included John Glynn & Son, running a fortnightly service to western Italy and Sicily; James Moss & Co, trading to Sicily, the Adriatic and the eastern Mediterranean; John Bibby to Lisbon and Oporto as well as to Italy. In 1844 transit sheds were appropriated to the Portuguese and Mediterranean traders, and by the middle of the century George's Dock was the centre for the fresh fruit trade.

Serious congestion resulted from the competition for berths and facilities from fishing smacks and from the Mersey flats that brought goods for transhipment from up country. In 1864 it was ordered that no goods requiring cartage were to be landed on the south quay of George's Basin, and that all such traffic was in future to come ashore on the broader quays of Harrington Basin.

From the beginning, too, there was conflict with the Mersey ferries which sailed from the dock, basin and foreshore. These ferries had a history dating back to the 14th century and their proliferation from the late 18th century reflected the port's growing trade and population. In 1815 the first steam ferry, *Elizabeth*, began to operate on the Mersey and, by mid-century, ferries were plying to eleven different places on the Cheshire shore. The cumbersome wooden drawbridges across the dock entrances were replaced in 1821 by iron, double-leafed, cantilever swing bridges that could be opened and closed in three minutes. These were similar to that designed for the London Docks by Rennie in 1803 and were supplied by William Hazledine who was already erecting two other such bridges. Ferry passengers were still liable to be stranded by the opening of these bridges, however, and by the 1860s congestion on the dock road had become so acute that a high-level foot bridge was built for ferry passengers from the Old Church Yard to the north end of George's Dock.

The Mersey's great tidal range created problems of embarking and disembarking from the ferries which were only to be finally solved by the building of a floating landing stage. Early 18th-century views show a wooden pier protruding into the river in the vicinity of the later Canning Half-tide Dock but such piers would have been an unacceptable navigation hazard as traffic on the river increased. In 1826 Marc Brunel was invited to design 'a landing for passengers from steam boats so as to be equally convenient at high and low water'[6] and the Corporation Accounts for the year 1833 record an expenditure of around £35,000 on landing stages with moveable piers, but it is not known if this first stage was built to Brunel's design. No other contemporary reference to a floating landing stage has been traced. The first floating stage of which records survive was designed in 1845 by William Cubitt and opened in 1847. This was a wooden deck 500ft long by 70ft wide, carried on iron pontoons of semi-circular section, connected to the land by two wooden bridges hinged at either end, and moored to the river bottom by four cables and fluked anchors. The new pier was appropriated to ferries for nine destinations in Cheshire, and to the tender for the ocean mails. A further landing stage to cope with the increased traffic was added in 1857. These two floating piers and the Ferry Goods Stage erected between them were collectively known as the Liverpool Landing Stage. It was destroyed by fire in July 1874 and rebuilt by the end of 1875. The eventual closure of George's Dock was due in large part to its increasingly impeding the growing ferry traffic.

1 Touzeau, 1910, ii, 485 ff.
2 LTB 6.vii.1758
3 Troughton, 1810, 232–3
4 DCM 2.vii.1811
5 MDHB Contracts Book 5.vii.1822
6 Beamish, R., *Memoirs of the Life of Sir Marc Isambard Brunel*, 1862, 199

Duke's Dock was unusual among the South Docks because it was built privately to serve inland trade. It was constructed for Francis, third Duke of Bridgewater, and intended for the transhipment of cargoes carried on the Bridgewater Canal (opened from Worsley to Manchester in 1764 and through to Runcorn in 1778) and on the Trent and Mersey Canal (with which the Bridgewater Canal made an arrangement in 1778).

The ultimate need for a Liverpool terminus had been apparent long before the Canal's completion, and in 1765 the Duke leased a piece of land immediately south of Salthouse Dock, strategically placed at the natural point of the future growth of the port. The 14,000 square feet acquired was augmented after 1765 by made ground on the foreshore, a process that was taking place all along the south shore, and in which the Canal engineers may have been able to employ experience gained from dealing with swampy ground around Manchester. The dock was nearly rectangular, some 70yds by 30yds, reached through a tidal passage. It more nearly resembled a canal than a harbour dock and was probably the creation of one of the engineers to the Bridgewater Canal, John Gilbert.[1] Construction was probably facilitated by the ease with which the company could carry building materials from up country; there was always more bulk cargo travelling inland from Liverpool than in the opposite direction, and space was available in barges and flats. The dock walls

20 Duke's Grain Warehouse, 1958.

were of sandstone, probably from the Runcorn area; the works were superintended by Thomas Wallwork, and were complete by 1773.[2]

For vessels of the inland trade, fast turnaround was essential, and carriers with guaranteed berths and warehousing enjoyed a considerable advantage over those without. Warehouses were needed especially by merchants engaged in the perishable commodity trades – grain and cotton for instance – which required long-term covered storage. Consequently, the Bridgewater undertaking, which carried large quantities of grain and cotton inland, was the first in the Port of Liverpool to build a dockside warehouse that was not separated from the dock by a public thoroughfare. This first quayside warehouse was built at Duke's Dock by Peter Hewitt & Co between 1780 and 1783; it was eight storeys high, of brick, 93ft long and 45ft deep.

In 1811 a grain warehouse with internal loading docks or barge holes, similar to the Grocer's Warehouse at Castlefield, Manchester, but with an internal iron frame, was completed at Duke's Dock. An 'iron warehouse' (presumably also an iron framed structure) was built between 1820 and 1828, at a cost of £3,062 to

19 Duke's and Albert Docks from the south-west, 1934.

accommodate the Staffordshire trade.[3] The 2-storey Great Western shed of 1857 seems to have had internal iron columns identical to those in a transit shed of 1870 on the north side of the Dock;[4] these columns bore the legend *Bridgewater Foundry Runcorn* and strongly imply that the Bridgewater organization had the capacity to undertake most of its own structural work.

Until the major reconstructions in the 1840s, in only one case, the extension of the river wall in 1811 as a result of the Liverpool Dock Trustees' extending their own river frontage, was work undertaken by the port authority rather than by the Bridgewater Trustees. Even that may have been as a result of pressure brought to bear by the Bridgewater Estate, and the £5,000 paid by the Bridgewater Trustees was probably no more than a token contribution to the cost.

21   Duke's Dock in the 1950s.

Shortage of capital in the 1820s and 1830s, caused largely by restrictive clauses in the Duke's will, led to neglect of maintenance. Though the dock walls were said to be crumbling and the dock gates held together with rope, the Trustees authorized only such repairs 'as will secure the walls and dock gates from falling down'. The river wall, too, was in a poor state. The shoreline represented piecemeal accretions over the previous fifty years, and lacked regularity of shape or structure. Some of the wall had been built by the Corporation, some by tenant shipbuilders, some by the Bridgewater Trustees. A shoal off the river entrance and queues of barges waiting in the river made the area off the dock hazardous to shipping, but no remedial action was taken until the 1840s.

A new river entrance and half-tide basin were built at Duke's Dock under the terms of the 1841 Act that sanctioned the building of Albert Dock. The work, for which the Bridgewater Trustees paid £9,181, was planned and executed by Hartley. The river wall and Duke's piers were founded on piles and sheathed in stone. Steam machinery and a large body of workmen made rapid work possible, and the half-tide basin was open to shipping by October, 1845. The dock improvements cut turn-round time; flats could enter and leave on the same day, taking advantage of the longer times of opening provided by the half-tide basin. The wider river entrance also allowed coasters to sail straight into the Dock. An eastern passage was built to the new Wapping Basin ten years later, and after 1945 when the river entrance was walled up, this became the only outlet; the Duke's Dock became in effect a branch dock off Wapping, only accessible by the Canning or Brunswick entrances. The Duke's Dock's own branch to the south was filled in in 1960 when the grain warehouse which it served had been demolished, and by 1982 only the two docks and the headquarters building put up in 1865 remained.

Operation

For all that coal had been a major factor in the Bridgewater Canal's promotion, it played little part in the trade at the Duke's Dock. Foodstuffs dominated it from early on, serving as it did the burgeoning populations of the industrial hinterland. Between 1780 and 1800, sugar, spices, tea, herrings, molasses and corn were forwarded, while the grain trade grew to such an extent that the seven-storey grain warehouse was built. Grain ships berthed in the King's Dock, immediately to the south, and could be discharged into the warehouse from which grain could be re-loaded into flats in the large barge holes beneath. Grain ships in Duke's Dock could also discharge overside directly into barges in the dock.

From the beginning of its history Duke's Dock was flanked by timber yards. The timber trade became so important to the Bridgewater operation that, around 1838, the Trustees built a new dock, called Egerton Dock, south of the old Harrington Docks for the exclusive use of timber merchants. The seasonal nature of this trade had caused acute operational difficulties: in March, April and May there were no ships in port from North America and the Baltic; in July, August and September they arrived in great numbers. It was impossible to accommodate these fluctuations without disrupting all other trades. Moreover, the whole timber trade of the port was moving south, following the opening of the Brunswick timber dock in

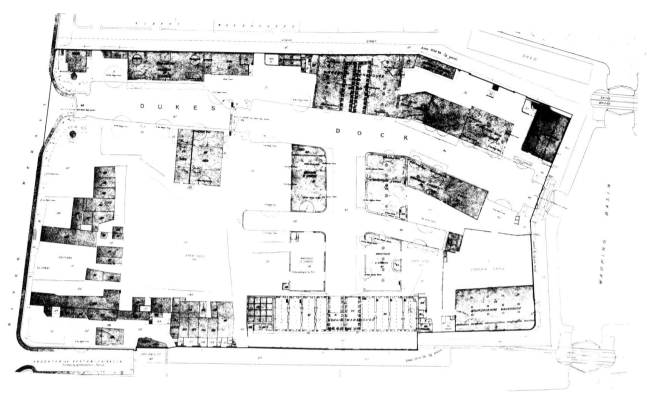

22   Site plan Duke's Dock, 1899.

1832. Timber continued to be handled at Duke's Dock, however, and various timber importers had premises there until the 1960s.

Another of the important cargoes to be carried in the Duke's flats from Liverpool to Manchester was cotton, in square bales from the East Indies and round bales from America. The cotton traders often used the carriers' warehouses for stock control, only withdrawing merchandise when they were ready to use it. The tendency of all carriers on the canal network to want storage space increased the demand for shed and warehouse accommodation at termini such as Duke's Dock where the quays were soon lined with buildings, many of them let. More structures were added every few years until 1899 when the schedule of buildings at Duke's Dock numbered one hundred and sixty-six. The ancillary installations included a copper yard, engine and boiler houses, various offices, a shipyard, joiners' shop, smithies, coal yard, stables, a number of dwelling houses and one henhouse.

The completion of the Trent and Mersey Canal in 1777

provided a water route from the Potteries which was particularly useful for the carriage of fragile, bulky earthenware. The Bridgewater Trustees consolidated their interest in this important trade when in 1848 they acquired the Anderton Company which specialized in the carriage of pottery from Staffordshire to the Mersey. Backloads included soda, flour and bulk materials used in the manufacture of ceramics. The Anderton Company built its own wooden narrow boats with characteristic barrel-shaped sides that enabled them to make the fast trips required by the potters, and it used the original type of boat until the 1950s.

The Bridgewater organization, too, built many of its own flats and barges, in the Duke's yards at Bangor on Dee. These vessels were carvel built of heavy timbers to withstand frequent groundings, with short single masts supported in tabernacles; they were beamy boats about 45ft long which carried about 30 tons of cargo. The river flats used on the Mersey and on the Mersey and Irwell navigation were much bigger – about 66ft long – drew up to 5ft and were too broad for the canal. The Bridgewater flats sailed on the river before steam haulage became common, and were drawn by horses on the canal. The sailing flats could be hard to handle:

'This morning we had four flats to sail out of His Grace's docks ... and had near 30 men to get them out and only one got clear without running against Rathbone wall – the other three stroke against it but not much damaged – but much of the flood was spent before they got off and I am not certain whether they would all get up to Runcorn in the same tide.'[6]

In 1781 Bridgewater had 26 flats; in 1790 the number had grown to 42 and by 1825 it was 75 in all. Steam tugs were introduced in the 19th century and by 1880 there were 20 tugs each capable of hauling 3 barges.

Acquisition of the Mersey and Irwell Navigation in 1844 for the sum of £402,000 brought the Manchester Dock under the control of the Bridgewater Trustees, and both helped to reduce water-borne competition and strengthened the Trustees in their dealings with the railways. In the 1850s an arrangement was entered into whereby goods for Liverpool and Manchester arriving by rail at Birkenhead from the south were transferred to Bridgewater flats and carried on by water. In 1853 a short branch line was opened between the Birkenhead railway to the Bridgewater Canal at Norton in Cheshire; thereafter Duke's Dock was increasingly used by cross-river traffic and by such coasting vessels as could clear the high sill of the dock.

In 1872 the Bridgewater Canal and all its associated properties and assets were sold into a joint stock company called the Bridgewater Navigation Company. This whole company was acquired in 1887 at a cost of £1,710,000 by the Manchester Ship Canal Company which needed the Mersey and Irwell Navigation for its own line – a fortunate circumstance as the opening of the Ship Canal in 1894 would have ended the Bridgewater's monopoly of inland water-borne trade out of Liverpool. Duke's Dock then became a base for the Ship Canal's coastal operations, though when cargoes landed in Manchester were subsequently barged back to Liverpool, far more trouble was caused than if they had been discharged in Liverpool in the first place.

Despite its limitations in size and the inconvenience sometimes arising from its operation in conjunction with the Ship Canal, Duke's Dock remained busy for some years to come. Commodities handled included grain, cotton, flour, linseed oil, sugar and animal feeds. In 1899 over three hundred thousand tons of cargo were handled, one third by private carriers and two thirds by the Bridgewater department of the Manchester Ship Canal Company; of the Company's share, half comprised lighterage from Birkenhead for the Great Western Railway and for the Pacific Steam Navigation Company.

In 1899, however, Duke's Dock was sold to the Mersey Docks and Harbour Board. The Ship Canal Company required the capital, the Dock Board wished to consolidate its ownership of the estate, and the purchase would end anomalies in the payment of port dues on goods imported through Manchester. The £522,000 selling price, decided by arbitration, reflected the strategic value of the site and the extensive range of buildings and facilities about the dock. The Bridgewater department itself retained tenancies of premises at Duke's until 1921. After the First World War the rapid development of road haulage increasingly limited the water-borne traffic handled by the Duke's Dock, and though the warehouses continued to be occupied until the early 1960s, for several decades before that the Dock had been '. . . a graveyard for Liverpool's unwanted derelicts; a most depressing sight, with mouldering tugs, barges and small craft of every description, slowly dying on the refuse-laden water'.[7]

1 Malet, 1977, 41
2 1773–1803 The undertaking governed by the Duke of Bridgewater
   1803–1872 The undertaking governed by the Bridgewater Trustees
   1882–1887 The undertaking governed by the Bridgewater Navigation Co
   1887–1900 The undertaking governed by the Manchester Ship Canal Co (Bridgewater Department)
3 Mather, 1970, 55
4 1870 shed recorded by Merseyside Docklands History Survey prior to demolition, 1982
5 Mather, 1970, 56
6 Malet, 1977, 136
7 England, 1981, 28

Manchester Dock and Chester Basin

Manchester Dock was built by the Corporation of Liverpool for barges and flats using the inland waterways. The construction of this small, originally tidal dock which lay between the Canning Graving Docks and George's Dock was probably undertaken to accommodate the crowds of barges near the then centre of the dock system. The growth in river traffic was partly due to the development of Mersey and Irwell Navigation Company terminals in Warrington and Manchester and to improvements in the Rivers Mersey and Irwell; Bridgewater Canal craft were accommodated in Duke's Dock but other vessels had no suitable, regular berths.

23   Manchester Dock, c1928, from the west.

The river craft were often a hazard to both navigation and operation, and at least by 1772 Henry Berry was authorized to build a quay to the west of the Dry Pier (ie the riverward quay of the Dry Basin of the Old Dock) and also to '... purchase or contract for an engine ... there for the weighing of coal at the expense of the Corporation'.[1] Picton reported that around 1785 the Corporation built a dock on the site,[2] and in 1789 the Corporation ordered 'the erection of sheds, cranes and other conveniences for the accommodation of the merchants, dealers and others in the loading and unloading of the goods from flats employed in the navigation of the rivers Mersey and Irwell'.[3] In 1790 the proprietors of the Mersey and Irwell Navigation were operating a daily goods service between Liverpool and

Manchester, using 23 vessels, and a carrying service between Warrington and Liverpool using 5 vessels.[4] Inland traffic was given another boost by the extension in 1795, of the Ellesmere to Chester section of what was to become the Shropshire Union Canal and in that year the Corporation constructed another tidal basin for river craft north of Manchester Basin. The new basin became known as Chester Basin.

24   Chester Basin, c1928, from the west.

In about 1815 the Corporation added gates and an entrance lock to Manchester Dock, enclosing a water area of just over one acre in the dock. During the next thirty-five years parts of Irwell Street and Mann Island, which bounded the Mersey and Irwell Navigation Company's yard to the east and north respectively, were developed as offices, warehouses and agents' residences. One of these buildings was a shed erected in 1841 by the Navigation Company for the use of, and presumably to attract, independent traders. Yet despite other attempts to improve a declining trading position relative to the railway companies in particular, the proprietors of the Mersey and Irwell Navigation Company eventually decided to sell their undertaking to the Bridgewater Trustees in 1844. In 1851 the Dock Trustees purchased both Manchester Dock and Chester Basin from the Corporation, though the Bridgewater Trustees continued to lease the surrounding land and buildings.

Operation

The use of Manchester Dock during the late 18th and early 19th centuries was dominated by the trades in coal and manufactured goods to Liverpool and corn and cotton back to the inland manufacturing districts. From at least 1793 coal yards around the dock are recorded. In 1825, each day, thirty-three flats could be loaded and unloaded; an average flat load was 30 tons giving a rough total of 1,000 tons of goods handled daily. Part of the dock was let to coasters whose cargoes were 'taken at once into the country' by the inland carriers. A scheme to develop the Manchester Dock site as a railway depot was proposed by John Bramley-Moore in 1846, and the Dock Trustees went as far as to agree relocation compensation with the existing tenants, but the project never came to fruition.

From the middle of the 19th century, Manchester Dock was used increasingly as a lighterage dock in conjunction with the railway companies, particularly those on the Birkenhead side of the river. In 1860 the Dock Board appropriated to the use of the Birkenhead Railway Company a covered berth in the south-east corner and two adjoining berths on the south side of Manchester Dock. By 1872 it was agreed that all of the Manchester Dock premises should be let to the London and North Western Railway Company (representing also the Shropshire Union Railway and Canal Company, the Great Western Railway and the Birkenhead Joint Lines). The Dock Board then undertook certain alterations to the buildings and machinery, and gave the tenants permission to further adapt the premises to their own needs. In 1875 the Great Western Railway Company erected an engine, boiler house, 5-ton crane and a road weigh-bridge; the

Shropshire Union Railway & Canal Company enclosed a portion of the north quay to make a coal depot. (A major fire destroyed many of the buildings at Manchester Dock in 1890, but most of these were replaced within a year or so.) Other additions to the cargo handling facilities installed at Manchester Dock included a 22ft radius, one-ton hydraulic crane (1909) and various hydraulic appliances in the Great Western Railway Company depot in Irwell Street (supplied from 1919 with hydraulic power from the Liverpool Hydraulic Power Company).

Competition, first from the Manchester Ship Canal (opened 1894), and later from road hauliers, contributed to a decline in the use of the inland carriers' docks and no regrets were voiced when the Manchester Dock and Chester Basin were closed and filled. By the mid-1920s the Shropshire Union Railway & Canal Company had given up its cross-river lighterage business and the Great Western Railway Company was considering discontinuing the use of Manchester Dock for barging. In any case, the whole site was settling dangerously as a result of the Mersey Tunnel excavations being carried out below. Once the decision had been taken to close the dock, it became necessary to fill it, and between 1928 and 1936 Manchester Dock and Chester Basin were filled with 60,000 tons of spoil from the tunnel works.

1 LRO. 352 CLE/TRA 1/2/22 Book 21
2 LRO returns relating to Liverpool Town Dues, etc, 1857, 41
3 Pope, D. J., *Shipping & Trade in the Port of Liverpool 1783–1793*, unpublished thesis, Liverpool University, 1970
4 Hayman, 1981, 17

King's and Queen's Dock

Between 1771 when George's Dock was opened, and the Dock Act of 1785 authorizing the building of two new docks, there was a sixty per cent increase in the number of ships using the port, and this despite the American War of Independence. The Act authorized the Trustees to borrow up to £70,000 – a sizeable increase over previous building costs, and independent of the cost of land bought for the Trustees by the Corporation. The new docks comprised two wet docks of $7\frac{3}{4}$ and $6\frac{1}{4}$ acres, two graving docks, two grid irons and a common, tidal, entrance basin. The docks may have had different designers as Berry resigned, at the age of seventy, from the post of Dock Engineer in 1789, the year after the opening of King's Dock. Thus his successor, Thomas Morris, may have been responsible for much of the work on Queen's Dock which was not completed until 1795, and Morris or the Corporation's surveyor, John Foster, for the graving docks which were completed in 1796.

The Corporation paid £27,315 for some fifteen acres of land for the new dock which it presented to the Trustees along with another fifteen acres already its property. (The cost of the land acquired by purchase was to be repaid out of port dues.) Most of this land had been reclaimed from the Mersey by Corporation tenants whose leases included covenants to enclose their foreshores. Most were merchants and shipbuilders, and though many could be dispossessed as soon as their short leases expired, others could only be removed after the offer (by the Corporation) of alternative sites. In these transactions, as in the original acquisition of land for the new docks, the Corporation was assisted by its powers to acquire land as and when it needed it; the Dock Trustees could only do so to carry out the express requirements of each Dock Act. Other land, however, was made by the Trustees themselves with spoil from dock excavations.

Construction started in 1785. Contractors for the masonry – the relatively soft, yellow sandstone from Brownlow Hill was used here for the last time – were Peter Buxton and Edmund Haighton (described as a miller) who were to provide labour and tools at 3s 8d per cubic yard for getting, carrying and setting, plus 11d per superficial yard for dressing the stone. Faces of the dock wall were of squared blocks laid in courses and scappled.

Shortly, however, the new docks began to be criticized. In 1800 the Harbour Master, Dock Master and Master

Pilots submitted to the Dock Committee a petition which *inter alia* drew attention to the mud in the docks and to the dangerous proximity of the Pluckington Bank to the entrance.[1] The Committee itself was concerned about the collapsing dock walls, and accordingly consulted the engineer William Jessop about this and about silting in 1800,[2] and approached John Rennie for fresh advice in 1809.[3]

25   East end of 1905 transit sheds.

Although no action was taken as a direct result of the consultants' recommendations, sluicing was improved over the next few years, and iron paddles fitted for the cloughs at Queen's Dock. Around 1800 the west pier of King's Dock was extended into the river, and between 1802 and 1810 the dock was deepened and widened slightly, with walls of ashlar backed with rubble. Queen's Dock was nearly doubled in size between 1810 and 1816. Pressure for dock accommodation was such that all ships which could take the ground without harm were left in the docks when they dried at ebb tides during reconstruction, while a chain across the King's Dock entrance prevented small craft entering the dock at an early state of the tide and impeding the work. Nevertheless, the much needed conversion of the entrance basin into a half-tide dock, despite repeated recommendations, was not undertaken until 1851–52, when two pairs of gates, 50ft and 70ft, were placed flanking an island at the river entrance. At the same time a passage was formed between the two docks, and Queen's Dock further deepened and its walls rebuilt.

King's and Queen's Docks   37

In 1843 the Corporation contracted for the construction of a lock and dock for inland carriers off the basin (also built by the Corporation, in 1825) called Clark's Hole. The new River Craft Dock, bounded by Etna Street, Queen's Dock and Coburg Dock cost some £25,000 to build and was operational by the middle of 1844.

26   The 1793 tobacco warehouse with bridge over entrance to Queen's Dock beyond, c1800.

The continuing growth of vessels and the lack of modern equipment that King's and Queen's Dock shared with all the older docks left them still at a disadvantage. The Mersey Docks (New Works) Act of 1898, generally known as the Southern Works Act, empowered the Dock Board to rebuild completely the group situated between Wapping Basin and Toxteth Dock. The provisions of the Act included the construction of an unbroken line of river wall from the entrance to the Duke's Dock to a new double entrance just north of Toxteth Dock, the enlargement of Queen's Dock by building two new branch docks at right angles to the existing dock, and the rebuilding of the King's Dock site to form two further new branch docks. Entrance thereafter was either by Canning Island or by Brunswick locks. The dock engineer, A. G. Lyster, explained the purpose of the work in 1900:

'*These docks were intended to provide for a class of vessel of somewhat smaller size than those for which the northern group was designed. The fact that all these docks were situated so far upstream, and that much utilizing them would have to run the gauntlet of all the traffic of the river ... rendered it advisable to limit the proportion of the scheme so as to suit a more moderate size of vessel.*'[4]

The landward approaches to the original King's and Queen's Docks were never as congested as were some of their predecessors'; not only were they situated slightly away from the town centre but also their construction neatly coincided with the passage of the first Liverpool Improvement Act in 1786. Almost from the first, warehouses began to be erected in the vicinity of the new docks.

A number of Virginia merchants, such as John Sparling and William Bolden, were established in the area before the docks were built, and the first warehouse to be erected by the Corporation was a bonded tobacco warehouse built in 1793 at the north east corner of King's Dock. This warehouse, described more fully on p155, measured 210ft by 180ft, and was intended to contain 7,000 hogsheads of tobacco. Largely demolished in 1824, a part of it was retained for a few years as a store for other goods, particularly for saltpetre.

27   Queen's Dock from the east with 1852 half-tide basin and river entrance in background.

Continued expansion of the tobacco trade caused the Corporation to replace this warehouse within 20 years by a larger warehouse built between 1811 and 1814, probably to the design of John Foster. It was a single-storey, brick-clad structure some 577ft by 241ft, with circular iron columns at 17ft and 52ft centres, timber beams and a timber and slate roof. Although it covered an area of over three acres and could hold 23,000 hogsheads of tobacco, the new warehouse had to be extended in 1846 and again in 1854 in order to accommodate the trade. Even so, it was necessary for the Customs authorities to sanction the use of parts of the north Stanley, Albert and Wapping Warehouses for tobacco storage after 1870. The King's Dock warehouse was demolished in 1904, and the tobacco trade was concentrated thereafter in the new warehouse at Stanley Dock.

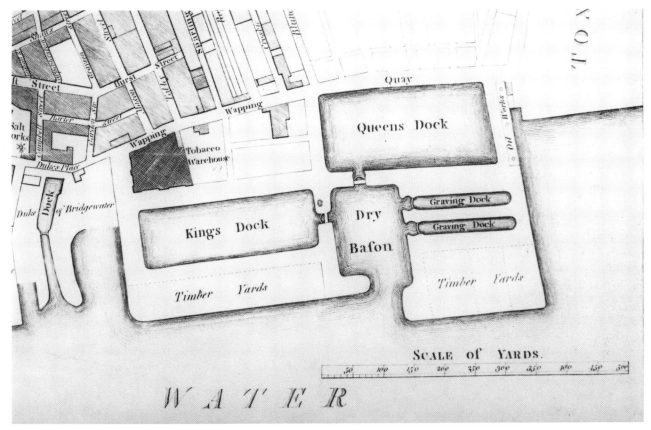

28   Detail from a plan of the Town of Liverpool, 1796.

Early proposals to build on the east side of the Queen's Dock were abortive until Foster built a single-storey, open-fronted shed there in 1818. This had iron columns and an iron roof and it stood until 1868 when it was replaced following irreparable collision damage by a lorry. It is described in detail on p132. By then most of the east and west quays of Queen's Dock were occupied by sheds, while the north and south ends and most of the land around the graving docks remained empty. A less usual building was the oil house built between No 5 Graving Dock and the river. Constructed at the expense of the Corporation between 1801 and 1803, it replaced Nat Kershaw's blubber house that had previously occupied part of the site of the docks. The Liverpool whaling trade was based here at the end of the 18th century, but the number of whalers belonging to the port declined from 21 in 1788 to 2 by 1814.

Dock accommodation was altered radically in the 1898 Southern Works Act programme. Double-storey transit sheds were built between the two King's Branch Docks and between the two Queen's Branch Docks, and single-storey sheds on either side of the roadway running down to the river from the Wapping–Queen's bridge. The sheds had open fronts with continuous sliding doors at quay level and large loading doorways opening on to the road behind. Some of the double-storey sheds were equipped with 30cwt electric roof cranes. The buildings were of brick with cast iron, fireclay-clad columns and steel roofs with granite setts on the ground floors and concrete floors on steel joists above.

Operation

Objections to the inadequate depth of the Old Dock, where most tobacco was traditionally landed, and to the smoke from the 'King's pipe' (the Custom House furnace where damaged tobacco was destroyed) prompted the removal of the tobacco trade to King's Dock as soon as the warehouse there was completed. Tobacco continued to be an important cargo at King's Dock throughout the 19th century, though by the 1870s it was also being landed elsewhere in the port and carted or barged to the tobacco warehouse. The growth in the volume of the trade and the absence of any overhead gear or hydraulic cranes in the King's warehouse eventually made it imperative to provide better accommodation, and a new tobacco warehouse was built in 1900 at Stanley Dock.

By the middle of the 19th century the trade of King's and Queen's Docks had become quite diverse. The Mediterranean trade was established early and continued to grow. African and South American traders were berthed in Queen's Dock, carrying piece goods, coal and salt outward in return for palm oil, cotton, hides and coffee. North American grain and cotton also came in here. Ships of the Cunard Line and Edward Thompson's Australian packets were also berthed in King's and Queen's Docks. While some of this trade was seasonal, coastal and inland traffic kept the docks occupied at all times; the Anderton Company rented a yard at the north end of King's dock in the 1830s, and in the 1850s and 1860s quantities of potatoes were landed. A mariners' floating chapel, converted from a former naval vessel by the last of the Liverpool whaling captains, William Scoresby, was also moored for some years in King's Dock.

Despite the successive displacement of shipbuilders by dock construction, shipbuilding continued, and Queen's Dock became the centre for the timber trade. Its 130-yard south quay was designated as a timber quay in 1805, and the east side in the 1820s. Further expansion was checked by the opening of the Brunswick timber dock in 1832, and by gradual encroachments on the Queen's Dock quays which impeded the Liverpool practice of discharging timber on to the quay (as distinct from unloading into timber ponds as practised in London). None the less in 1835 the Liverpool and Manchester Railway built a line along the eastern quays of Queen's Dock specifically for the timber trade, and by 1840 there were lines of railway to the foot of King's Dock.

The provision of two graving docks and two grid irons was a considerable attraction for ship repairers. Their facilities, first commissioned in 1796, must have been of a high standard as they accommodated such notable vessels as, in 1846, the *Great Britain* (at 3,270 tons the largest ship afloat) and in 1848 Cunard's transatlantic steamer *America* (1,826 tons). Some time after 1852, 20-ton masting shears were erected on the south quay of the half-tide basin near the entrance to No 2 Graving Dock. Overhauled in 1883, these were a permanent installation equivalent to the mast-houses found in London and continental docks.

The 1900–07 reconstruction of King's and Queen's Docks deprived them of their own river entrance. The new 240ft by 80ft and 350ft by 100ft locks at Brunswick provided alternative entrances of adequate length and breadth for large ships, but the Pluckington Bank always limited the available depth of water. This resulted first in the concentration in King's and Queen's Docks of ocean traders of shallow draught, and later on coastal vessels, and led finally – with all the southern group – to their closure. Around 1910, companies with appropriated berths included Alfred Holt & Co, Ocean Steamship Co Ltd, China Mutual Steam Navigation Co Ltd (all in Queen's Branch No 2) trading to the Far East, the Booth Line (King's No 2) to South America, and the Hall Line (Queen's No 2) to South Africa and India. In the 1920s these had been joined by the Palm Line (Queen's No 2) established to import the vegetable oil processed by Lever Brothers at Port Sunlight.

After the Second World War, of the ocean-going traders, only Booth and Palm Lines remained. Others now were MacAndrew's and Swedish Lloyd to the Baltic and the Mediterranean, British and Continental Steamship Company to the Netherlands, Currie Line to north Germany, and the Irish and Mersey Company and the Limerick Steamship Company to Ireland.

1 DCM 6.viii.1800
2 DCM 1.v.1800
3 Rennie, *Report to Dock Committee*, 28.xii.1809 (Gladstone colln, Liverpool Athenaeum)
4 Lyster, A. G., *Works recently carried out & in contemplation at the Port of Liverpool*, International Navigation Congress, Paris, 1900.

Canning Dock

The Act of 1811 which granted powers to fill the Old Dock also sanctioned the conversion of its tidal entrance basin to a wet dock. This basin had been reconstructed under the 1737 Act, and sections of wall dating from these works can still be seen. The delay in filling the Old Dock equally affected progress with the conversion of its basin, and it was not until February 1826 that Hartley prepared the specification for excavating the bed of the basin to 2ft below ODS. In July he submitted to the Dock Committee his plan for diverting the sewers which emptied into the dock. By December 1829, gates had been added and the Dry Dock was reopened as a wet dock, and re-named Canning Dock in June 1832.

The conversion of the Dry Dock to a wet dock necessitated the development of an alternative method of draining the adjacent graving docks, the ownership of which had been transferred, c1825, from the Corporation to the Trust. Connected as they were in 1829 to a dock which was to remain flooded for most of the time, emptying the graving docks once vessels had come in on the top of the tide posed a problem. On the advice of their surveyor, the Dock Committee resolved to provide syphons for docks Nos 1 and 3 and a sluice for No 2. Later they decided to fit all three graving docks with iron syphons.

In the 1840s the construction of the Albert Dock affected all of the surrounding docks. The southernmost of the three graving docks was buried under the masonry of the new south wall of what was to become the Canning Half-tide Basin. The bottom of the Canning Dock was excavated to a depth of 9ft below the level of the Old Dock Sill. The pier between the two remaining graving docks (re-named Canning Graving Docks in 1840) was lowered by about 3ft, with the object of obtaining increases in quay room above and illumination below. The dock floors were lowered to the level of ODS, the walls rebuilt in sandstone coped with granite and the gates replaced or repaired, at a cost of some £6,500. One section of a typical shed, now bricked up between the iron columns and roofed with corrugated iron, remains standing at the north east corner of the dock.

The Canning Half-tide Basin, which functioned like a large lock, was built mostly on the site of the narrow inlet which had linked the Dry Dock to the open river. Construction work commenced in January 1842 and by

June the Surveyor was able to report that '. . . the sill and greater portion of the masonry for the gates from the Canning Dock to the West Basin have been constructed . . . The wall along the bottom of the late No 1 Graving Dock, forming the south side of Canning Dock Basin is being proceeded with, the foundations of which are necessarily laid upon piles.' The half-tide basin was completed in 1844.

The new Canning river entrance consisted of two 45ft passages separated by an island on which was built '. . . . a round house to exhibit a light . . .', and similar slightly smaller buildings were erected on each of the pier heads. Open and closed transit sheds were erected on the north and south quays of the half-tide basin, and on the east and south sides of Canning Dock at various times during the rest of the 19th century.

The north gates of the river passage were sealed off by a concrete dam in 1937 and the southern gates were fitted with valves to admit water from the river. Some of these tide flaps were removed when the South Docks were made tidal after their closure in 1972.

Operation – Canning Dock
Designed for sailing vessels in the early years of the 19th century, Canning Dock was hampered throughout its history by its relatively small size, and the useful space within the dock was further reduced by the need to keep three passages clear. Nearly half of the east side of the dock also had virtually no quay since the two Canning Graving Docks opened off it here. By the end of the century, many of the vessels in the dock were Mersey flats and fishing smacks. (The fishery trade had long been of significance to the port of Liverpool, and as late as 1937 the Liverpool City Council was asked to consider guaranteeing a loan to be used to purchase a 45-vessel trawling fleet. The Council declined to participate in the venture despite the promoters' optimistic predictions of employment and profits.) Canning Dock also maintained the tradition of importing building materials and two local sand and gravel firms, Joseph Cooper & Sons of Widnes and Abel & Company of Runcorn were based there almost until its closure. The dock also shared in the coasting trade which remained important into the 1960s, and the Furness Withy Group had appropriated berths in Canning where their small refrigerated ships unloaded cargoes of fruit.

29 Canning Dock from the south, in the 1920s.

iron ships were also accommodated, though the masters of these vessels had to provide thick, hardwood caps to prevent damage by iron keels to graving blocks. The size of ships using the Canning Graving Docks had to remain virtually the same, but the class of vessels changed from

30 Canning River Entrance with gatemen's hut on Canning Island and Pilotage Buildings on the pierhead behind, *c*1920–30.

A special function of Canning Dock was as a base for the Mersey Docks and Harbour Board's fleet of dredgers. The earliest record of dredging in the port of Liverpool dates from 1717 when the Council agreed to the construction of a boat for carrying mud out of the Dock. In the 1960s, all of the 3,000 tons of sand and silt which entered the Brunswick Dock at each 'tide time' when the gates were open had to be removed by dredging. The 32ft 6ins accumulation of silt in the decade since 1972, when dredging ceased in the South Docks, is evidence of the importance of dredging to port operation. Both grab dredgers and bucket dredgers were moored in Canning Dock which was itself cleared of sand and silt by the grab dredgers Nos 14 and 15. After the construction of the Pilotage Building in 1883 the Dock was also used as a base for Liverpool pilot schooners and steam cutters.

Operation – Canning Graving Docks
In spite of the evident differences in scale between the Canning Graving Docks and their 19th- and 20th-century successors, the graving docks at Canning continued to be well used throughout two hundred years of working life. That the Corporation built three docks for ship repair at a time when there were but two wet docks in the port indicates the level of demand for ship repair and maintenance facilities. At first, the vessels using the graving docks were sailing ships with wooden hulls. Later,

the transoceanic merchant ship to the humble coastal flat and river dredger. As significant as, and no doubt linked to, the relatively limited capacity of the 18th-century graving docks was the remarkably low level of technical provision for ship repair. Two of the iron pitch boilers of 1810 are still *in situ*. When *Lloyd's List* announced that the Canning Graving Docks would be closed at the end of February, 1965, they were not mourned: 'These docks are very old and lacking in facilities such as cranes, compressed air and ballast. They will not be badly missed.'[1] These graving docks are now part of the Merseyside Maritime Museum established in 1980.

Appendix 2 shows how their dimensions compared with later graving docks.

1 *Lloyd's List* 5.ii.1965

Apart from the tiny Union Dock, there were no new docks built in the port between Queen's, opened in 1796, and Prince's in 1821, while the amount of traffic continued to grow; some sixty per cent between 1800 and 1810 and a further ten per cent in the next decade. One of the points on which the Dock Committee consulted Rennie in 1809[1] was the direction for future expansion, and he had suggested that the area south of King's Dock could be developed more quickly and more cheaply than that north of George's.

£1,200,000. However, problems of land acquisition now presented themselves. The Dock Committee had tried unsuccessfully to obtain the site of Jackson's Tide Mill immediately after the passage of the 1811 Act, and negotiations continued until 1827 when a jury was empanelled to decide the value of the various leasehold interests. The property in question comprised two reservoirs, a dwelling house, mills and machinery for which Jackson's assignees were awarded nearly £50,000. The rest of the land required for development was in the

31   Gatemen's hut, Brunswick Dock, 1905.

32   Building the Brunswick River Entrance, November, 1907.

The 1811 Dock Act embodied some of Rennie's recommendations, and two points in particular in the design accompanying the Act may have been his and foreshadowed later development: the arrangement of graving docks to give maximum protection from the prevailing wind, and the minimizing of direct river access. At the time, however, no action was taken. The Trustees were heavily in debt, and though a Treasury loan was obtained in 1813 under a further Act of Parliament, the construction of Brunswick Dock had to be postponed until after the completion of the extension of Queen's, the rebuilding of Canning and the filling of the Old Dock, and the construction of Prince's and Clarence Docks.

Detailed planning was finally able to commence under the terms of the two Dock Acts of 1825, which also increased the Committee's borrowing powers to

possession of the Corporation, and the part bounded by Queen Anne Street, Hill Street, Warwick Street and the strand had been leased to shipbuilders such as Dawson & Company. The appointed juries assessed the value of the Corporation's land at some £60,000. Yet another Dock Act was passed in 1828 to explain and amend the 1811 and 1825 Acts for the improvement of the port, and to pay for lands purchased under the Acts.

The adopted design of the 12½-acre dock with its half-tide entrance basin and two graving docks incorporated some features proposed by Rennie and some by Hartley. Rennie had earlier recommended the construction of a dock for the exclusive use of the timber trade, and Brunswick Dock was the first to be built for such a purpose. Here Hartley built sloping quays which facilitated off-loading through bow or stern ports, and provided special mooring arrangements which allowed ships to berth end on to the quay. The space between the west quay and the river was allocated to shipbuilders, and two 460ft long graving docks, the first to be constructed by the Dock Trustees, were built at the south end of the west dock. Since Brunswick Dock was to be built at the extremity of the dock estate, an extension of the line of river wall was also needed. A report on this subject was commissioned in 1822 from the civil engineers Joseph Whidbey, William Chapman and John Rennie, who recommended the construction of a wall as far south as the site of the Herculaneum Pottery.[2] Detailed records of the dock's construction are lost, but it is likely that a contractor was responsible for the excavation while the Dock Surveyor undertook the masonry for the dock walls. The hollow quoins were of limestone and the quay edges coped with granite. The docks were begun in November 1827 and opened in April 1832.

Some reconstruction was needed almost at once when some of the foundations of the dock walls failed in 1836 and cost some £36,000 to rebuild. The north passage to Coburg Dock was widened from 42ft to 60ft at the time of amalgamation of Union and Coburg Docks. In 1875–78 a branch, barge dock, 950ft by 70ft, was built off the eastern side, to replace Egerton Dock which had been purchased as a part of the site of the new Toxteth and Harrington Docks. The branch dock was connected to Brunswick Dock by a passage 200ft by 25ft, spanned by an Armstrong hydraulic bascule bridge and with two pedestrian subways from Sefton Street to the east and south quays of Brunswick Dock passing beneath it. The 1873 Act authorizing new docks to the south of Brunswick allowed for sills 12ft below ODS while the existing docks had sills only 6ft below ODS. To enable these older docks to accommodate vessels using the new docks an impounding system was introduced in 1890 with a pumping station at Coburg Dock to draw in water for distribution to the docks in the Brunswick to George's group. The resulting difference in levels was overcome by a locked passage between Brunswick and Toxteth. This passage, 450ft by 125ft with 60ft gates at either end, was constructed in 1883 and was known as Union Dock from 1889 (the former Union Dock to the north having been absorbed in Coburg in 1840).

The improvement was not a total success, however, nor was the water area itself increased. The Southern Works Act of 1898, already mentioned in connection with King's and Queen's Docks, was passed to make possible necessary reconstruction. Under its terms – which were altered slightly by subsequent legislation – a new river entrance

was built into Brunswick Dock, with locks 350ft by 100ft and 240ft by 80ft, with a depth 19ft 6ins below ODS and facing upstream to provide maximum protection for the vessels using them. Brunswick Dock itself was deepened to 21ft below ODS and lengthened to 1,800ft following the demolition of the two graving docks and the closure of Brunswick Branch Dock and its passage. The passage between Brunswick and Coburg Docks was enlarged, as was that to Toxteth Dock, with a depth of 17ft 6ins below ODS. Specialist suppliers of hydraulic and other machinery included W. G. Armstrong, Tannet Walker, C. & A. Musker, Francis Morton & Co, and Whitaker Bros. The general works were undertaken by the Board's own labour force and largely completed by 1905. The former half-tide dock was sealed off from Brunswick Dock on the landward side but remained open to the river.

The only buildings to be erected on the quaysides during the period when the use of Brunswick Dock was dominated by the timber trade (up to about 1865) were two small transit sheds put up on the north side of the half-tide basin and at the north-west corner of the dock in 1842. Following the enlargement of the Brunswick–Coburg passage to 60ft and the removal of part of the timber trade north to Canada Dock, a large shed was built along the north side of the west quay of Brunswick Dock in 1865. This building incorporated a novel cargo handling device which consisted of a large bogey some 12ft square that ran in a channel from dockside to roadside across the shed; the top of the travelling platform was level with the floor of the building. By the 1870s Brunswick's role as a timber dock had been largely superseded, and more sheds were needed for other cargoes. Following the rebuilding of the sloping quays a 600ft shed was built on the north side in 1872–73 and a similar shed with moveable 30cwt cranes on the south in 1878–79. A large corrugated iron shed was erected on the south end of the west quay in 1898.

From the beginning, however, accommodation was required for shipwrights and for dock officials. A 50ft shed with iron columns was built as a carpenters' store in 1836, and saw pits and a smithy in 1840. A pumping engine house was built in 1841 and replaced in 1887. Two more shipwrights' sheds were built in 1842 and 1848. Two dock gatemen's huts were built in 1836, either side of the river entrance to the half-tide dock, small, octagonal, freestone structures, with windows on seven sides and a door on the eighth, winch machinery inside, a vaulted coal cellar, a coal stove, and benches round the walls. Hartley had first built such huts at Clarence Dock, and the pattern was to be followed by him at nearly all later pier heads. In 1832

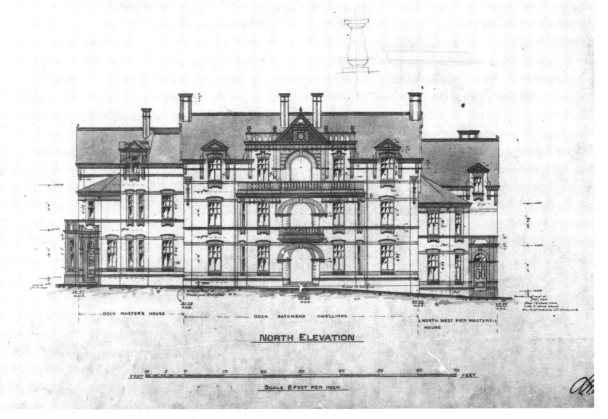

RESIDENCES NORTH END OF BRUNSWICK BRANCH DOCK

NORTH ELEVATION

SCALE 8 FEET PER INCH

33   Houses for Dock Master, Dock Gatemen and Pier Master,
Brunswick Dock 1891.

a two-storeyed dock master's house was built, also octagonal and also with windows all round: the dock master was liable for duty 24 hours a day. Accommodation for gatemen and other dock officials was provided on the north quay of the Brunswick Branch Dock in 1891 (Fig 33).

Most of these buildings were swept away during the 1900–08 reconstruction, and new buildings included a 500ft transit shed on the quay north west of the river entrance, a 1,290ft transit shed on the east quay, a triangular shed on the west quay, and new houses for the dock master and his assistant. The largest building in Brunswick Dock, however, was to be the granary erected in 1935–37 by the Liverpool Grain Storage and Transit

Company (LGST) at the north end of the east quay, built of concrete by William Thornton & Sons on a system of moving shuttering, devised by W. L. Phillip, which permitted continuous pouring. The granary is a tripartite structure comprising a 235ft working core flanked by two silo buildings containing 140 bins each 10ft 6ins by 8ft 6ins and 116ft deep and is still in operation.

Operation
Until 1865 up to eighty-five per cent and never less than forty per cent of ships entering the dock were laden with timber, from the Canadian and Baltic ports and from West Africa and the West Indies. Cargoes of timber were best carried in purpose-built ships, and these had bow and

stern ports and removable 'tween-decks', which were needed only for the outward passage with other cargo. A railway line along the east quay, laid in 1835, added to the dock's specialized facilities. Its very attractiveness, however, led to its sometimes disastrous throttling, when after a spell of head wind as many as 50 sail might be seen bound up the Mersey for Brunswick Dock. By the end of the 1850s ships were being delayed for an average of 30 days while waiting for a discharging berth. The opening of the Canada Dock as a timber dock in 1859 led to the relocation of the timber trade, however; only a quarter of the ships in Brunswick Dock in 1875 were discharging timber and fewer than one per cent by 1895. The shipbuilders, whose requirements had complemented the trade, were also gradually to decline; their long and ultimately unsuccessful competition for land was to lead increasingly to their re-establishment on the Cheshire shore.

The later users of Brunswick Dock, even after reconstruction, tended to be those ocean traders who, because of the nature of the ports to which they sailed, required ships of relatively shallow draught. Trading to West Africa were Elder, Dempster & Co, with an appropriated berth from about 1890 to 1970, the Guinea Gulf Line and the Palm Line. T. & J. Harrison traded to Brazil and Mexico and to the cotton ports of the southern USA. The Booth Line also traded to Brazil, R. P. Houston to New York and the River Plate, and Larrinaga & Co and Booker Line to the West Indies. The South American lines would typically carry heavy machinery and manufactured goods, coal and salt out, meat and hides,

ore, guano, general cargo and sometimes fruit home, the African ships returning with latex, tin, cocoa, palm kernels, lime juice, sawn timber and logs.

The reconstruction did no more than keep up with the increasing size even of the shallow-draught vessels, and both before and afterwards many companies also maintained deep water berths in the North Docks and Birkenhead. For a century after Brunswick ceased to be the principal timber dock, there was a sizeable Mediterranean and coastal trade, and between 1875 and 1960 the proportion of ships under 500 tons using the dock seldom dropped below forty-five per cent of the total.

Many of the larger vessels using Brunswick Dock in the 20th century were grain ships which discharged to the Coburg granary by means of a pneumatic elevator installed on the north-east Brunswick quay in 1932 and then direct to the Brunswick granary from 1937. The new granary had a capacity of 60,000 tons and grain dischargers which could handle 500 tons an hour. Both granaries were served by railway sidings and provided with machinery for virtually automatic sack and bulk delivery to rail and road hauliers. The Brunswick river entrance remained open to vessels trading at the LGST granaries until 1975, but by then most grain cargoes were discharged from large bulk carriers at the modern grain terminal at Seaforth and the Coburg and Brunswick granaries could be supplied by road.

1 DCM 9.viii.1809
2 DCM 25.v.1822

The site of Coburg Dock was first developed as a small dock and a tidal basin known as Union Half-tide Dock and Brunswick Basin, which were sanctioned under the 1811 Dock Act and built around 1820 to the south of Queen's Dock and north of the future (and intended) Brunswick Dock. Union Half-tide Dock formed an improved entrance to Queen's Dock, as enlarged under the terms of the same Act, and was too small (around 2 acres) to be of use as anything else. Brunswick Basin, in turn, formed the entrance to Union. Both were probably begun in 1817 following completion of the Queen's Dock extension, and they were operational by 1823. At the same time the river wall was extended and the South Ferry Basin, a small tidal basin and a slip, were built on the south side of Brunswick Basin for river boatmen.

The Union Dock and Brunswick Basin walls were of an ashlar face of Aberthaw limestone, backed with rubble and reinforced with stone counterforts encased in brick; part of the north wall was rebuilt, however, two years later by William McConochie and this may have been by way of repair. A scheme of 1825[1] to convert the dry basin into a wet dock came to nothing, and it was not until 1840 that the Brunswick Basin was fitted with gates and renamed Coburg Dock in honour of Prince Albert. When this was done, however, the width determined upon was 70ft, and transformed the dock at once into one of the most important in the port, able to receive ocean-going paddle steamers. The only other steamship dock at the time was Clarence Dock, where the gates were only 47ft wide. In 1841 the dock was further improved by deepening to 7ft below ODS (save for its south-west corner which remained at 5ft). Two single storey sheds were erected on the south quay. Later, the quay walls were raised by 4ft throughout.

Major reconstruction was undertaken in 1857–58 when the Union and Coburg Docks were enlarged and united. At the same time the passages to Brunswick Dock to the south and to Queen's Dock to the north were widened from 42ft to 60ft, and fitted with a double pair of gates to enable each dock to be run dry independently of the others. Yet further alterations resulted from the rebuilding of Queen's and Brunswick Docks under the terms of the 1898 Southern Works Act. The passages out of Coburg were realigned and further widened, from 60ft to 100ft and their sills deepened to 17ft 6ins below ODS, and a

channel through Coburg Dock, between the two, was deepened to 19ft 6ins below ODS. The greenheart gates for the 100ft-passages were operated hydraulically by machinery supplied by C. & A. Musker (Coburg–Queen's) and Tannett Walker & Co (Coburg–Brunswick). Rivetted steel slewing bridges and operating machinery were supplied by Francis Morton & Co. The embayment on the north quay of Coburg Dock was fitted with a timber wharf 60ft by 45ft with a ferro-concrete deck supplied by Hennebique. The new north passage was completed and in use by 1902, and the deepened channel dredged by the *Vulcan* by 1905. However, the building of the new Brunswick river entrance, thought to be clear of the Pluckington Bank, made the Coburg entrance largely redundant, and from November 1905 the entrance was permanently closed (with an estimated saving of £4,000 a year). A wall was built across the closed entrance in 1907.

Operation

The early Brunswick Basin and Union Dock were almost certainly used mainly as passage docks, but the fitting of the 70ft-gates to the former immediately transformed its value: it was soon being used by the British and North American Royal Mail Steam Packet Co (the fore-runner of the Cunard Line). The liner traffic was short lived, however, and the disadvantages of the dock were summed up by David MacIver, one of Samuel Cunard's partners.[2] It was dangerous for large ocean-going steamers to come up the Mersey at speed among the small craft of the river. In spite of its enlargement, Coburg Dock was too small to contain many big ships (for instance, *Hibernia* which was 58ft wide and 240ft long including her figurehead) at once. There was not the strict segregation from sailing ships that was desirable. Moreover, the dock was apparently liable to dry out by accident through some syphoning action of the culvert system of the adjacent docks.[3] As larger docks in a more favourable northern situation were built, so the North Atlantic liners moved there from Coburg Dock. The opening of the Prince's Landing Stage and the beginning of works for the 1857–58 alterations provided the final incentive for the departure of the transatlantic ships.

Another consequence of the exceptional entrance into the dock, however, was to attract to it large ships in need of repair or refit. In 1843 a large machinery hoist was removed to Coburg Dock from Trafalgar Dock, and large masting shears were in use in the dock in 1848. A 290ft slip was built in the dock at the west end of the north quay in 1844. In 1865 a 25-ton hydraulic crane was erected on the east quay, and remained until 1899, when it was removed to make way for the granary.

Transit sheds were erected on the north and south quays for firms that included G. H. Fletcher & Co and Bahr, Behrend & Ross. During the 1880s and 1890s these companies were joined by other appropriated berth holders, namely Serra Tintore, MacAndrews, the African Steamship Co, the British and African Steam Navigation Co, Elder Dempster, and Yeoward Bros, who traded to Spain and Portugal, the Canaries and to West Africa. Serra Tintore also operated a service to Puerto Rico. General cargo was predominant, with fruit, palm oil and kernels from West Africa. Intermittent users were the Cork Steamship Co to Le Havre around 1846, the Black Ball Line of Australian packets from about 1856 to 1871, the China Mutual Steam Navigation Co in 1922 and Coast Lines Ltd trading to Belfast in the early 1940s. During the greater part of the 20th century, however, the dock was more important as a passage than as a commercial dock. A fair amount of the port's expanding grain trade was centred on the Coburg granary from 1906, but its importance to the dock diminished after 1932 when pneumatic elevator plant was installed on the north-east Brunswick quay to discharge vessels too large for Coburg. After the building of the Brunswick elevator, only coasters and barges used Coburg Dock.

An impounding station was constructed at Coburg Dock in 1887–89. The location was probably chosen as central to the area of docks to be served, near to the dockyard for repair to machinery, and unlikely to interfere greatly with trade in a dock whose use was already declining. Three Gwynne centrifugal pumps with 54in suction pipes drew water at high tide in order to increase artificially the depth of water at sills, basins and passages. Impounding was successful for a time in permitting the use of the South Docks by larger ships, but in the long

term the limitations imposed by silted fairways and narrow entrances were greater than could be overcome by such means, and in 1931, after some 40 years operation, the pumping station was taken out of commission.

An operational feature unique in the South Docks to Coburg Dock after 1842 was the dockyard, a compound established to provide, under the supervision of the Dock Surveyor, facilities for the repair and maintenance of machinery, plant and structures, a materials store, workshops, and a headquarters for the design and execution of new works. The dockyard had been growing on the site ever since the building of the Brunswick Basin, but the impending eviction of the Surveyor and of his plant from the former dockyard at Trentham Street (prior to the redevelopment of the site as Albert Dock) led to his designing and building, in 1841–42, within a boundary wall, foundries, smithies, sawpits, millwrights' and wheelwrights' shops, a buoy store, a gate shed and offices. By the early 1870s the original site could no longer contain the facilities necessary, and the dockyard was extended. Its final closure began with the foundry in 1969, and only the sawmill, a relatively modern installation of 1960, survived. All of the original dockyard buildings were demolished in 1982.

The South Ferry Basin, between the dockyard and the Coburg river entrance, provided a ferry slip and a free landing place for the local fishermen. Ferry services had operated from 1820, but had ceased long before the Mersey fishermen gave up the cockle hole, as they called it. Those who fished the Mersey in small and often home-made boats continued to use the basin until well into the 20th century, and their retention of old ways has created a nostalgia for the sandstone basin rarely found elsewhere in the docks. Fishermen have returned again since 1982 after the closure of the Brunswick entrances.

1 DCM 29.1.1825
2 Ib
3 Minutes of Evidence, Liverpool Docks Bill, 1844, 39

Its five great stacks of warehouses are the principal feature of Albert Dock, and obtaining powers to build them was the primary object sought by the 1841 Dock Act. Albert Dock was the first of the South Docks to be designed with warehouses as an integral part of the scheme even though the potential of such provision had been investigated by the Corporation as long ago as 1803,[1] the year in which the Act establishing bonded warehouses in London was passed. Under this system, duties on goods unloaded into a bonded store were only payable on discharge from the store rather than immediately on landing. Thus ships could be unloaded whether or not excise men were on hand to sample cargoes, mixed cargoes could be moved from the quay for sorting and merchants could wait to pay duties until their goods were sold. These were great advantages, and the Corporation was disappointed when in 1805 the Board of Customs and Excise decided that security in the Port of Liverpool was too lax to allow the extension to Liverpool of the London system. For over thirty years thereafter all proposals for the provision of public warehouses in Liverpool were thwarted by the vested interests of private warehouse owners.

In 1838 the Finance Committee ordered an inquiry into docks and quayside warehouses, and the report submitted in 1839 contained descriptions of the major closed dock systems in London and dwelt on the advantages of these.[2] Strong objections were received from the Liverpool Shipowners' Association and from the Associated Land and Warehouse Owners who stressed seven main points:

1 Successive Corporation leases had compelled lessees to build warehouses; these the Corporation now proposed to put out of business by building warehouses themselves.
2 Dock revenue ought to be spent on docks.
3 The costs of building warehouses would lead to an increase in harbour dues.
4 By 1838 an estimated £4,000,000 had been invested in private warehouses; the Corporation offered no compensation.
5 The practical advantages to the excise could be achieved by a more efficient use of their staff and a more flexible system of sampling.
6 Quayside warehouses were a fire risk in an enclosed dock.

7 The reclaimed land proposed to be built on would not bear the weight of multi-storey warehouses.

Some of these points were unanswerable by the Bill's promoters, who could only accuse the Liverpool warehouse owners of seeking to perpetuate an outmoded system for selfish reasons. However, a system whereby the Trustees' own employees would unload cargoes into secure warehouses had many advantages: pilferage would be diminished, the risk of fire much reduced with fireproof buildings and closer supervision of the Trust's own staff, and risks of damage on the quayside would be lessened. The practice of each consignee sending his own labour to offload his cargoes as they came ashore made for confusion and delay, as did the need for excise men to sample cargoes as they were landed; henceforth Dock Trust staff would unload complete cargoes into warehouses for sorting and sampling.

The proposed warehouses were to follow the general form of those at St Katharine's Dock in London. In 1839 a Mr Falcon from the Town Clerk's Office and a Mr Clint were sent to London to examine the installations there, and they reported:

'The warehouses round these docks project close upon the edges of the quays, and are open backwards 15 yards. There are recesses in the building for cranes for discharging the ships .... There are also small cranes over small doors, from the upper storeys downwards, wrought by a gang of eight men .... These cranes are kept constantly at work by means of relieving gangs of men, and are chiefly used in the discharging and loading of carts and barges .... The warehouses are in general six storeys high. The lower storey is in some places divided into two by a sort of half deck.'[3]

However, a number of details required elucidation, and between 1841 and 1843 Hartley prepared six alternative designs for warehouses of fireproof or semi-fireproof construction, at prices estimated to be from £33 10s per square yard for a scheme with 'a common warehouse floor as used in Liverpool'[4] up to £70 14s for a proposal with iron columns and iron beams spanned by iron plates carrying sand and flags. The alternatives were tested practically in 1843. Model arches built according to design No 5, though spanning 12ft rather than the full size of 19ft were erected at Coburg Dockyard, where Hartley attempted unsuccessfully to break them down. Fire resistance tests were carried out, in the Trentham Street Dockyard, on a reduced model with brick arches between iron columns and beams, and on a timber building lined with sheet iron. The experiments were conducted in a purpose built structure 18ft square by 10ft high, which was packed with eight tar barrels, three barrels of pitch and about a ton of dry split wood, and then ignited. The iron-lined wood structure resisted catching fire for 45 minutes, but quickly ignited once the timber was exposed to the air. The brick and iron structure was clearly to be preferred. Cast iron was chosen for the quayside columns in preference to granite; at £51 7s 6d it was cheaper than granite by a pound. On many technical points Hartley corresponded with Philip Hardwick who had designed the St Katharine's warehouses and with George Aitchison, the then surveyor to the dock, but many details were Hartley's own, such as the use of 4ins × ¾ins iron bond bars built into the walls to counteract any tendency to differential settlement and the building of brick piers within the hollow cores of cast-iron columns of the quay frontage. On one critical point, however, Hartley adopted Hardwick's recommendation that '. . . in constructing the quay walls at St Katharine's inverted arches were turned in them, from column to column to equalize the bearing. We observe you do not consider this necessary at Liverpool, but a large brick pier has been carried up under each column instead of them. The inverted arches extending from pillar to pillar lengthways of the building are extremely necessary . . .'.[5]

Besides the building of the warehouses, the Act authorized a river wall at Duke's Dock with 'a parade for the recreation of the public', the filling up of No 1 Graving Dock, the construction of railways on the dock estate, and necessary alterations to Salthouse and to Canning Docks. The new dock was to be built on the site lying south of the entrance basin to Canning Dock, west of Salthouse Dock and north of Duke's Dock. It was to contain 7¾ acres of water, with passages to Salthouse Dock and to a new half-tide basin with a double river entrance. The land acquired was ripe for development, lying as it did surrounded by existing docks and having gradually been reclaimed during the 18th century. In June, 1841, the Surveyor was authorized to give to the fifty-nine occupiers of the Albert Dock site immediate notice to quit. By far the greatest area of the site was occupied by shipbuilders, including such notable names as Grayson, Clarke, Humble, Milcrest, Clover, Rathbone and Haselden, but it also included a dozen or so warehouses, a

few offices and houses, a cooperage, a pub and the Trustees' own dockyard. This latter comprised, as well as sheds and workshops, a foundry, smithies, stables, an engine house, a counting house and a basin or slip. The dockyard was relocated at Coburg Dock. Land acquisition was completed within twelve months at a cost of some £27,500 including purchase of land and subleases, removal expenses and arbitrator's fees.

Work began in November 1841 when Canning and Salthouse Docks were run dry in order to begin work on the passages to Albert Dock. Three or four thousand elm and beech trees for piling were ordered at up to 1s 7d a foot. The contract for deepening Canning Dock was awarded to John Orell, at 2s 10½d per cubic yard, and when bad weather had delayed the works, a railway was laid down on the quayside to assist with the removal of spoil. Chillington Ironworks tendered for two hundred tons of cast-iron sheeting piles and cramps at £6 15s per ton, but subsequently had to decline the contract because Hartley wanted the piles cast vertically. A fresh contract at £7 10s was then given to Bury, Curtis & Co, who were able to do so. In May 1842, Canning Dock was re-opened to ships, with work well advanced on new dock entrances and on the clearing of the Albert Dock site.

In January 1843, the contract for excavating the new dock was given to John Waring, who was to provide:

'*All the labour of every kind required for carrying on and performing the said work and also all waggons, blocks, ropes, powder, lights, planks, wheelbarrows, stages, railways (except the permanent railway already laid down by the said Trustees and extending from the southward corner of the Salthouse Dock to Beacon's Gutter on the North Shore . . . .*'[6]

Work was to be continuous, for 24 hours a day save for a break of a few hours after midnight on Sunday. While Waring was digging, Hartley was building the new river wall, some 400ft of which was ready by June to receive its coping. By then, foundations for warehouses on east and west were begun, and 5,270 piles had been driven. Hartley wrote 'The nature of the ground on the west side of these works renders the progress very tedious.'[7] Contracts for structural ironwork for the warehouses went to the Haigh Foundry and to J. & E. Walker of Gospel Oak ironworks. Bricks at £1 11s 6d per thousand delivered were supplied by S. & J. Holme, from clay dug partly on the Trustees' own land on the north shore. Holme could not supply bricks fast enough, however, and Hartley had to supplement them with bricks from a Mr Rowson at an extra 1s 8d per thousand. By the middle of the following year, most of the dock was finished and the blocks of warehousing well forward: tenders were accepted from Gospel Oak for the galvanized roof plates and from W. H. Ogden for cast iron window frames. The cast-iron swing bridges based on the Rennie design that Hartley had already employed at Clarence and at Brunswick Docks and supplied from the Haigh Foundry were also in place. The dock was opened to lying-up shipping in February 1845, and for general use, with the south-east and eastern stacks

of warehouses, on 30 July, 1846. Also in 1846 a fly bridge comprising a pair of weighted arms for the convenience of 'foot passengers and persons having business with Canning Graving Docks'[8] was erected across the east entrance of the Canning Half-tide Dock. The remaining warehouses were finished the following year. The works had cost in all over £700,000, of which the warehouses accounted for about half.

While the warehouses had been Hartley's work tempered by Hardwick, the dock office was designed by

34 Ground plan of Albert Dock and Warehouses, c1848.

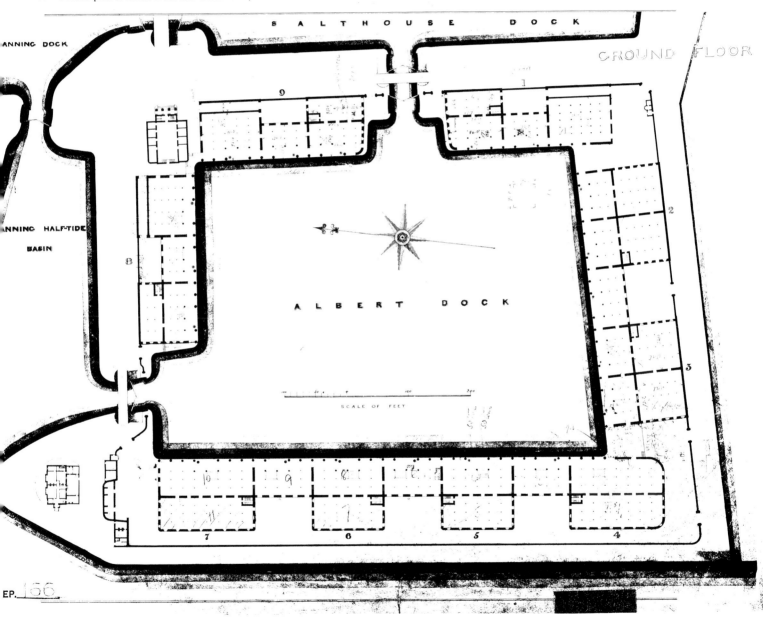

35 Naval vessels moored against the west quay of Albert Dock, looking
    towards the passage to Canning Half-tide Basin, c1935.

36 (*opposite*) Handling a hogshead of tobacco using wall crane typical
    of those converted from manual to hydraulic operation,
    Albert Warehouses.

Hardwick and altered by Hartley. This comprised a
central public hall open to the roof with offices off it at
two levels and a basement underneath, with a cast-iron
Tuscan portico and pediment. It was completed in 1848,
but in the following year Hartley added a top storey over
the offices to provide accommodation for the principal
clerk at the dock office. Hardwick also designed the houses
for the dock master and his assistant and for the
warehouse superintendent, which were built in 1852 on
the south pier of the Canning river entrance; Hartley
designed the minor dwellings, dock master's office and
cooperage there. The west and east ends of the south
stack of warehouses were added in 1853–54, in response to
demands for more accommodation, and differ slightly from
the originals. The infill in the south-west angle has granite
columns on both the quay and cart bay sides and groined
brick arches spanning the ground floor. Hardwick's final
contribution to the project was a design for a clock turret
which was erected on the north-east stack of warehouses
in 1848.

Careful consideration of cargo-handling methods was
evident from the first. The London docks provided
alternative examples of building types and machinery –
top-storey iron cranes worked by two-handled ground
floor jiggers at West India Dock, iron cranes of various
powers at St Katharine Dock, wooden cranes with tread
wheels at London Dock and common luff tackle at East
India Dock. At Albert Dock, the warehouse bays between
the dock and the cart area were designed to function as
transit sheds from which cargoes could be forwarded to
the rest of the warehouse or to a waiting vehicle for inland
distribution. The warehouses originally contained 21
internal hoists for moving goods vertically above the quay.
The vaults were served by iron cranes fixed at quay level
to the outside of the cart bay walls; installed in 1845, most
of these cranes were converted to hydraulic operation in
1882 and they still remain in position. In 1846, after
complaints about the inadequacy of crane provision,
jiggers 'like those in general use in the warehouses of the
town' were installed, on the top floor, above the main

delivery doorways.[9] Many of these also remain in the warehouses. Iron dockside cranes, placed close to the large columns so as to swing through the arcs provided in the front of the warehouses, were ordered from Johnson and Murray in 1845. It is likely that all of these were replaced in 1878 when Lyster extended the hydraulic system.

The warehouses were entirely enclosed by a wall except in the north-east angle where large iron doors could be used to cut off access to the buildings. The openings in the perimeter wall were policed from purpose-built watch huts. Circulation inside the wall but outside the warehouses was restricted to individual stacks, and secure internal subdivisions were limited by the number of stairways in the warehouses (one in each of the north,

north-east and south-east stacks; two in the south stack and four in the west).

By 1843 Hartley at least had been contemplating the possibility of powered goods handling and in that year he had investigated a vacuum apparatus devised by John Hague of London. This scheme proved abortive, but in 1847 Hartley travelled to Newcastle to examine W. G. Armstrong's hydraulic crane. At once he ordered two cranes for £1,000 and two hoists and had them installed by Armstrong at the east end of the south stack. The pipes through which municipal water was supplied were made and laid by the Corporation. It is not known whether or not an engine house built at the south end of the west stack was intended to supply power for the early

37   Albert Warehouses, west stack, with Dock Board Camels in the dock, c1930.

38 Cart bay, north-east stack Albert Warehouses, 1982.

hydraulic machines. Likewise, it is not clear if there was a functional connection between the hydraulic power centre Lyster built in 1877–78 and the 'old engine and chimney' which were taken down at the same time.

Operation

The opening celebrations were attended by Prince Albert, and included a grand luncheon in a room in the warehouses specially decorated by a Mr Troutbeck of Hanover Square, London:

'The pillars and arched brick ceiling were painted of stone colour, the pillars being also ornamented with gold bands which encircled the capitals. The walls were lined with glazed calico, fluted in alternate colours of pink, blue and white. The hangings to the windows were the same with white drapery and pink rosettes, the division below the arches at the windows being fitted with purple moulding.'[10]

Until about 1890 Albert Dock was used mostly as a discharging dock for deep-sea traders from the Far East, India and the Americas whose typical cargoes were tea, silk, dyestuffs (indigo, gambier), rice, hemp, cotton, sugar, tobacco, and spirits. The pattern of trade established by T. & J. Harrison (one of the major users of Albert Dock) to India, the West Indies, Mexico, Brazil and the east coast of the USA was common to a number of shippers. Bulk cargoes such as railroad iron, salt and coal were carried out from Liverpool to Calcutta, where rice, stores and coolies to work the sugar plantations were loaded for Demerara, Trinidad and Guadeloupe. Rum and sugar from the West Indies or cotton, grain and tobacco from the USA were then shipped back to Liverpool. In the two-way trade with India, ships would return with cotton, rice, tea and jute. Having discharged cargoes at Albert Dock, vessels would proceed to Salthouse for loading, and the pressure for loading berths sometimes led to vessels entering Albert Dock light in order to jump the queue, thereby adding to the congestion.

Despite its initial success, however, the fate of the dock was linked to the decline of sailing vessels in the port as a whole. Although sailing ships still accounted for some sixty-four per cent of the vessels using the port of Liverpool in the 1880s, after that there was a sharp decline and by the end of the century they accounted for a mere seven per cent of the total. Docks built for the sailing ships of the 1840s could not compete for the later deep-water steamship trade. Despite the utility of bonded storage and of the 1878 improvement of the hydraulic cargo-handling machinery, the warehouses were old fashioned in relation to the transit sheds required by better bulk handling equipment and modern distribution schedules (the point is discussed further on p163). The 1880s and 1890s saw the greatest number of large vessels in the dock; thereafter, with the expansion of the northern docks and the work undertaken under the Southern Works Act, the use of the dock declined precipitately. In 1890 only twenty-nine per cent of ships in the dock were of under 1,000 tons; there were ninety-four per cent by 1920. The proportion of dues collected from ships in Albert Dock, compared to those of the port as a whole, similarly reflects this dramatic decline from 3.05 per cent in 1870 to 0.04 per cent in 1920.

The north-east stack of warehouses was converted in 1899 for the Riverside Cold Storage and Ice Co. Parts of the building were lined with timber and cork for insulation, and refrigeration and ice-making machinery were installed on the top floor 'so that no smells can pass up the building, and the heat from the boilers, etc, does not penetrate through the building'.[11] The siting on the top floor was a testimony to the strength of Hartley's construction. The ice manufactured there was passed through an electric crushing machine and loaded into ships' holds by means of a shoot, or lowered in blocks by a lift. The users of the cold store included the Liverpool Steam Fishing Co (based on the west side of Canning Dock) and the importers of butter and bacon from Ireland and of carcases from the River Plate. The Riverside Cold Storage and Ice Company was ultimately taken over by Vestey Bros, and the building continued as a cold store until about 1952.

From 1920 onwards there was almost no commercial activity in Albert Dock. Most of the vessels which continued to berth in the dock did so while waiting for space in the graving docks, or were Dock Board vessels awaiting duty. From 1930 the pilotage service used Albert river wall to land and embark pilots. During the Second World War hundreds of Admiralty ships, including requisitioned merchant ships, landing craft and small warships such as HMS *Acanthus* and HMS *Eglantine* were berthed in Albert Dock, bringing the number of ships for a brief time to the highest total ever recorded. But almost all were of under 300 tons. Only sixty-eight ships entered the dock in 1955; forty-two of these were Dock Board vessels, twenty-three were waiting, and three carried cargoes of oyster shells. The last regular users were Crossfields' barges from Warrington with a berth at the north-east corner. Albert Dock was defunct for many years before it was closed in 1972.

1 LRO *Report of the Committee of Finance of the Town Council . . . on the Subject of Docks and Warehouses on the Dock Quays*, 1839, 41
2 Ib 42
3 Ib 10
4 DCM 14.i.1843
5 DCM 30.viii.1843
6 MDHB Contracts Book 25.iii.1843
7 DER 1843
8 DCM 27.ii.1845
9 DCM 15.x.1846
10 *Liverpool Mercury* Supplement 31.vii.1846
11 *Journal of Commerce* 24.vii.1899

As early as 1809 Rennie had commented adversely on the piecemeal development of the dock system and particularly on the lack of communication between docks[1] and this was a theme that Hartley was to take up on his appointment in 1824 and return to on many occasions. Thus when he reported in 1845 on his proposal for what was to be the Wapping Dock, he claimed that:

'One of the greatest inconveniences connected with the Liverpool Docks has been the want of a connection between the north and south docks. Vessels having discharged their cargos in any of the docks in the South division and required to take in their outward cargos in the Northern division have hitherto been obliged to take in ballast to enable them to go into the river, as well as to employ a steam boat [i.e. a tug] and Pilot ... and not only has there a great necessity been felt for a more convenient water communication, but a still greater necessity for a better land access to the different docks of this particular locality ...'[2]

The Wapping docks, therefore, were built largely for tactical reasons: not only to provide more dock space, but also in order to facilitate the use of the other docks in the southern division. They lay inland from King's Dock, and south of Salthouse and the Duke's Dock, where they could provide a link between two separate groups of south docks, one group to the north comprising George's, Salthouse, Canning, Albert and the Duke's Dock, and the other to the south consisting of King's and Queen's and Brunswick. Also, in order to achieve his last objective, Hartley proposed a new arterial road to relieve the pressure on traffic that would be created by the new dock, and a railway between it and the Wapping terminal of the Liverpool and Manchester line.

Wapping Dock was built on the landward side of King's Dock, a position that had the advantage of requiring no special works to keep the water out during excavation, nor of occupying valuable shoreline. Immediately to its north, east of the Duke's Dock and connected to it and to Salthouse, came Wapping Basin. Each of these new docks had three entrances, necessary to enable them to fulfil their function as links though diminishing the lengths of quay available. On the other hand such a position involved the displacement and compensation of a large number of established businesses including a cooper, a gunsmith, shops and warehouses, a

timber yard, a pub, a ropery, dry salters, a ship chandler and an iron store. There were houses, too, whose removal (it was reported to the Lords' Committee on the Bill) '...would in every respect be an advantage ...'. The area was, in fact, occupied by just those businesses one would expect in such a place, but their removal was a matter of expense and delay despite the Trustees' powers of compulsory purchase under the 1846 Dock Act which enabled Wapping Dock to be built. The site was not clear for work to begin until 1851, when Hartley reported on 'the construction of a small portion of wall, near the north-east corner of the King's Dock, upon which a mortar mill and limekiln have been erected, and, together with a pump well for taking off the water, are in readiness for the commencement of the work'.[3]

39 Sectional gate on wheels, *c*1855, boundary wall, Wapping Dock.

Excavation began in 1853, when a contract was let to William McConochie whose firm had undertaken a number of contracts for the Trustees since 1824 when he rebuilt the passage linking Canning and George's Dock. Stone was supplied by J. Blakeley at 3s 3d per ton for wall stone and 2s 3d per ton for rubble. The dock walls were founded on rock, and faced in Kirkudbrightshire granite from the Trustees' own quarries at Kirkmabreck. Walls were 7ft 6ins and 14ft 6ins thick at top and bottom, and the dock floor was 36ft 6ins below quay level. Though these contracts had been let for stone and for digging, it is likely that the bulk of the construction work was done by the Surveyor's own labour force. The new street was nearing completion in 1853, and the docks were opened to shipping on 9 May, 1855.

40   Rear of Wapping Warehouse from the north-east, 1982.

The warehouse that Hartley built along the eastern quay owed much to his earlier designs at Albert Dock. (A matching warehouse on the west quay was not built and a single-storey transit shed substituted.) Wapping warehouse has crane bays to the quay similar to those at Albert Dock, with cast-iron Doric columns that differ from those at Albert Dock in their being slightly splayed. The ground floor was similarly open to the quay. To the rear, however, the warehouse lacks the cart bays of its predecessor, and has a straight wall, probably adopted because it was from the first intended to run a railway line the length of the building. A covered cartway two storeys in height and containing a railway running the length of the warehouse, was built against the perimeter wall, while a second line ran within the shed. The Wapping goods terminus of the Liverpool and Manchester Railway Company was partly demolished for the Wapping dock

works, but railway connections to the dock were reinstated subsequently. The warehouse is of six floors, divided vertically into five equal parts, thus facilitating its use by a variety of occupiers, and hydraulic goods-handling was provided from the first. It was complete with its machinery and railway by July 1856. By 1859, however, it was reported that the railway turntables inside the warehouse had not been used during the previous two years and that the space they occupied was needed for storage. Instructions were then given to store goods as if no line of railway existed, and the turntables and rails were removed altogether in 1878.

In 1855, W. G. Armstrong supplied a steam engine and accumulator for powering the hydraulic system at Wapping, and this Hartley installed in a tower of his own design, octagonal with random granite rubble facing and vaguely mediaeval ornament of a character uniquely his. Building began in December, 1855 and was finished in April, 1856. Equally distinctive were the other ancillary structures. The boundary wall, which was only pierced by two railway arches, terminated in massive, sculptural gate piers into which multi-leafed wooden gates rolled on wheels. At each entrance, north and south, were ovoid conical gate houses with equally odd decoration and vaulted interiors. Their surfaces were similarly faced in granite rubble, probably saved from the waste of the huge blocks in the dock and river walls.

Equal care and inventiveness were bestowed on the warehouse structure (described more fully on p152). Significantly, Hartley did not repeat his use of a metal roof as at Albert Dock Warehouses. Although there are similarities in the metal roof trusses, at Wapping, instead of galvanized sheets for roof covering he used slates over boards carried on wooden purlins. Another difference between Albert and Wapping is the extension of the Wapping vaults below the cartway to the line of the rear boundary wall; at Albert they occur beneath the warehouses only. Varying internal subdivisions of the warehouses at the two docks perhaps reflect Hartley's perception of a need for longer uninterrupted spaces: in Albert, the maximum distance between cross walls is 110ft (minimum is 72ft 9ins) while in Wapping the regularly spaced cross walls occur every 150ft 6in.

The warehouse and railway connections were completed by July 1856 and the following year an open shed on iron columns was erected on the west quay. This shed was enclosed in brick in 1862 and a brick-walled transit shed was erected on the west quay of Wapping Basin in 1864; there was little room for other structures due to the number of dock entrances. Bridges were of the manually operated, cast iron, double-leaf design that Hartley had already installed at the Albert Dock and elsewhere, and were supplied by Beercroft, Butler & Company of Leeds.

By the Brunswick–Wapping improvement scheme of 1889 an increased depth of water was provided at neap tides between Brunswick and Wapping Docks, by means of an impounding pumping station at Coburg Dock. This was successful, and caused little additional work at Wapping other than the enlargement of certain culverts and the raising of the planking of dock gates. By the time pumping had been discontinued in 1909, the dock had been deepened under the Southern Works Act.

By this Act, the King's Dock, to the west of Wapping, was replaced by the two King's Branch Docks, 1 and 2, both reached by the demolition of the west wall of Wapping dock. Only a section of the centre of this wall was retained, to serve as the east wall of the tongue dividing the two branch docks. Wapping Dock itself was deepened to 19ft 6ins below ODS, the same depth as the

new docks off it. The entrance from Queen's Dock was widened and a new hydraulic bridge fixed in 1905. Other improvements included a telephone link in 1881 and telegraphic communication with the pier master at the Herculaneum river entrance in 1884. An electric generator was installed by the Liverpool Electric Supply Co to provide light in 1893.

The hydraulic engines were first modernized in 1873, and the boilers replaced in 1878. In 1897 'spans' of steel wire rope, carried on brackets, were fixed at the top of the dock faces of the warehouse walls, and ring bolts fixed in the dock walls for carrying leads from the portable hydraulic jiggers on the quay up to the saddles on the spans; similar travelling, lifting equipment had been installed at Albert Dock in 1894 and had proved very successful. Ten new fixed hoists were installed at the same time. An additional accumulator was provided at the south end of the warehouses in 1900. All the hydraulic pumping engines were dismantled in 1906, however, and thereafter

41 Wapping Warehouse from the south-west, *c*1930.

the Wapping machinery was worked off pressure supplied from the Toxteth and Herculaneum centres.

A proposal of 1905 to demolish Wapping Warehouse and to replace it by a transit shed was not implemented, and the only subsequent changes were those brought about by a bomb dropped on the southern end during the Second World War. In 1982 most of the warehouse was still in use as a bonded liquor store, and among the wooden casks lying in the valuts below the quays, the passage of the years seemed virtually imperceptible.

Operation

Not surprisingly, the operation of the Wapping docks was related to the reasons for their construction. Since they were built primarily as a linkage between other docks, much of their 'trade' was through traffic. Furthermore, a good deal of the passing traffic consisted of vessels which were light, because in such relatively unstable conditions they were safer within the dock system than without. The construction of the dockside warehouse and transit sheds on the quays of a passage dock indicates somewhat confused thinking on the part of the Dock Committee. Identifiable patterns of trading did develop over the years, nevertheless, and even when there were major changes in the whole of the South Docks, the patterns established at Wapping were altered rather than destroyed.

The coastal and cross-channel trades using the Wapping docks were mainly Scottish, Irish and Southern European. From the ports in these places came general cargo, stone such as setts and chippings, and bonded wines and spirits. General cargo, coal and manufactured goods filled the holds on the outward trips. After the construction of the half-tide entrance to the Duke's Dock in 1845, Irish coasting vessels had been allowed to use this dock, and later they moved on in to Wapping Basin. The tiny basin with its three passages was never the scene of very much loading or discharging activity because there was so little space available in and around it, but the coasting trade made fair use of Wapping Dock.

The deep-sea vessels which found berths in Wapping Dock came from the Americas, the West Indies and West Africa, bringing cotton, tobacco, wool, nitrates, sugar, rum and ivory into the warehouses. Their outward cargoes were textiles, heavy engineering and railway equipment and re-exports, but few of these were shipped at Wapping. When more and more of the international deep-sea trades began to be deflected from the older docks which could not accommodate the increasing size of ship plying these routes, the Wapping Dock retained much of its original custom. The ports of West Africa and South America had never been deep-water harbours, so deep-draughted vessels could not use them in any case. Thus, for example, the iron barque *San Lorenzo*, 488 tons, $9\frac{1}{2}$ft draught, was typical of the ships sailing between Wapping and Valparaiso in the 1870s. The warehouses were not used solely for storage: a certain amount of sorting and sampling, in the case of wool, and rudimentary processing, in the case of tobacco, was also undertaken. On the whole, the Wapping Dock and its warehouses had been designed to handle sailing ships whose turn-around time in port was not very fast. Though one of the trans-oceanic vessels might spend several weeks in port, this time was a relatively small proportion of the total journey time and it thus did not greatly matter that the length of quay, and thus the capacity for working cargo, was relatively small in comparison to the quay room provided for steamers.

1 Rennie, *Report to Dock Committee*, 1809
2 DCM 13.i.1846
3 DER 29.vi.1851

Herculaneum Dock

The earliest dock on the future Herculaneum site was built by Charles Roe, late in the 18th century, to serve his copper smelter established in 1767. It was probably an irregular tidal basin, enclosed by walls but lacking gates.[1] In 1791 the dock and the buildings in the vicinity were acquired by the undertakers of the Herculaneum Pottery Co. The company's promoters were shipbuilders, and for a time the pottery carried on a substantial export trade, particularly with the United States. The Herculaneum Pottery Co specialized in maritime subjects and individual commissions, the latter generally relayed to the pottery by the Liverpool agents of American tobacco, timber and grain merchants. From the 1830s, however, the business was in decline; by the end of the decade it had dwindled to nothing, and the remaining buildings were dismantled soon after 1840.

The Acts of Parliament for the development of the site as a privately-promoted dock were passed in 1840 and 1846. The directors of the Herculaneum Dock Company, who no doubt hoped to capitalize on the rapid expansion of the trade of the port, were Joseph Bailey the younger, William Potter, Marcus Freeman Brownrigg, John Laird, John MacVicar, Robert Barbour and Joseph Travis Clay. Bailey and Laird were also involved with the earlier development of Birkenhead. The Act gave powers to raise capital of £600,000, plus £200,000 on mortgage. Yet in spite of these sanguine beginnings, nothing was done, and in 1848 the site was transferred to the Liverpool Dock Trustees. The Trustees took no further action for some years, though in 1858 the suggestion was made that a development similar to that of Sandon Dock (a 10-acre basin with 6 large graving docks, opened in 1851) would be appropriate.[2]

Herculaneum Dock was the first major work on Merseyside of G. F. Lyster, appointed Engineer in Chief to the Dock Board in 1861, and though the general scheme seems to have been decided in advance of his arrival in Liverpool, the overall execution is his. Preliminary drawings[3] show an additional dock where Harrington Dock (qv) was to be constructed some 20 years later, and a locked entrance. As built, however, the dock had a double entrance (south 60ft, north 8ft) with single pairs of gates, a basin of 3 acres, and two 755 ft graving docks. Lacking entrance locks, it was known as Herculaneum Half-tide Dock until 1885, indicating that it

was viewed primarily as an entrance basin either for the graving docks or to the as yet unbuilt dock to its north.

Details of the design also make it likely that preliminary work, at least, had been done by John Hartley, who was still Dock Engineer (in succession to his father) until a few months before excavation began. The stonework of the pier head and graving dock entrances and of the entrance island, complete with typically whimsical huts for gatemen, was indistinguishable from that of the elder Hartley; the remaining masonry of the docks, however, was very much less idiosyncratic and more typical of Lyster's later work elsewhere. The walls of the wet dock were 'veneered'. First of all the face of the bedrock was cut back to 2ft–4ft back from the intended face of the dock wall. Then vertical dovetailed grooves were cut into the rock at 20ft intervals, and, into these were slotted large blocks of ashlar dovetailed to fit these slots and also dovetailed outward to hold in place the masonry panels intervening between these dovetailed counterforts. Stone employed for this lining was Runcorn sandstone, used also in a conventional manner in the two first graving docks. As built, these were of exceptional length, some 190ft longer than the next newest and largest, those at Sandon Dock.

Excavated material was removed and dumped some ten miles out to sea by five new hopper barges each of 500 tons capacity, and with them the contractor Thomas Monk removed some million cubic yards of rubble, most of which had to be excavated by blasting. The half-tide dock was opened in 1866, two years after the opening of the first two graving docks. Work on a third graving dock was begun at the same time to take advantage of the presence of plant on the site and to cut down on necessary disturbance to dock users later when it would be decided to complete it. Work recommenced on this third dock in 1876, three years after the passage of a further Dock Act authorizing the dock's extension. This work, and also that for the dock's enlargement, was carried on behind dams formed of unexcavated material left in place; the new graving dock was excavated from bedrock and lined with concrete. A fourth graving dock had been proposed as early as 1869, but was not built until 1902. Baldry and Yarborough were the contractors.

The work authorized by the 1873 Act was completed in 1882, with the building of a branch dock on the east side. This work involved cutting away a rock outcrop some 70ft high, and this site may have suggested to Lyster[4] the opportunity offered for providing secure storage for petroleum and other inflammable products which had already been discharged in the dock for some years: in 1878 the north quay had been approved as a permanent unloading place for barrels of petroleum. Lyster provided the remarkable casemates excavated from the rock of the east and south sides of the new branch dock. These are barrel-vaulted chambers dug at regular intervals, each one 20ft high, varying in depth from 39ft to 51ft, and separated from its neighbour by 5ft of solid rock. They are faced in concrete, with rusticated decoration cast *in situ*.

A buoy store was required in the early 1880s to replace the original store on the site of the new Toxteth Dock, and this was established at the south-west corner of Herculaneum Dock where a shed, cranes and railways could be built adjacent to the river. Other accommodation designed by Lyster and built in the 1880s included accommodation for customs officers and for dock gatemen.

The gates at Herculaneum river entrance were the first in the south docks to be worked by hydraulic power. An Armstrong accumulator was installed in 1865. The first two graving docks had manually operated gates, but hydraulic gate engines were installed for the third dock when it was built in 1881. Five years later a second accumulator and pumping engine were supplied by the Hydraulic Engineering Co in order to power the increasing number of hydraulic appliances in the docks. The remaining manual gates and cloughs were converted to hydraulic operation in 1897.

The most remarkable of the hydraulic installations were the coaling cranes: two 25-ton moveable cranes and a 25-ton stationary hoist. The cranes, one by Armstrong Mitchell and the other by the Hydraulic Engineering Company, were installed in 1895 and 1897 respectively, and towered some 65ft over the east quay of the branch dock. They were hauled into position by hydraulic capstans. Their maximum reach was 30ft, and they could tip waggons loaded with 15 tons of coal straight into a ship's hold. The hydraulic hoist was installed on the south end of the branch dock by C. & A. Musker, in 1907.

In 1862, Lyster had declared optimistically that the double entrance to Herculaneum Dock was:

'. . . in deep water and everywhere clear of sandbanks . . . nor is it probable that any such accumulations will take place, owing to its being a salient point of the river, along which the currents scour with considerable rapidity'.[5]

In 1883 the sills of the entrances were deepened by 4ft to 12ft below ODS, while the foreshore in front of the

entrance was dredged to 14ft below ODS. Continuous dredging, however, was necessary on the basis of the harbour-master's fortnightly soundings, but neither the lowered sills nor the dredging made the entrance always easy of navigation. The next attempted solution was simply to close one of the entrances. The 60ft south entrance was closed experimentally for two months in 1912, and then permanently. In 1932 the north entrance was closed as well (thus compelling all ships to use the Brunswick Dock entrance) but this resulted in increased siltation in Herculaneum and Harrington Docks, and the appearance of mud in Toxteth Dock which had previously been clear. In 1939, with the onset of war and a 50 per cent government grant towards the cost, both entrances were made operational again. The graving docks were in constant use throught the Second World War, and most of the ships entering them passed through the Herculaneum river entrances.

During the twelve months to September, 1962, however, the greatest number of vessels using the entrances on any tide had been eleven coasters, and on fifty-seven tides no ships had passed the entrances at all. Both sets of gates were closed again, and once more all ships were obliged to enter the system through Brunswick Docks. Four months later the inner gates at Brunswick 100ft lock were closed for repairs, and the 80ft Herculaneum entrance recommissioned; thereafter it remained open for oil traffic from the Dingle to the Clarence Dock electricity generating station, and in 1967 new steel gates were installed by Head Wrightson Teesdale Ltd at a cost of nearly £123,000.

Operation

Operations at Herculaneum were dominated by maintenance and repair at the four huge graving docks, not exceeded in size until the building of the single 1,060ft dock at Gladstone Dock in the north in 1913, and by the coal and oil trades. The graving docks were in frequent demand for the Board's own vessels. Lyster wrote in 1883:

'. . . we have to provide for the frequent repair of a large number of craft of various kinds, such as 6 dredgers, 8 steam hoppers (soon to be increased by the 800 ton hopper now building on the Clyde), 16 sailing and derrick flats, 40 wooden hopper flats and the 30 ton floating crane now in course of construction . . . also the steam tug Hodgson, the surveying vessels Alert and Vigilant . . . several light ships . . . all requiring constant examination and overhaul in a graving dock',

Use of the graving docks was continuous, though reaching peaks of activity during the two World Wars when Liverpool was the terminus for North Atlantic convoys and the merchant ships were joined by many of the Royal Navy.

Repair and maintenance were also the foremost activities in the nearby Buoy Store. It was said of this establishment, in 1951, 'Not only buoys, cables and sinkers are the concern of the workers in the shed. They also clean and overhaul craft employed on taking river soundings, sand suckers used on wreck salvage and the boilers that power them.'[6] In addition to the 'shed' were a smithy, shackle store, secure stores for gas cylinders, petrol and oil, a gas house, yard, offices and a shipwrights'

open-fronted shed with a boilerhouse and steaming facilities attached. Buoys in need of repair were brought to the Herculaneum river wall by Dock Board vessels such as *Vigilant* whence they were lifted by quay cranes (hand operated until 1914) and lowered on to bogeys and wheeled into the fitting shed. Most of the men employed in the Buoy Store worked for the Mersey Docks and Harbour Board, but at various times this force of smiths, platers, rivetters, holders up and shipwrights was supplemented by contract labour from independent firms including the shipbuilders H. & C. Grayson Ltd. As electric arc welding replaced rivetting as a means of joining parts of steel buoys, the Board's boilermakers became redundant whilst more outside welders were

42   Herculaneum Dock and Graving Docks Nos 1–4, and north end of Dingle tank farm, 1964.

employed. In the 1930s amalgamation of the work of the Buoy Store and that of the Coburg Dockyard was considered, but no such union took place.

Oil products and coal monopolized the trading in the dock from the outset. By 1873 pressure from oil importers had led the Board to set aside an approved quay for the landing of petroleum, and on account of its remoteness from other installations Herculaneum must have seemed a natural choice. The casemates, when completed, could accommodate 60,000 barrels (9,500 tons) of petroleum. The Board never allowed one party to rent all of the casemates at once, but major tenants in the 1880s and 1890s were Meade-King and Robinson, Samuel Banner & Co (agents for the Kerosene Co), A. Hopps & Sons and Bigland Sons & Jeffreys, who paid 20s a week for large casemates and 15s for small ones. In addition, other inflammables – turpentine, resin and explosives – were landed at Herculaneum and stored in the casemates.

At first, oil was carried in barrels, then in sheet iron drums packed two to a wooden case. The earliest bulk cargoes (often carried in sailing ships in the '80s and '90s, that required no great turn of speed, merely plenty of unbroken cargo space, and which were cranky and unpleasant to sail) were pumped by hand into storage tanks on the quay and thence run off into barrels. Regulations laid down that no more than 200 barrels were to be left on the quay overnight, and the use of lights was forbidden. In 1891, however, a bulk storage depot was opened by the Dock Board immediately to the south of Herculaneum, at Parkhill, where in 1894 there were five 32ft-high tanks of wrought-iron plates with an aggregate capacity of 12,500 tons. Oil was pumped from ships berthed on the west side of the branch dock via underground pipes to the storage tanks built on a terrace cut in the face of riverward slope of the Parkhill Estate, some 15ft above the Herculaneum Dock quays. Oil was

43 East quay Herculaneum Dock, with oil gantry in foreground and coaling cranes beyond, c1920–30.

delivered from the tanks by gravitation to a two-storey filling house 11ft below the level of the tanks. There was railway and roadway access to the filling house, and a special barrel elevator ran from the dock quay to a coopering yard. Meade-King, Robinson and Co inaugurated the new stores by delivering 2,700 tons of oil, using their ship's own pumps, in June, 1891. The provision of the tank farm in time diminished the need to land oil on the quayside, and in 1895 petroleum was confined to the south end of the dock. After the erection of the coaling cranes on the east quay, there were further restrictions imposed, and petroleum spirit was never able to be handled in bulk in the Port until after 1923.

44 Barclay fireless locomotive MDHB No. 45 outside petroleum casemates, Herculaneum Dock, c1920–30.

In 1902 a steamer was bunkered with fuel oil at Herculaneum Dock by a small steamship that had brought the liquid fuel from London, and oil bunkering continued in this fashion until 1919 when permanent oil bunkering facilities were provided on the Dingle Bank estate on the Board's land. Oil companies established here from the first were the Anglo-American Oil Co, which was bunkering a ship within seven months of the start of construction. The Dingle station and Herculaneum Dock were connected by means of two 3,000ft lengths of 10ins diameter pipe through which fuel oil could be pumped to ships berthed in the dock, or to railway waggons or to bunkering barges. A huge gantry was erected along the south and east sides of the dock to carry the feeder pipes overhead, keeping them clear of the quays and allowing several vessels to bunker simultaneously.

In 1923 a river jetty was built near Dingle Point to accommodate the oil and petroleum tankers, and the

National Benzole Co built tanks at Parkhill for the storage of petroleum spirit and benzine in 1925. Barclay fireless engines were employed to haul railway tank waggons from the oil loading gantry to the steam engines waiting at the south-west corner of Herculaneum Dock, which then took them on to the main goods station.

The construction of two mooring buoys and, in 1928, a second jetty was in response to the continuing growth of the oil trade and the voluminous storage capacity (173,500 tons in the port, of which 122,500 tons capacity was at Herculaneum, Parkhill and Dingle) in the Mersey Docks.

The ultimate decline of the South Docks facilities followed from the continued silting of the approaches to the Herculaneum river entrance and to the Dingle oil jetties, and from changes in the pattern of the trade as a whole. The provision of storage for imported, refined spirit was increasingly unnecessary with a shift to the importation of crude oil to refineries, and with the establishment of oil refineries at Ellesmere Port and at Stanlow on the opposite bank of the Mersey there was no incentive to continue to use the oil stores attached to Herculaneum Dock. Both the Dingle jetties were closed in

45 Casemate, Herculaneum Dock, 1983.

1967, and a temporary buoy berth erected that year in deeper water was so badly damaged when a tanker collided with it in 1976 that it was not repaired.

The coal trade at Herculaneum Dock was established a little after the oil trade, and was shorter lived. Though the coal traffic had always been of importance to the Port of Liverpool, during the late 19th and early 20th centuries Herculaneum was one of only four docks whose operations and cargo handling equipment were specifically geared to coal shipments. The Hartleys initiated the provision of specialized coaling machinery in Liverpool when they built the high-level coal railway with its hydraulic appliances at Bramley-Moore Dock in 1857, some four years after the opening of a large (1100ft × 350ft) specialized coal dock at Garston, some three miles to the south, by the St Helens & Runcorn Gap Railway. By the 1880s the railway companies in particular were pressing the Dock Board to provide coal traffic accommodation in the South Docks, but it was not until the late 1890s that the quayside railways and the 25-ton hydraulic cranes which travelled along them were installed at Herculaneum Dock on the north and east quays. By the late 19th century, coal had assumed a new importance as a marine fuel. In the 1860s the proportion of sailing to steam ships in the port had been 88:12;in the 1880s, 64:36, and by the end of the 1890s, 7:93, a dramatic turn around.

Berths at the coaling cranes were allocated by the Herculaneum Dock Master. The provision of bunker coal always took precedence over that of cargo coal, but there was also the necessity of handling coal for the Toxteth and Herculaneum hydraulic power stations. Coaling a 5,000-ton ship frequently occupied about 48 hours, but bunkering was liable to interruption to allow the movement of other vessels. Not only did the Herculaneum Dock have a water area slightly smaller than that of the Albert Dock, but its quays were interrupted by entrances: two to the river, one to Harrington Dock and four to the graving docks. The restricted length of the quayside available for loading and discharging had to accommodate the travelling coaling cranes, the hydraulic hoist, the weighing machines, weighbridges and rolling stock of the railway network round the dock, the pillars for the gantry carrying the oil pipelines, and the business of the buoy store.

Crises also affected the operation of the dock, and because of the concentration on fuel and ship repair at Herculaneum, strikes and wars made a greater impact on the operation of that dock than on most others. Coal strikes in 1912 and 1926, the rail strike in 1919 and the two World Wars all resulted in dramatic drops or rises in activity. The tonnage of coal handled in the Liverpool docks began to decline in the 1920s. As the petroleum trade was handled increasingly from the Parkhill and Dingle installations, the Herculaneum casemates were used for a widening variety of purposes. The characteristics which had recommended them as oil stores made them suitable for the storage of explosives (c1902, 1914–18, 1939–45) and radioactive substances (1963). A number of the casemates were bonded for wine storage in 1919, and at various times they were also used to store cotton and general cargo. Entirely lacking in mains supplies of power or water, and damp, the casemates never attracted substantial rents and they were eventually occupied by the types of businesses which, elsewhere, would have moved to a railway arch. A fair number of these businesses remained in occupation long after 1972 when the adjoining dock was finally closed to ships.

Two years after Herculaneum Dock was closed by the Mersey Docks and Harbour Co, one last vessel entered the dock. This was *Eem*, a cutter suction dredger of the Westminster Dredging Company, which was delivered in pieces by lorry, assembled on the quayside and lowered into the dock by crane. In two weeks she removed 477,373cu yds of silt and pumped it through an overground pipeline into Toxteth Dock. Herculaneum Dock itself was thereafter filled with 980,905cu yds of sand from the Devil's Bank, a sandbank between the Garston and Eastham shipping channels in the Mersey, and Boskalis Westminster Construction Co sealed the Herculaneum Dock gates by piling 15,000 tons of stone from North Wales against the outer and inner sides of each entrance. The site of the dock, branch and graving docks has been developed as a spine road, car park and some public open space adjacent to the site of the 1984 Liverpool Garden Festival.

1 LRO 1867 Hf 387.1 MER
2 MDHB Committee on Dock Extension on the Lancashire side of the Mersey 1858
3 Ib
4 DER 1881
5 DER 1862
6 *Liverpool Post* 16.v.1951

Harrington and Toxteth Docks

A casual observer of the Harrington and Toxteth Docks in 1980 might well have been forgiven for dismissing these two long, narrow basins with transit sheds along both quays, as among the dreariest in the docks. Their origin and development, however, was more complex than their later appearance would suggest.

The earliest dock to be built on the site was the work of the Bridgewater Trustees, in 1837–39, who were probably led to develop it by the area's already being partly industrialized. Towards the end of the 18th century the Earl of Sefton had leased some fifty-two acres of land between the later Parliament and Northumberland Streets for building, but the residential attractions of the area were reduced by the relocation of industries from the centre of Liverpool. These included Charles Roe's copper smelting works and Richard Clare's turpentine distillery. Roe built a coal quay on the foreshore. His premises were subsequently taken over by the Herculaneum Pottery Co, and other parts of the site were occupied by shipyards, and by the Mersey Forge (later the Mersey Iron and Steel Co) established in 1810. The Bridgewater Trustees' dock, known as Egerton Dock, was a small affair of 340ft by 60ft, with a 20ft entrance, and intended primarily for river boats carrying timber.

The first Harrington Dock was promoted by a private company, though since a number of those with interests in the concern were members of the Corporation it is hardly surprising that they should have employed Jesse and John Hartley as their engineers. The Hartleys designed two rectangular basins 350ft long by 80ft wide and angled so that their entrances faced upstream. Each entrance was 40ft wide, but only the northern one was fitted with gates. When opened in 1839 they were known as Harrington Dock and Harrington Dry Basin.

At the same time, the Dock Trustees were themselves constructing another dock for coasters and small craft on the south side of Brunswick Dock. This, Toxteth Dock, was 500ft by 90ft at the west and broadening to 130ft at the east; the sill was 5ft below ODS, the gates were 40ft and were sheltered by the extension of the Brunswick shipyards into the river to the north. Thus by 1841, there were four small docks to the south of Brunswick Dock: Egerton, Toxteth and the two Harrington Docks.

The Harrington Dock Company did not prosper, partly in consequence of its failure to secure exemption from

harbour dues for vessels using its docks. Powers given to the Company to build further docks were not taken up, and by the Liverpool Dock Act of 1844 the Trustees were empowered to buy the company's assets. In 1848 the Dock Trustees acquired further land in the immediate vicinity of the Egerton Dock, while the Egerton Dock itself was sold to the Midland and to the Manchester, Sheffield and Lincolnshire Railway Companies in 1857, following the Bridgewater Trustees' moving their operations to Stanley Dock in the North Docks.

Improvement of facilities at these small docks under the Trustees' ownership was desultory, partly on account of the vociferous and conflicting demands of the timber traders and the ship builders. Some had been long established there; others found there temporary homes after being displaced from the sites of Brunswick and Albert docks. However, there was not really sufficient room for shipyards on the narrow Harrington site, and the Trustees concentrated their efforts on providing for the timber trade. The ground in the vicinity of Toxteth and Harrington Docks was levelled, and railways were laid between Sefton Street and the timber ground in 1851. In 1854 the whole timber ground was reorganized to provide 25ft wide strips of land served by common gangways of 20ft. Railway connections were further improved in 1856 with the provision of sidings by the London and North Western and Lancashire and Yorkshire Companies. Among individual timber traders' installations, Chaloner and Fleming's mahogany shed of 1851 probably contained a travelling overhead crane.

After the opening of Canada Dock in 1858, the focus of the timber trade shifted from south to north, though even while it was pre-eminent it was not exclusive. Barges discharged copper and silver ores at Todd, Naylor and Co's works on the south side of Harrington Dock; Bridgewater vessels used the dock, and so did the Mersey Iron and Steel Co. In 1863 the Mersey River Steam Boat Co built a landing stage off Harrington Dock wall whence they operated ferry services until 1876. But after the departure of the bulk of the timber trade, Toxteth and Harrington Docks were in a sad way. Toxteth Dock was far enough from other activity to allow it to be used for cargoes that were dangerous, such as gunpowder, or unpleasant, such as Corporation refuse. It was described as 'the only spot in the long line of Liverpool docks where grass grows on the quay',[1] and in 1872, when part of Harrington north wall collapsed and sank the flat *Caroline*, the dock was closed to shipping altogether.

Plans to redevelop the Toxteth, Harrington and Egerton Docks had been in existence since the building of Toxteth and the purchase of Harrington, and several schemes had been mooted between then and 1872 when a sub-committee of the Trustees was appointed to take up the matter. One reason for the Trustees' long delay in developing the site was their concentration from 1858 on works at Birkenhead which tied up most of their resources for nearly twenty years. Plans submitted with the Mersey Docks (Liverpool Dock Extension) Bill of 1872 showed two rectangular docks parallel to the river, connected to Herculaneum Dock and to each other; a connection to Brunswick Dock was added at the construction stage. The alignment chosen was prompted by the desire to use as much as possible of the existing structures in order to keep down costs, and the site was restricted also by dense urban development and by a sandstone outcrop. At Harrington and Toxteth Docks, in consequence, the dock estate is at its narrowest. The 1873 Act also gave the Dock Board powers to refurbish the river wall, to acquire Egerton Dock, subject to providing the occupiers with alternative and equally favourable accommodation, and to finance the works by borrowing up to £4,100,000 in amounts not exceeding £500,000 per annum.

The northern dock, known initially as Dock I, and only later as Toxteth, was to be connected to the river by means of two locks, one built on the site of the former Harrington Dock and the other making use of the old Toxteth Dock sills. The dock was to cover 11¾ acres, and to be 1450ft long by 300ft wide at the south and 380ft wide at the north end. The other dock, first known as Dock K and later as Harrington, was to have no direct river entrance and was to measure 7 acres in extent and to be 1,330ft by 300ft, with 60ft passages at each end. Road and railway connections were, it seems, only resolved as work progressed. The dock sills were proposed at first to be 8ft below ODS, the same as at Herculaneum. Later, Lyster recommended their lowering to 10ft. In the event, they were built at 12ft below ODS, largely in response to public pressures expressed in a meeting of the Toxteth inhabitants anxious to ensure the building of docks that, with a long life before them, would guarantee local employment for the foreseeable future. (The river entrance at Herculaneum was deepened to 12ft below ODS in 1883.) The sheds erected were to be the first of the large double-storey type in the Liverpool docks, built after inspection of examples in London. Their proponents

described vividly in 1883 the need for dock installations to match the new generations of ships:

'*These steamers now discharged night and day, and frequently the first information which the consignee of the cargo had of his goods having arrived was a notice that the time had begun to count against him during which goods might remain upon the quay. He at once sent carts and men down to take delivery, and when they arrived they found things in a state of utter confusion. Some huge steamer carrying some 4,000 or 5,000 tons of cargo was discharging from five hatchways as fast as steam winches could tear the stuff out of her hold. The quay was more like the falls of Niagara than anything else, and he was utterly unable to get possession of any portion of his goods upon the quay.*'[2]

Further advantages were that double-storey sheds could be built on sites that were too narrow for single-storey sheds of equal floor area, and that if under-employed the upper floors could be used for warehousing. In the event the Board decided to build double-storey sheds on the narrow east quays and single-storey sheds on the broader, west quays of the new docks.

Excavation of Dock K from the rock began in December 1875, and the spoil was dumped at sea by hopper barges; a small 22ft-wide river lock constructed in 1878 and additional to the original plans may have been partly for their use. The projected depth of excavation had been reached by July, 1882, but the decision taken to lower the dock floors and sills to 14ft and to 12ft respectively below ODS had lengthened the construction time by a year. Water was admitted to Dock K in July 1883, and the first ship to enter, the *Parthia*, berthed in December. The new dock was known as Harrington Dock from 1885. Work on Dock I had been authorized in May 1882, and by July 1885 three quarters of the excavation of the dock itself, all of the south passage to Harrington, and the foundations for the 50ft lock were complete. Water was admitted in April 1888 and the dock named Toxteth Dock. The girder swing bridges spanning the two 60ft entrances and the 50ft and 22ft locks were made in the Coburg Dockyard; their driving machinery was supplied by Armstrong, Mitchell and by Tannett Walker.

The river wall, begun in 1876 opposite Dock K, incorporated considerable sections of existing masonry. Where old walls were available, these were cut down as necessary to make possible a sound bond with the new, which were of concrete. The overall height of the finished river wall, backed with material excavated from the dock basins, was 31ft above ODS. In the dock walls themselves, Lyster adapted the system of veneering that he had already employed at Herculaneum, in which ashlar was dovetailed to the bedrock.

Work on the 1,200ft double-storey transit shed on the east quay of Dock K began in the summer of 1883, with iron and steel components supplied by Eastwood Swingler & Co, Sampson Moor & Co, and the Widnes Foundry Co. By October, work was sufficiently advanced to allow the installation on a trial basis of an Armstrong travelling roof crane, with a jib of long reach to cover ships' hatches alongside. By 1888 the shed had received seven of these cranes. Plans to build a similar shed on the west quay were abandoned on grounds of cost, and instead a single-storey shed 1,067ft by 143½ft was put up and ready by October, 1885.

The transit sheds of Dock I were similar to those of Dock K, with a double-storey shed on the narrow east quay and a single-storey shed 1,300ft by 150ft – then the widest on the docks – on the west; these were finished by

1889. Structural components for the double-storey shed were supplied by Pearson and Knowles, and by E. C. & J. Keays.

The modern hydraulic machinery required greater supplies of water than were available from the Herculaneum power centre, and in April, 1889 the Engineer was authorized to build an hydraulic station at the north-east corner of Toxteth Dock. By June of that year, the shortage of water had become so acute that emergency supplies had to be obtained from the Liverpool Hydraulic Power Company. The new station was completed by the next year, with Armstrong pumping engines and accumulator, Green and Sons economizer, and Joseph Foster steel boilers.

A similar state of unreadiness was revealed in the course of construction with regard to road connections, and Lyster was forced to recommend the lowering of a stretch of Sefton Street some one mile long between Horsfall

46 T. & J. Harrison ships typical of those using Toxteth and Harrington Docks in the early 20th century.

Road and Park Street. Though negotiations were protracted an incline to Horsfall Street was eventually built. From 1885 the main line of dock railway was extended to serve the Harrington Dock single- and double-storey sheds, and later the double-storey shed in Toxteth Dock. The Toxteth Dock single-storey shed remained without railway access.

Under the provisions of the Southern Works Act of 1898 the 60ft passage between Union and Toxteth Docks was widened to 100ft and deepened to 17ft 6in below ODS. At the same time, more powerful impounding engines were installed at Herculaneum to maintain a water level of 27ft over the Union–Toxteth sill. As a result of the decision to extend the reconstructed Brunswick Dock over the site of Union Dock and the Brunswick Graving Docks, Toxteth became connected directly with Brunswick Dock and the 100ft and 80ft Brunswick river entrances became the northern approach for vessels entering the Toxteth–Harrington system. The now largely redundant Harrington and Toxteth locks, 22ft and 50ft respectively, were filled in in 1913, and transit sheds extended over them.

Later improvements included major repairs between 1950 and 1952 to the Harrington west wall, which had moved; a wall 7ft 9in deep was built in front of the old sandstone masonry. The steam engines in the Toxteth power station were replaced by Mather and Platt and Hydraulic Engineering Co electric engines in 1913, and the Toxteth east shed hydraulic roof cranes replaced in 1962 by Stothert and Pitt 1½-ton electric cranes. Part of the Harrington Dock east shed was demolished after bomb damage, and the quay left open for the landing of tropical hardwoods. A 550ft × 100ft shed for the fruit traders was built in 1966. The first ship to use the new shed was the 3,070-ton Furness Warren Line motor ship *Olau Knud* which discharged 85,000 cases of apples and some general cargo, and she was typical of the ships, small in size by contemporary standards, now best suited to Harrington and Toxteth Docks. Big modern vessels required a greater depth of water, while modern cargo handling called for wide quays and good road access, neither of which were notable features of these docks. For many years the facilities in these two docks had been kept up-to-date by the efforts of the companies using them rather than by those of the Dock Board, and as the companies' interest waned, so the docks were doomed to closure.

Operation
From the outset the double-storey sheds with their hydraulic cranes and hoists proved efficient and popular with shipowners, with consignees and with the Board. Alfred Holt described the new docks as the only truly commercial docks to be built in the south since 1832, and an account in the *Liverpool Courier* in August 1886 described their operation in glowing terms:

'*The* Astronomer *ss from Calcutta, with a cargo of 5,460 bags rice, 6,170 bags wheat, 2,288 cases castor oil, 18,895 bags linseed, 1,693 bales gunnies, 604 bags saltpetre, 125 bags turmeric, 125 bags ginger, and 250 bales hides . . . worked with her own steam power on the lower quay, and employed three cranes on the upper floor, the whole of the cargo weighing 3,643 tons being landed in 25 hours or an average of 146 tons per hour . . .*'[3]

Shipowners began immediately to press for appropriated berths, pressure that the Dock Board at first attempted to resist, perhaps fearing detrimental consequences for older and less well-equipped docks. Thomas Hughes of T. & J. Harrison, for instance, asserted in a letter in the *Daily Courier*[4] that the granting of appropriated berths could provide regular employment for the large number of artisans, seamen and labourers in the Toxteth area, still depressed after displacement of the ship building and timber trades. The first two companies to be granted berths were Harrisons and R. P. Houston, both of which companies had formerly held berths in Brunswick Dock. Shortly afterwards Elder, Dempster and the African Steamship Co acquired appropriated berths in west Toxteth and east Harrington. By 1909 three out of the four transit sheds were appropriated, and fourth was used as temporary appropriation.

Some of the appropriated berth holders, notably Elder, Dempster & Co further improved the facilities by installing specialized equipment at their own expense. Two 7-ton Goliath travelling cranes were installed on the east side of the west Toxteth shed between 1913 and 1922, with which the company moved 56,000 bags of palm kernels in one week. A paraffin-driven electric battery charging engine was installed in 1918. Other Elder, Dempster equipment including Lansing Road Craft electric tractors, Stulyard weighing machines of up to 8½ tons, and electric bag-sorting apparatus. The Harrison berths were provided with additional electric cranes including two 20cwt run-abouts. On the docks, however, as elsewhere, the introduction of new mechanical aids was not always greeted with approval. The Chief Traffic Officer reported in 1917 that:

'*when a trial was made of a Semac sack-filling machine at the East Harrington Dock, filling wheat into sacks, all the men in the shed struck work, stating that they would not*

47 View looking south-west across the railway towards Harrington Dock transit sheds, 1969.

work the machine or work in the shed where it was working and that the working of the machine had therefore to be stopped.[5]

The typical patterns of trade evident in the working of Harrington and Toxteth Docks were manufactured metals, machinery, textiles and salt exported in return for ores, seeds and grains, other raw materials and foodstuffs. Rails and sleepers made in Lancashire and South Wales were barged to Harrington Dock for export to India, Brazil and Mexico. Much of the galvanized metal sheeting manufactured in North West England and North Wales was shipped out of Harrington; J. Summers & Sons carried such products in flats from their works at Shotton

to the premises they rented at Harrington. Elder, Dempster ships brought in manganese, copper and iron ore to supply the works inland. Barge traffic was significant in both docks, bringing general cargo and, most of all, salt to the outward bound ocean-going ships.

The West African traders generally discharged commodities such as palm kernels, palm oil, groundnuts, cocoa and manganese ore in Toxteth Dock. Having bunkered at the Herculaneum coaling cranes, they were warped to their main loading berths in Harrington. Harrison vessels followed a similar pattern, discharging cargoes such as rice and jute from India, and cotton from Galveston, New Orleans and Brazil before proceeding to Herculaneum to take on Haydock or South Yorkshire coal,

48   Swing Bridge, South Docks.

and then loading at their appropriated berths in
Harrington, or at Birkenhead. Nearly all of the goods
shipped from or landed at Harrington and Toxteth were
packaged; the spacious single- and double-storey transit
sheds were ideal for grading and sorting all non-bulk
cargoes. Grain, alone, had to be bushelled on the quays
because generally it was delivered by rail in box trucks to
the export port and transhipped in bulk.

Additional power was provided at the Toxteth hydraulic
power centre in 1898–99 when a new Tannett Walker
accumulator was installed. Power was augmented again in
1911–13 when new pumping engines were connected to
the hydraulic mains. At about this time, however, the
Harrison line was bearing the cost of having electric
cranes erected on the east Toxteth shed, and in the 1920s
numerous complaints of the inefficiency of the hydraulic
roof cranes were received by the Board. The unspecified

shortcomings of these appliances were most likely related
to their having fixed jibs. By 1929 a number of different
firms had taken over portions of the Toxteth and
Harrington sheds for use as warehouses. Niger Co,
J. H. Rayner & Co, William Porter & Sons, Lete & Sons,
Bibby & Sons and Paterson Zachonic & Co Ltd stored
grain, sugar and cotton in the sheds for up to six months
at a time.

The unprecedented depression in trade in the early
1930s laid up ships or caused them to be run at a loss;
very much reduced fleets were worked in order to
maintain skeleton services and thereby an interest in
particular routes. In 1933 the number of ships discharging
in Harrington and Toxteth Docks fell to little more than
half of the 1923 number; the number of vessels loading
was down to eight per cent of the 1923 figure. The
quantity of cargo discharged was fifty-four per cent less

than in 1923 and the quantity loaded was sixty-seven per cent down. Regular trading patterns were subsequently established once more, only to be disrupted by the outbreak of war. Ships were loaded with bigger cargoes than in peacetime, and they discharged at fewer ports. Cargoes needed to be moved through the docks as quickly as possible to reduce the risk of bomb damage. Sorting to grades, packaging and passing shipments through customs, normally carried out on quays or in sheds, were performed during the war at inland depots. More goods were moved away from the docks by rail, and the main lines of dock railway along the Toxteth shed were improved so as to provide sidings for 189 wagons. The number of heavy lifts increased substantially and in January, 1943, for instance, nineteen landing craft were unloaded on the Harrington Dock quays.

After the war, the major berth holder was Elder, Dempster which became a member of the West African Lines Conference in the 1950s. WALCON held two berths at west Toxteth and a follow-on berth at south-west Toxteth. In 1961 the Conference companies formed a joint stevedoring company which thenceforward undertook all of the wharfingering and master porterage for WALCON liners, 'assisted by recent developments in containerization and palletization'.[6] Accordingly the Dock Board was pressed to widen and strengthen the West Toxteth quay aprons in order to receive the ten-ton containers of the Conference's recently established subsidiary African Container Express Ltd. The necessary adaptations which were completed in 1965, included the cutting back of the quayside bay of the transit shed, the extension of the quay margin by some 20ft and the resurfacing of the quay with concrete. Yet despite these improvements, and the building of the new fruit shed already described, the age of the dock and its capacity were too great disadvantages to be overcome. In 1970 Elder, Dempster moved from Toxteth to Huskisson Dock, and by 1972 the only occupants were the haulage firms, garages, plant hire companies and pallet and oil drum repair firms which rented the redundant transit sheds.

1 Picton, 1873, II, 605
2 *Liverpool Mercury*, 9.ii.1883
3 Ib
4 *Daily Courier*, 20.x.1886
5 MDHB Sub-Committee of Traffic, 10.iii.1919
6 Davies, 1973, 345

Development of the South Docks, Liverpool.

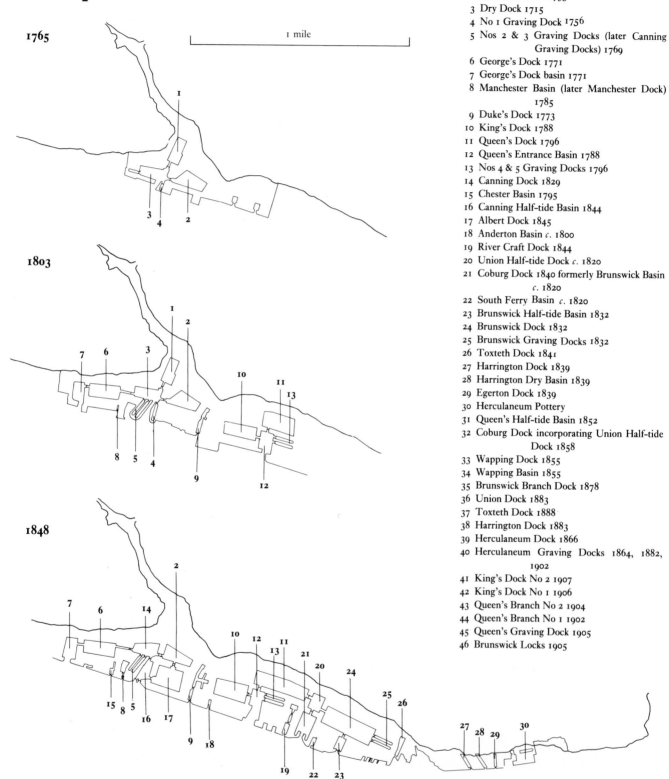

1765

1 mile

1803

1848

Key - Dock name and date of opening

1 Old Dock 1715
2 Salthouse Dock 1753
3 Dry Dock 1715
4 No 1 Graving Dock 1756
5 Nos 2 & 3 Graving Docks (later Canning Graving Docks) 1769
6 George's Dock 1771
7 George's Dock basin 1771
8 Manchester Basin (later Manchester Dock) 1785
9 Duke's Dock 1773
10 King's Dock 1788
11 Queen's Dock 1796
12 Queen's Entrance Basin 1788
13 Nos 4 & 5 Graving Docks 1796
14 Canning Dock 1829
15 Chester Basin 1795
16 Canning Half-tide Basin 1844
17 Albert Dock 1845
18 Anderton Basin *c.* 1800
19 River Craft Dock 1844
20 Union Half-tide Dock *c.* 1820
21 Coburg Dock 1840 formerly Brunswick Basin *c.* 1820
22 South Ferry Basin *c.* 1820
23 Brunswick Half-tide Basin 1832
24 Brunswick Dock 1832
25 Brunswick Graving Docks 1832
26 Toxteth Dock 1841
27 Harrington Dock 1839
28 Harrington Dry Basin 1839
29 Egerton Dock 1839
30 Herculaneum Pottery
31 Queen's Half-tide Basin 1852
32 Coburg Dock incorporating Union Half-tide Dock 1858
33 Wapping Dock 1855
34 Wapping Basin 1855
35 Brunswick Branch Dock 1878
36 Union Dock 1883
37 Toxteth Dock 1888
38 Harrington Dock 1883
39 Herculaneum Dock 1866
40 Herculaneum Graving Docks 1864, 1882, 1902
41 King's Dock No 2 1907
42 King's Dock No 1 1906
43 Queen's Branch No 2 1904
44 Queen's Branch No 1 1902
45 Queen's Graving Dock 1905
46 Brunswick Locks 1905

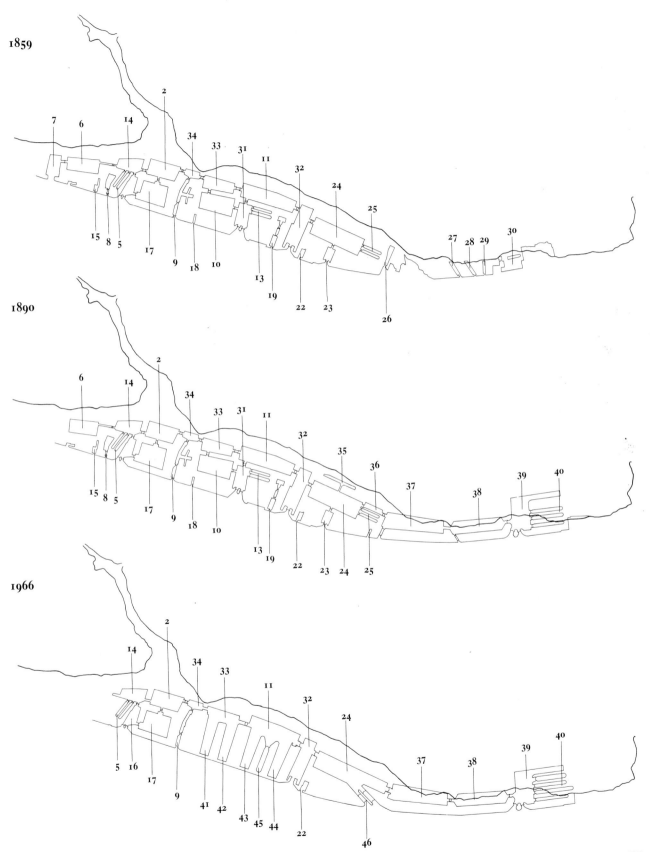

1859

1890

1966

49 Docker wearing safety harness, controlling crane.

50 Working a points lever on the dock railway.

51 Dock gatemen.

76 *Liverpool's Historic Waterfront*

Port of Liverpool building, headquarters of the Mersey Docks and Harbour Board, upon completion in 1907.

53 Stanley Warehouse, 1907.

Management and port labour

Constitution, policy and finance

Up to 1709 and the passage of the first Liverpool Dock Act the Corporation developed and operated the harbour at Liverpool on a small scale, paying for the limited works partly with the revenue from the petty customs or town dues and partly with the hallage collected in respect of goods stored in the public warehouse. The inhabitants occasionally contributed to the maintenance of the physical fabric of the port. The construction of a wet dock, however, was beyond the technical and financial means of the Corporation, which consequently applied to Parliament for the Act necessary to fund the building of the first dock, and retained the services of an experienced engineer, Thomas Steers.

The 1709 Act appointed the Mayor, Aldermen, Bailiffs and Common Council of the Borough as Trustees for the objects of the Act, and gave them powers to finance the work by the issue of short-term bonds and by the collection of dock dues (to be levied on ships using the port, and distinct from the town dues levied by the Corporation on goods). The issue of short-term bonds remained a means of financing dock development until the 20th century. Liverpool was thus created a non-profit trust port.

During the 18th and early 19th centuries, the management of the docks was very gradually removed from the immediate legal control of the Corporation, though at the same time the Dock Trustees remained the members of the Corporation until 1857. Initially, management was by a committee appointed by the Corporation as Trustees, and the Corporation seal was used whenever necessary in dock business. Subsequent 18th-century Acts of Parliament sanctioning further dock construction perpetuated the powers of the Corporation as Trustees for successive docks, and the Act of 1761 specifically vested the dock property in the Trustees and authorized them to take legal action in their own name. Under the 1811 Act, the Trustees of the Liverpool Docks were incorporated and granted their own seal, while the Dock Committee responsible for the day-to-day administration of the docks was to consist of 21 members chosen from among them. The same Act granted the Trustees additional financial resources by enabling them to levy dues on goods entering and leaving the port.

But while the Corporation and the Dock Trustees were becoming more legally discrete, their identical membership and complementary powers were causing increasing confusion in the development of the port. The Corporation paid for the construction of graving docks, which remained its property (as distinct from the Dock Trustees') until the Trustees were authorized to acquire them between 1825 and 1845. The Corporation paid for the building of the tobacco warehouses, and by the terms of leases controlled the development of other building immediately adjacent to the docks and complementing their use. When the Trustees, who were barred from speculative land development, wished to build new docks, they might acquire the necessary sites from the Corporation by free gift, by purchase at cost price, or at a price fixed by agreement, by arbitration or by statute. (The advantages to the Trustees of the Corporation's ability to acquire land long in advance of dock development were considerable, of course; the sites of the future Albert Dock and of other docks, to the north and south, were bought early in the 19th century by the Corporation with usefully vague objectives: 'to make alterations and improvements on the property so purchased, in order to render it of public use, and as far as is practicable productive of annual revenue'.[1])

However, the disquiet which arose from a situation in which two corporate bodies with an identical membership were exchanging real estate and money (some collected for the town, some for the port) grew to alarm following the disclosure of irregularities within the Dock Trust. In consequence, the Dock Committee was reconstructed under an Act of 1825, so as to consist of twenty-one members, of whom thirteen including the chairman were to be appointed by the Trustees and eight elected by the dock ratepayers, who were mostly Liverpool merchants and ship-owners. In addition to this infusion of actual port users, the Committee was given greater authority than before: and the Trustees could only confirm or veto, not direct, the Committee's proceedings. More power and freedom from Town Council control were sought in a Bill of 1836 by which it was proposed to strip the popularly elected (under the provisions of the 1835 Reform Act) Council of all control over the Dock Trust, but the Bill failed in the Commons. Then in 1851 the constitution of the Dock Committee was altered once more, making the total complement twenty-four members, of whom twelve including the chairman were to be elected by the Town Council from their body and twelve were to be elected by the dock ratepayers. Autonomous management of the port was secured eventually on the passage of the Bill promoted in 1857 by the Manchester Chamber of Commerce, the Manchester Commercial Association and the Great Western Railway which created the Mersey Docks and Harbour Board.

The two main grievances of the supporters of the Bill were that freemen of Liverpool were exempt from the payment of town dues (levied on cargo) and that the monies accruing from the dues paid by others were used for the benefit of the town and not the port. It was also acknowledged, with particular reference to the recent acquisition of the assets of the Birkenhead Dock Company on the Cheshire side of the river, that the whole interests of the Mersey ought to be merged in one, public management.

The newly constituted Board agreed to pay to Liverpool Corporation the sum of £1,143,000 in respect of the Birkenhead Docks and £1,500,000 as compensation for the loss of the Town Dues. Additionally the Board assumed responsibility for a bond debt of some six million pounds. The total consideration for the port as it then was (ie, from the first Harrington Dock in the south to Canada Dock, under construction in the north and the unfinished Birkenhead system) was therefore about £8,500,000. The Board inherited and perpetuated the system of securing money borrowed to finance dock construction on the income of rates and dues, and consolidated under an Act of 1858 powers to allocate a proportion of rates to river conservancy and to charge rates on vessels proceeding up river.

The franchises adopted for the election of Board members and for the right to vote were the payment of £25 and £10 in dock dues respectively in the year preceding the election. Port policy thereby rested with port users. Port management was undertaken by means of a number of committees – Finance, Traffic, Docks and Quays, Works, Marine, Pilotage and so on – to direct their respective departments. The committee system continued in use until 1965, proving generally satisfactory at the outset but less so later on when policy formulation, which was the Board's primary responsibility, tended to become confused with operational detail, which was the responsibility of the executive. Likewise, the system of electing Board members remained fundamentally unaltered until the re-organization of the Board as a Company in 1971.

This kind of conservatism was also a characteristic of

the Board's financial history. When the Board had to apply to Parliament in 1859 for additional borrowing powers the opportunity was taken to obtain sanction to set up a sinking fund and the subsequent Act required the Board to transfer to this fund surpluses on the revenue account up to a maximum of £100,000 per annum. By 1887 the Board was persuaded that steps should be taken to fund its debt, and a Bill to do so was accordingly promoted in that year. However, when the chairman of the Lords Committee insisted that if the new powers were granted the Board would be obliged to set aside a definite sum annually (instead of the permissive power then enjoyed), the Board withdrew the Bill. It was not until 1935 when it had become clear that the existing reserves would not be sufficient to replace many capital assets and that past policies had become untenable that provisions for a new sinking fund were made and enacted under the Mersey Docks and Harbour Board Act 1936. The new fund had two faults: it failed to take account of the advanced age of some of the assets, and the contributions to it were inadequate (as they were geared to 90 years of life from 1935 or later). The situation was not rectified because the Board felt that more realistic depreciation provision and the building up of capital funds would result in ship owners and traders pressing for reductions in rates and dues.[2]

War damage cost the Board over £13,000,000, nearly £11,000,000 of which was payable by the Government in 1948. In 1949 work started on the Canada–Langton improvement scheme; the project cost £20 million and no direct increase in revenue resulted. The £4,000,000 invested in 1960 in the Tranmere stages, however, produced a handsome revenue surplus. Overall, the port of Liverpool shared with nearly all of the other major British ports in the 1960's financial difficulties occasioned by a number of factors. Port capacity, especially for small ships, was excessive; revenue from profitable activities was used to offset losses elsewhere; modernization schemes were retarded by shortage of resources; labour costs rose substantially and it was not always possible to take advantage of the economies of mechanization; annual charges for interest rose as money borrowed earlier at low rates was replaced by money borrowed at current rates; premature obsolescence became more important than ever before.

In 1969, the Board's revenue account after charging interest and depreciation showed a deficit of nearly £2,000,000. Over £22,000,000 of the outstanding debt was borrowed at a rate of 8 per cent or more. According to a forecast of the position for the next five years, each year the operating surplus would be exceeded by the charge for interest which would rise to £10,750,000 by 1974.[3] The total estimated cost of Seaforth Dock had now risen to £39,000,000. The only alternative to the process of gradual transformation of the Board's finances was a sudden adjustment by means of a capital reconstruction. In 1971, an Act was obtained to reconstitute the insolvent Mersey Docks and Harbour Board as a statutory company, the Mersey Docks and Harbour Company, transforming the port authority from a self-governing trust to a public limited company, and transferring all of the rights and responsibilities of the Board to the Company.

The board of the Dock Company is made up of three directors appointed by the Government, seven who represent the shareholders, one who works for the company, one trade union representative and two associate, non-voting directors. The company's executives are the Chairman and Deputy Chairman and Managing, Finance, Port Services, Cargo Operations and Personnel Directors who together run the four main departments.

The Act which established the Dock Company was passed on the faith that the trading position of the port of Liverpool would be viable in the future. The causes of the Board's financial crisis of 1970 had been identified and all concerned with the setting up of the statutory company were committed to avoiding previous mistakes. One such error had been undoubtedly the maintenance and manning of under-used docks; it was partly rectified by the closure to commercial shipping of the South Docks in August, 1972, and the subsequent sale of the site to Merseyside Development Corporation in 1981–82.

Professional, administrative and clerical staff of the port authority

Liverpool's first dock engineer, Thomas Steers, worked for the Dock Trustees as a consultant and though he held other Corporation appointments including Water Bailiff and Dock Master, he was never engaged full-time to build or maintain the fabric of the docks. Henry Berry took over the supervision of the works on Salthouse Dock from an aged and ailing Steers in the early 1750s, but his position as Dock Engineer with a salary of eighty guineas a year was not confirmed until 1766. Berry's successor, Thomas Morris, served the Trustees as Dock Engineer from 1789 to 1799 when he resigned his one hundred guineas a year situation to work in London for a salary eight times greater. These engineers appear to have been the only officers engaged during the eighteenth century exclusively for the dock works. The Trustees' statutory duty to prepare annual accounts of receipts and disbursements was

54   Charles Turner, MP, first Chairman of the Mersey Docks and Harbour Board.

probably undertaken by the Corporation's treasurer, and likewise, the Trustees would have used the services of Council lawyers.

When John Foster was appointed Surveyor for both docks and city in 1799, the Dock Trustees lost the exclusive services of their own engineer. Foster must have found his dual roles demanding and difficult, not least because he was also acting as Secretary to the Trustees from around 1810. The number of eminent outsiders – James Walker, John Rennie, William Jessop, Thomas Telford – brought to Liverpool during Foster's incumbency suggests that he may not have had the range of engineering knowledge required by his office. Eventually, in 1823, a resolution of the Town Council was passed to appoint a person 'not concerned directly or indirectly in any trade nor in any other occupation whatsoever saving that of an engineer and surveyor'[4] in the capacity of Deputy Surveyor. Furthermore, the Trustees were not willing to consider applications from any individual already in their employ. Fourteen candidates were interviewed, Jesse Hartley was chosen and a fortnight later Foster's resignation signalled the start of a new era:

'A letter from Mr William Foster containing his father's resignation of the office held by him under the Trustees of the Docks was read and letters from Mr Leonard Addison, Clerk and Superintendent of the Dock Works under Mr Foster and of Mr Henry Heyes, Measurer of the Dock Works, containing the resignations of their situations were also read ... Mr William Foster having already acted for many years as Assistant Secretary to the Trustees of the Docks and to the Dock Committee to their entire satisfaction, Resolved that he be now appointed to the office of Secretary at the salary of five hundred pounds.'[5]

Hartley's salary was confirmed as £1,000 in April, 1825 at the end of his twelve months' probation. By this time his staff included, at least, Gilbert Cummins, Chief Clerk (£200 per annum), Thomas Parkinson, Junior Accountant (£55 per annum), Joseph Smith, Draughtsman (£3 per week) and John Cross, Clerk. The Dock Trustees first published the names and annual salaries of their employees in the accounts for the year ending 24 June, 1829:[6]

Surveyor's Office

Jesse Hartley	Surveyor	£1500–0–0
Gilbert Cummins	Clerk	200–0–0
John Cross	Clerk	120–0–0
William Wigley	Clerk	135–0–0
George Thornton	Surveying Clerk	200–0–0
William Anderton	Draughtsman	175–0–0
Thomas Parkinson	Storekeeper	80–0–0
		£2410–0–0

Secretary's Office

William Foster	Secretary	£500–0–0
Daniel Mason	Clerk	137–10–0
		£637–10–0

Treasurer's Office

Robert Pickering	Treasurer	£800–0–0
John Buckhouse	Receiver of duties on goods	400–0–0
Richard Jones	Assistant receiver of duties on goods	120–0–0
Henry Sudlow	Receiver of duties on tonnage	200–0–0
William Marrow	Check clerk	100–0–0
George Tanton	Check clerk	100–0–0
John Evans	Check clerk	96–0–0
Thomas Jones	Book Keeper	250–0–0
Pryce Davies	Assistant Book Keeper	100–0–0
		£2166–0–0

Ten years later, the salary bills for the Secretary's and Treasurer's Offices had dropped, while the Surveyor's had risen to £3076. By 1847 all three departments had expanded considerably, but the principal officers' salaries were £1,000 p.a. each for the Secretary and Treasurer, and £3,500 for the Surveyor.

Upon the formation of the Mersey Docks and Harbour Board, the heads of the Board's departments were the Engineer in Chief, Secretary, Solicitor, Marine Surveyor, Water Bailiff, Harbour Master, Treasurer and Superintendent of Pilotage. New posts were created for a Principal Accountant (1866), Chief Traffic Manager (1878) and Chief Warehouse Manager (1892). The Office of Secretary became that of General Manager and Secretary in 1894. Until then most port users had sufficient faith in the Board's committees to feel that a general manager was unnecessary, but it was also admitted that, for instance, a shed had been planned and sanctioned before it was found to be quite unsuitable for working.[7] The two offices were separated in 1963. (It is noteworthy that the Board's first General Manager, Miles Kirk Burton, began his career with the Board as an apprentice in the warehouses in 1857 for 8s a week.) The offices of Marine Surveyor and Water Bailiff were combined in 1909.

The office of Water Bailiff was the most ancient in the port and it carried the responsibilities for preventing obstructions and supervising the mooring of ships. The first Liverpool Dock Act stated that the harbour should be buoyed. The next Act, a plea for additional time and money for completion of the works sanctioned at first, listed the buoys and landmarks as work which had not been undertaken. And the following Act (1737) stated that part of the dock revenue should be applied to '... erecting and placing ... proper land marks, buoys and other directions at the mouth and entrances into the said harbour ...'. In subsequent years, the navigable channels were marked with buoys, including bell buoys, but being without lights their usefulness in fog or mist and at night was limited. The 1761 Act established a harbour authority for Liverpool, and from this time, the port as a whole and the docks in the port were afforded equal attention by their developers. Lighthouses were built on the Wirral peninsula at Leasowe (1763), Hoylake (1764) and Bidston (1771), and the first scientifically designed parabolic reflectors in Britain were made in 1763 by the Liverpool Dock Master, William Hutchinson.

The port's first Marine Surveyor was the distinguished Admiral Henry Mangles Denham who spent seven years from 1833 surveying the Mersey. Largely as a result of Denham's work, a river conservancy bill was promoted and passed as the Mersey Conservancy Act of 1842. The Act appointed a Commission consisting of the First Commissioner for Exercising the Office of the Lord High Admiral, the Chancellor of the Duchy of Lancaster and the Chief Commissioner of Woods and Forests whose main purpose was to preserve the regime of the river and to prevent encroachment upon the storage capacity of the upper Mersey estuary.

River conservancy duties include the maintenance of approach channels, dredging, surveying and charting the tideway, removing or dispersing wrecks and obstructions, preventing pollution, salvage, regulating traffic, providing and maintaining moorings, lighting and buoying, supervising the foreshore and licensing lightermen and watermen. Since the passage of the first Liverpool Pilotage Act in 1766, the port authority has been responsible additionally for the administration of the pilotage service. These manifold duties could only be performed under the direction of suitably qualified professional men adequately supported by administrators and clerks.

Between about 1860 and 1900 two of the major occupations of the population of Liverpool were unskilled water front jobs and clerical work. The clerical work generated by the operation of the port caused the Dock Board to become an employer of one of the largest groups of clerks in the city. In 1868 the Board employed 264 clerks and apprentices and approximately 60 'extra clerks'[8] (who held their posts subject to a week's notice and were not allowed to receive increases of salary). Typically, the Chief Traffic Manager's clerical staff comprised 1 chief clerk, 2 ungraded clerks, 9 first grade clerks (6 of whom were clerks to District Traffic Managers), 20 second grade clerks, 11 apprentices, 7 extra junior clerks, 11 female clerks, 1 boy messenger, 15 extra clerks and 3 weighers.[9] First grade clerks received cash on account of quay rent and the use of machines, and supervised the general work in the office, second grade clerks spent half their time recording orders and making out accounts of charges for the use of machinery, and half their time, together with the whole time of the other clerks, recording the landings and removal of goods from the dock quays, calculating the quay rents and dealing with appeals against various charges. Promotion from a clerical post to assistant traffic manager was possible: 'It has been customary in the past to train all youths in the office until they have attained, and retained for many years, the position of Clerk to a District Traffic Manager'.[10] Prospects were not so bright for female clerks who were considered capable of performing only work of a more or less routine nature under the supervision of experienced male clerks.

Port labour: dock and warehouse management

The first dock master in the port of Liverpool was Thomas Steers, who held the job from its creation in 1717 until his death in 1750. He is thought to have been succeeded by Capt William Hutchinson, who served from at least as early as 1759 to 1801, with the aid of an under dock master. By the early part of the 19th century a hierarchy which included dock masters, pier masters and gatemen had evolved to handle the daily workings of the docks. While the numbers of men employed swelled as the line of the docks was extended, their designations and responsibilities remained virtually immutable.

Many of the men who became dock masters were pilots or master mariners. In general, a dock master's main responsibility was to ensure the safe and efficient passage of vessels through his dock. He was expected to be present around tide times (day and night) to oversee the movements of ships and smaller craft, to allocate berths, to see that the quays were maintained in a clean condition, to co-operate with the men engaged on dock sluicing, to direct the activities of his gatemen and watchmen and to keep a record of the principal events of every day. Dock masters were ordered in 1806 to prevent the practice of men and boys going down into the docks, when they were let dry, to pick up ropes and other articles, the 'Committee having reason to think that great loss is sustained by merchants and shipowners in having rigging etc designedly thrown into the docks for the purpose of being picked up'.[11] Dock masters were on call at all times and so were provided with service houses free of rent and taxes. Until about 1840, suitable dwellings in the vicinity of the various docks were rented by the Dock Trustees for their tenants, but after that date (to around 1900) purpose-built residences were erected within the boundaries of the dock estate.

The annual salary of John Elsworthy Fortunatus Wright, Dock Master of George's Dock, was recorded in 1799 as one hundred guineas. In 1838 the system of paying dock masters additionally according to the tonnage using their docks was investigated but found still suitable despite the fact that it encouraged dangerous overcrowding in the popular central docks near the town warehouses. In 1861 the docks were classified as 1st, 2nd or 3rd and annual salaries for the masters of each class were set at £250, £200 and £100 respectively and a house. Amongst the first-class docks at the south end were Albert, Salthouse, King's, Queen's and Brunswick.

The need for pier masters, whose duties were largely confined to those required in taking vessels in and out of the docks, arose when dock congestion made it impossible for the dock masters to oversee the general operation of their docks and deal with the detail as well. Dock masters were still required to be present on the pierheads at tide times, as theirs was the ultimate responsibility for the safety of the ships. The pier masters gave directions and assistance as to 'laying on, slackening or casting off the ropes of vessels hauling into or out of the basins' and seeing that no damage was done to the 'piers, mooring posts, chains or mushrooms'.[12] Following instances of inconvenience and accidents said by river pilots and shipowners in particular to have arisen for want of sufficiently accurate job descriptions for pier masters, their duties were more closely defined and the men became liable to instant dismissal for breach of any of their conditions of service or regulations.[13] Most pier masters were promoted from positions as head gatemen, and their remuneration in the 1850s and 1860s was a salary of £80, a uniform and a house or housing allowance. Head gatemen were generally recruited from the gatemen.

Employed by the Dock Trustees since at least 1748 (when they were paid seven shillings a week), dock gatemen performed much of the manual labour involved in operating gates and bridges and kept watch at night over the docks and shipping. For some years there were not enough dock gatemen: 'Now, when ships are coming into the dock, with a southerly wind, they require people on the quay to take hold of a rope, but there is nobody connected with the dock to receive it. The pilot, or the captain, will perhaps call out for somebody; or rather, the men will say from the shore, Do you want anyone to take hold of the rope? They call out "yes" and then perhaps 50 men get hold, when one would do.'[14] The service was eventually re-organized and equipped in the 1840s, and if the number of gatemen's hats ordered from Joseph Wright in 1846 might be taken as an indication of the numbers of gatemen, there were 114 then in the employ of the Trustees. The rest of their uniforms, apparently first supplied at the same time, included a jacket, double breasted waistcoat and trousers '... of cloth not inferior in quality to that worn by the Police'[15] and a flannel-lined pea coat with the insignia LD and an anchor on the collar, and gold-coloured buttons bearing the Dock Seal. From 1864 they were also allowed a free pair of shoes.

The six new gatemen hired when the reconstructed Coburg Dock was opened in 1858 ranged in age from 26 to 32 years with the exception of Samuel Price, aged 40, who had been in the lightships for the previous five years. The Board recruited from seamen who were already familiar with the basics of ship-handling which were so important for the efficient performance of their jobs as

gatemen. The move to shore based employment ensured a regular wage and the opportunity of better living conditions and safer working conditions, but it also imposed a regimentation which was not always easy to accept. In addition to submitting to all the rules and orders made by the Dock Committee, gatemen were liable to be fined for a series of offences including not turning the bridge rails down when passing vessels through the dock entrance, using insolent language to the public, smoking on duty and coming late to the tide. The fines were paid into the Dock Gatemen's Burial Fund.

By 1854 it was a condition of employment that pier masters and dock gatemen should become members of '... some respectable Sick Club or Benefit Society'.[16] Because such societies were formed by sectional groups of workers, they were precursors of the trade unions which emerged near the end of the 19th century even though they had no record of militancy or political action. However, led by the locally notorious William Simpson (caterer, orator and champion of unskilled workers in Liverpool) in 1872, the dock gatemen demanded and were granted an increase in their minimum wages from 21 to 25 shillings a week. The Board continued to post its annual advertisement prohibiting the giving of Christmas Boxes to its employees.

The Dock Trustees built their first warehouses around the Albert Dock, so all of the jobs which were eventually organized under the jurisdiction of the Chief Warehouse Manager date from 1846. In January of that year the Sub-committee of Management drew up a list of officers and clerks necessary to work the south and south east stacks of warehouses.[17] One of the warehouse keepers and the managing foreman of the tea department were recruited from the East and West India Dock Warehouses, London.

In addition to these officers, more than 40 labourers were hired to work the two new stacks of warehouses, with relatively few mechanical aids, since hydraulic lifting gear was not extensively provided in the warehouses until the late 1870s.

Port Labour: cargo handling
Prior to the establishment of public warehouses run by the port authority, it was the responsibility of the master of a ship to arrange for its discharge by a lumper and his labourers. Lumpers approached ships' masters with offers to discharge their cargoes, usually for a lump sum; respectable lumpers were said to charge around £15 in the 1830s, whilst the unscrupulous ones undercut this price and made up the difference by plundering the holds. Once the cargo was on the quay it became the responsibility of

various consignees, each of whom employed his own gang of porters, to move his goods from quay to cart; the same porters then unloaded the carts into warehouses in the town. Each consignee also employed his own clerk to superintend the landing of goods and to weigh them. Similarly, the stowage of ships was undertaken following private arrangements between owners or forwarding agents and lumpers or stevedores.

In 1846 the Dock Committee took powers to introduce a system of master porterage providing for the licensing and regulation of Master Porters, and the Dock Board's Consolidation Act of 1858 re-enacted these clauses. Thenceforward the Board controlled cargo handling in the port, though it never became a major employer of dock labour. Thus most of the 'dockers' who did most of the work were not part of the port authority's direct labour force. In general, stevedores were responsible for dealing with cargoes once they were aboard; porters handled goods to and from ships' sides. Master stevedores and master porters were gang masters who oversaw the work of their men and they could be self employed, or employees of a large firm of stevedores, porters or both.

55   Cargo-handling: cases of red salmon.

Strictly speaking, these water-front workers were without a trade and unskilled because they served no apprenticeship. In fact, the jobs of porters and stevedores were not only quite distinct but each comprised its own particular expertise. By the latter part of the 19th century the designation of lumper had nearly died out in Liverpool, and the stowing and unshipping previously undertaken by lumpers was done by highly skilled stevedores. In stowing a ship, account had to be taken of the weight, density and other characteristics of the cargoes

as well as the order and port (in terms of depth of water and availability of machinery and labour) of discharge. With the increase in the number of steamships in the port, the new job of coalheaving was created. Even within jobs there was differentiation: quay porters never dealt with outward cargoes at all, and it was from their ranks that came even more specialized porters. Fruit porterage for instance, was highly skilled. Once the fruit was delivered on the quay the fruit porters judged and classified it, making up a catalogue for the brokers who traded on the basis of the catalogue, the porter delivering the goods to the buyer on the production of the broker's order. Cotton merchants and provision merchants also employed special porters.

56   Overhead travelling crane at Harrington Dock.

A strike in 1866 had secured a day rate of 4s for quay porters and 4s 6d for stevedores. Following the settlement of the 1890 dock strike, sample rates of pay exclusive of overtime rates for dock works were agreed to be:[18]
Shipmen: stevedores 7s a day; labourers 5s a day; headman of gang breaking out screwed cotton 6s a day; filling in hold sulphur, manganese, valonia and bones 6s a day;
Quay porters: quay porters 4s 6d a day; lotters, weighers, scribers and sackholders 5s a day; shipping grain on the quay 4s 6d a day;
Coal labourers: When working by day work, 6s per day. When working by piece work $1\frac{1}{4}d$ per ton per man.

A long-standing problem, not resolved until the 1920s, was the casual nature of dock work. During the sailing ship era periods of unemployment occurred when adverse winds or storms prevented vessels from entering or leaving port. The intensification of steamship traffic eliminated the

57 Cargo-handling: meat.

58 Interior of transit shed with runabout crane, 1919.

delays caused by weather problems, but introduced a demand for quick turn around in port which also led to concentrated periods of work alternating with periods of unemployment. There were also seasonal fluctuations, and during some periods the waterfront worker was lucky if he averaged a couple of days a week at work. The Shaw Enquiry's recommendations in 1920 foreshadowed the National Dock Labour Scheme of 1947 which was based on four main principles:

1 limitation of entry to dock work by the registration of both port employers and dock workers and the restriction of employment on dock work to registered dock workers;
2 centralized hiring of dock labour;
3 payment for attendance for work if no work is available;
4 a guaranteed minimum weekly wage for all who report regularly for work.

The implementation of these principles protected the dock worker from seasonal and trading variations and gave him, in effect, a steady job for life.

A witness before the Royal Commission on Transport in 1930 said that the machine age had not yet been accepted in the ports, and the Working Party on the Turn-around of Shipping reported in 1948 that in most ports many operations were performed by hand which could be partly or wholly mechanized. Port authorities persisted in the use of a large labour force which was not

only cheaper (in the short term) but also more flexible than machinery, while dockers resisted the introduction of mechanical aids which they thought threatened their livelihoods. In 1948, 16,000 registered dockers were employed in the port of Liverpool and as late as 1970, there were 10,000; in 1982 there were 2,000. These men are all employed by the National Dock Labour Board which agrees a quota of dockers with the port authority and licenses that authority to have the use of the necessary dock labour.

1 LRO returns relating to Liverpool Town Dues 1857, 43
2 MDHB *The Financial Crisis*, 1970, 4, 10
3 Ib 173
4 DCM 11.viii.1823
5 DCM 7.iv.1824
6 Dock Trustees' Accounts 1828–9
7 Mountfield, 1965, 75
8 MDHB WUP Treasurer's Department, unclassified
9 Ib
10 Ib
11 DCM 4.iv.1806
12 DCM 16.i.1840
13 DCM 9.ii.1843 & 5.i.1854
14 *Report of Committee of Finance . . . on the Subject of Docks*, 1838, 162
15 DCM 29.i.1846
16 DCM 5.i.1854
17 DCM 22.i.1846
18 *Liverpool Mercury* 29.iii.1890

Dock works and South dockyards

Linked to the growth of the dock system in Liverpool were the growth of a work force to build and maintain the fabric of the port and the establishment of yards where building materials were stored and worked. At first, such places were simply called work yards for the purposes of the docks, but by about 1825 they had become known as dockyards. Since the term generally signifies a building and repairing yard for naval vessels, it is important to understand that in the Liverpool docks a dockyard was connected to dock-building rather than to shipbuilding. The earliest dockyards were used mainly to dress stone and to grind mortar, while the later yards included workshops, foundries, sawmills, stores and offices. The dockyards are noteworthy not only in terms of the technological history which inevitably they reflect, but also in terms of their social and industrial history. For the period covered by available records (c1835–1960), the numbers of men employed on the dock works and associated with the operation of the dockyards were always in the hundreds and sometimes in the thousands. This army of men built the docks and the buildings which stood on the quays: they made boilers and cranes, dock gates and capstans, and they repaired almost anything.

The reference in 1808 to the recently deceased William Street's forty-four years of service as Superintendent of Labour implies the existence of a permanent direct labour force from at least the time when the construction of George's Dock was begun in the 1760s. However, it seems that no dockyard was established before 1800 when the Dock Committee leased a plot of land on the west side of Salthouse Dock to use as a work yard and store. In 1805 an application was made by the Trustees to increase the size of the dockyard riverward particularly for the purpose of floating dock gates under repair, and two years later permission was sought to embank a piece of land west of the dockyard.[1] Two small tidal basins shown on Sherwood's map of 1821, near the north-west corner of the Trentham Street yard, may have been built in connection with such purposes. In 1826 the Prince's Dock lime works were removed to the south side of the South Ferry Basin marking the start of the development there of Coburg Dockyard. The Trentham Street Dockyard continued to flourish in the central docks until its site was re-developed during the construction of Albert Dock.

In 1835 the dockyard comprised two millwrights' shops with lathes and drilling and screwing machines, three smithies with fifteen hearths altogether, a punching machine and trip hammer, a brass foundry, pattern shop, offices, stables and stores. The one hundred and fifty or so people employed there in 1838 included clerks, storekeepers, book-keepers, measurers, draughtsmen, tradesmen, labourers, carters and two charwomen. They undertook most of the building and maintenance work on the dock estate then with the general exceptions of excavations, provision of raw materials and supply of manufactured articles. Contractors were able to mobilize more easily the large labour forces needed for major earthworks, and materials were often best obtained from specialist suppliers. Some bricks were made in the dockyards, and once the granite quarry at Kirkmabreck was opened, the Surveyor could obtain ashlar and setts direct from this source. He had to continue to buy in sandstone and limestone. The dockyards produced gate machines, capstans, sluice gates and the myriad fixtures and fittings (mostly iron and brass) required for the works.

The dockyards evolved in response to a need and they were perpetuated in the twin interests of efficiency and economy. Hartley, for instance, reported that the cost of designing, surveying, supervising and accounting for the dock works between 1824 and 1835 was just $2\frac{1}{2}$ per cent of the total outlay.[2] Old materials were re-used regularly; in 1839 nearly £400 was expended on the wages of men working up scrap iron using the dockyard tilt hammer. One of the most effective of Hartley's innovations was the leasing in 1826 of the granite quarry at Craignair in Kirkcudbrightshire. In 1830 a 30-acre quarry at Kirkmabreck was leased from Sir Alexander Muir Mackenzie and others and developed by the Trustees of the Liverpool Docks who built a loading jetty, cranes and railroads as well as cottages for the agricultural tenants of the non-operational parts of the holding; this quarry supplied all the granite required on the dock estate for nearly a century. It was worked by contractors who were required to pay an annual rent for the use of the machinery provided by the Trustees, who also undertook to receive not less than 10,000 feet of ashlar blocks and 5,000 tons of square setts each year; the appointed contractor was at liberty to sell additional granite to other parties. The stone was transported from Scotland by sea, in vessels chartered by the Trustees (as many as 11 at a time in the quarries' busiest years) and in their own ship, the *Oak*, 'a very strong vessel [built] for the purpose of conveying large blocks of granite and timber',[3] and the cargo was weighed on one of the public machines upon arrival. Hartley was able to report in 1836 that, in spite of the cost of opening and working the quarry, he had already found a saving of $8\frac{1}{2}d$ per foot on ashlar, and $6\frac{3}{4}d$ per ton on setts over the price of stone formerly obtained from Craignair in Galloway.

The extension of the river wall southwards from the shipyards on the west side of Queen's Dock and the construction of the tidal basin which came to be known as South Ferry Basin were probably undertaken around 1820, when the Corporation completed major waterfront works in that area. The reclamation of the site of the Coburg Dockyard began almost immediately thereafter when the excavated material removed from Brunswick Basin was placed '. . . in a hollow . . .' on the south side of the ferry

basin.[4] The offensive lime kiln and mortar mill relocated from Prince's Dock in 1826 were required in any case for the re-construction of the Brunswick Basin. Between 1825 and 1837 the growth of the new dockyard was accretive and by 1835 an inventory of the machinery and materials in the South Yard and carpenters' shed included crabs, pumps, diving bells, boilers and a 12ft diameter Mather, Dixon and Co flywheel.

At the end of 1840 the Dock Committee had resolved to contract out for all new works, alterations and repairs because the members thought that the dock works could be undertaken more cheaply by contractors. The List opposite shows that the numbers of employees and their wages bill were indeed high, but Hartley was a determined champion of the direct labour system and by May, 1841, he had persuaded the Committee to reverse its earlier decision and assert:

59 Reconstruction of Brunswick Dock, *c*1905. A steam navvy is on a gantry and a contractor's railway on the dock floor.

'... that the various works have been executed on very *reasonable terms, and at lower rates than they could have* *been in any other way. The interests of the Dock Trust in the* *conduct and management of the Mechanical Departments of* *the Surveyor's establishment have been materially promoted* *by the system which has been pursued; and as long as that* *system is kept up in the same orderly, vigorous and efficient* *manner ... no better system can be devised for the general* *benefit of the Trust. The establishment being highly creditable* *to the Dock Surveyor whose indefatigable zeal and industry* *cannot be too highly commended'.*[5]

Following this policy statement and the commencement of works on the Albert Dock site it became imperative that the whole of the old Trentham Street Dockyard be removed and rebuilt as soon as possible. During 1841–42 the Surveyor planned and built the replacement dockyard at Coburg Dock. His decision[6] to obtain a 14-horsepower condensing engine which could be delivered from stock by Boulton & Watt within a week rather than to follow the standard tendering procedure was an indication of the urgency with which the new works were carried out.

60 The coaster *Oak*, built in the early 1830s to carry granite from the Kirkmabreck Quarry to Liverpool docks.

Surveyor's Department 1840–41

NUMBERS EMPLOYED[7]

32	carpenters	46	paviours & assistants
2	coopers	46	smiths & assistants
1	blockmaker	5	pairs of sawyers
1	brazier	304	labourers
1	shipwright	1	book keeper
18	millwrights	7	accountant clerks
61	masons	1	draughtsman & 2 apprentices
2	painters		

535 Total Persons

COST OF WAGES[8]

Foremen & labourers	£22,148
Masons & bricklayers	£3,940
Carpenters	£3,897
Millwrights	£2,032
Paviours	£1,867
Smiths	£3,050
Sawyers	£749
	£37,683

Coburg Dockyard occupied a riverside site bounded north and south by South Ferry Basin and Brunswick Half-tide Dock. The various buildings were enclosed within a boundary wall with two entrance gates. The main

61 Construction gang on steam navvy, Brunswick reconstruction works, *c*1905.

Coburg Dockyard 1869

1 Dwelling house
2 Lodge
3 Stores
4 Weighing machine
5 Stables
6 Coach house
7 Manure heap
8 Steam hammer shop
9 Smiths' shop
10 Iron store
11 Engine house
12 Millwrights' shop
13 Mortar mill
14 Galvanising shop
15 Cooperage
16 Printers' shop
17 Sawpits and Carpenters' shed

18 Wheelwrights' shop
19 Dining room
20 Plate furnace
21 Floating platform
22 Crane
23 General offices
24 Foundry
25 Gate shed
26 Sawmill
27 Timber slip
28 Time office
29 Loose box and cart shed
30 Stable yard
31 Mold stores
32 Millwrights' stores
33 Mahogany stores
34 Pattern stores

35 Gantry rails
36 Boiler house
37 Timber measurement office
38 Engine house with pattern room over
39 Millwrights' shop with pattern room over
40 Fitting shed
41 Steamhammer
42 Steamhammer shop
43 Tinsmiths' shop
44 Boilermakers' shop fited up with punching, rolling and drilling machine and over-head gantry
45 Shipwrights' shop
46 Gate shed and carpenters' workshop fitted with gantry and planing and bandsaw machinery
47 Brass foundry
48 Tide gauge

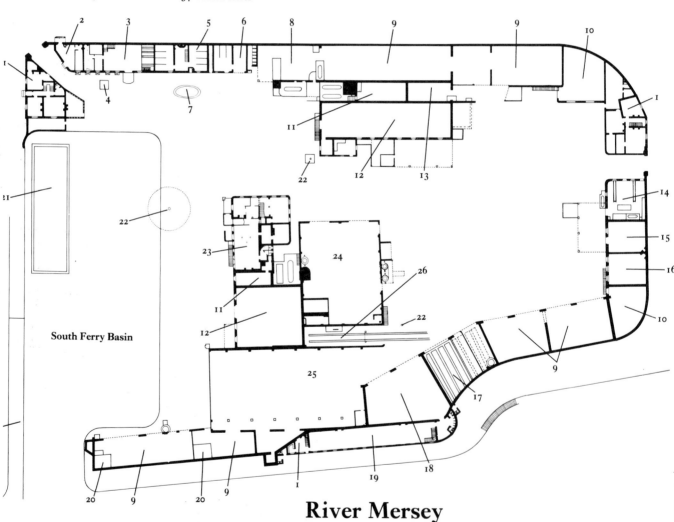

South Ferry Basin

River Mersey

Coburg Dockyard 1882

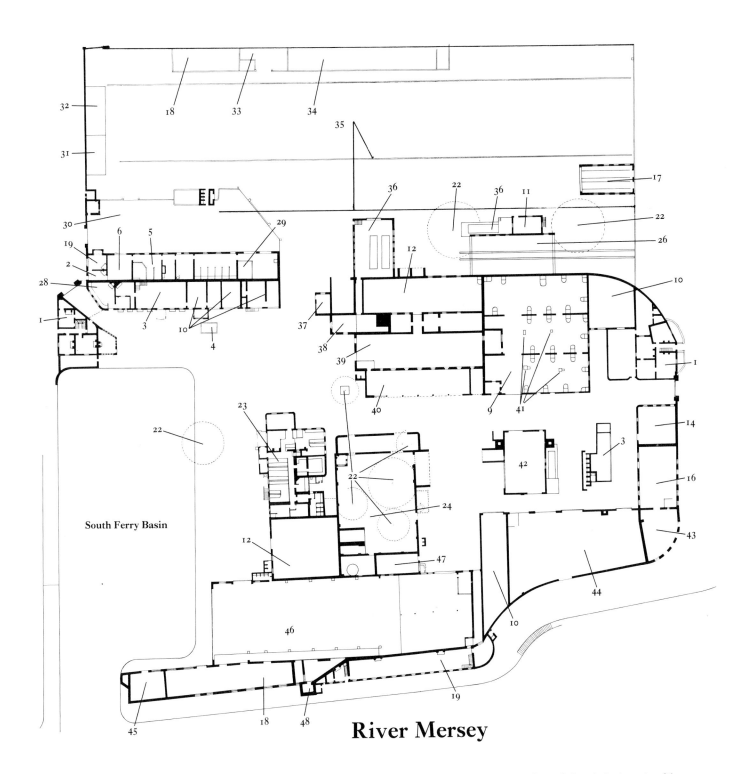

South Ferry Basin

River Mersey

functions of the yard were to provide facilities for the repair and maintenance of machinery, floating plant and dock fabric, storage space for materials, workshops for wood- and metal-working, and a headquarters for the direction and implementation of new dock works.

The Dock Trust's first items of floating plant were workboats such as the 'proper stout boat of about 20 tons burthen for the purpose of conveying mortar from the mill on the west side of Prince's Dock and materials from place to place at the dock works and for clearing away the mud from about the dock gates and for such other purposes as the said vessels may be found useful'.[9] By the time Coburg Dockyard had been established, Hartley had bought the coaster *Oak* and two flats, *John* and *Crown & Anchor*; he hired the flats at £1 per day each to the parties who had contracted to convey sand to his mortar mills. Until the relocation of the buoy store from Coburg to Toxteth in 1848, the buoy-shunting vessels joined the other workboats and the dredgers at the Coburg river wall and in the ferry basin and the Brunswick Half-tide Dock.

62   Masons working on a dock sill *c*1920.

An iron store of unusually heavy timber and brick construction was included amongst the buildings originally erected in the new dockyard, but it is unlikely that orders such as the 250 tons of railway bars delivered to the yard by Guest & Co, could have been stored under cover. Nor would the following order for timber have been easy to store:[10] 10,000 to 20,000 cubic feet of American Rock Elm for wagons, barrows and flats; 10,000 cubic feet of the same 45ft to 60ft long, and not less than 12in square at the small end, for dock stages; 80 to 100 logs of good sound Baltic in lengths not less than 24ft 6in and to

square not less than 16in, for two pair of inner gates for the Prince's Dock. Considering the varying quantities of diverse items and materials delivered to the dockyard, it is not surprising that the storekeeper was one of the more important of the Trust's employees.

Amongst the dockyard buildings originally erected for the working of ferrous metals were the smithies and steam hammer shop and a foundry with cupola furnace. In the absence of evidence of moulding or pattern shops in the early years, it must be assumed that iron was often cast in moulds made in the wheelwright's shop or the gate shed which were the only buildings available for the wood-working trades. The ironwork typically produced in the dockyard was of relatively small size, including such items as bollards, chain posts, capstans, boiler fittings and machine parts. A galvanizing process was in use from 1849 for the production of bolts, boilers, roof coverings and outsized drain pipes. A brass foundry seems to have existed in the dockyard from at least 1862, and by 1874 shops for tinsmiths and coppersmiths had appeared on plans of the yard. Brass was used mainly to make intricate components for machinery, especially valves and bosses, whilst tin and copper were utilized in sheet form to make oil cans, funnels, lanterns and pipes.

The four sawpits originally built between the wheelwrights' and carpenters' shops next to the second gate shed had been replaced by two new pits and a steam powered sawmill on the other side of the yard by 1874. In general, the wood-working trades were of less significance than the metal working trades in the dockyard. A small complement of wheelwrights was housed in a shop where they fashioned wheels and other wooden parts for the wagons, carts and barrows which were the predominant means of transport on the dock estate. The gateshed carpenters worked in a shed nearly 60ft wide by 125ft long and open at the northern end adjacent to the south-west quay of the ferry basin; this structure and situation facilitated the handling of enormous balks of timber and dock gates. The gate shed was fitted with a gantry crane, planing machinery and a band saw.

The other buildings erected inside Hartley's boundary wall included dwelling houses (at the entrance gates), offices and a dining hall for the Dock Surveyor and his staff, stables and coach house, a cooperage, two millwrights' shops and a buoy store. Within thirty years the scale of operations had increased to such an extent that expansion beyond the limits of the 1840 site was inevitable.

In the early 1870s the major physical changes in the

dockyard were the extension of the gate shed, the conversion of the western smithies to a boiler makers' shop fitted up with a travelling gantry crane and punching, rolling and drilling machines, the construction of a big, new steam-hammer shop and the erection of the new sawmill with two circular saws, and a large crane at each end. The machinery required for dock construction and operation was increasingly complex and therefore increasingly purchased complete from outside suppliers. Repair work became more important than new work, with the exception of special items such as dock gates and small complementary parts for outside commissions. A letter from W. G. Armstrong & Co to G. F. Lyster in which reference is made to the provision of 30cwt cranes at Albert Dock illustrates the procedure for collaboration between the Dock Engineer and contractors: 'It was your intention we believe to supply from the Dock Yard the casting which will have to be fixed to the wall to carry the top socket. We therefore send herewith a tracing of the top socket so that the casting may be made to suit.'[11]

A complete set of new machinery was installed in the gateshed around 1890. Arranged so as to deal with pieces of timber up to 60ft long and 3ft square, it could surface either a flat plane or in a curve, bore, mortice and cut out tenons. Gates for all of the estate were built at Coburg Dockyard and then dismantled for removal to the passage for which they were intended and there re-assembled and erected. Cast-steel fittings such as collars, collar straps and bolts could not be made in the dockyard and these components were supplied by contractors including Rolls & Brown, Francis Morton & Co and the Widnes Foundry. In 1895 machinery to work greenheart was installed in the gate shed by Thos Robinson & Son Ltd of Rochdale.

During 1897–98 the eastern side of the dock yard, where timber storage grounds and a pattern shop had been established over the previous 20 years, was sliced off to make room for a new 45ft wide road to the rear of the adjacent 1865 Brunswick Dock transit shed. At the same time the north quay of Brunswick Half-tide Basin was formally allocated to the dockyard, and the shed there (built 1842) was fitted out as a workshop and store for the Dock Board's floating plant which had gradually become the exclusive users of the half-tide dock. A big new millwrights' shop was then erected beside the converted shed and fitted with two overhead cranes and more than a dozen new lathes. A narrow-gauge railway was laid throughout the dockyard and carried into several workshops and to the timber storage area in 1899. Other improvements made at the turn of the century included extensions of various stores and offices for the

draughtsmen and timekeepers and the installation of a number of gas engines to replace auxiliary steam engines. Occupation of the south quay of Brunswick Half-tide Dock was consolidated between 1898 and 1906 when this site was used as an operational base for the works done under the Southern Works Act. In December, 1907, the Engineer's Department was transferred from Coburg Dockyard to the new offices in the Port of Liverpool Building at the Pier Head, thereby removing from the yard one of its four original functions.

While the Engineer was based at Coburg Dockyard, it was the operations centre for the whole dock estate, but the dock works were not confined, of course, to the dockyards. Between about 1830 and 1905 it seems to have been common practice to have the stone needed for the dock works delivered in the rough and dressed on site. Likewise, mortar was ground and mixed on site. Small quantities of bricks were made in the dockyards early in the 19th century, but later on bricks were supplied by contractors and delivered to construction sites to be laid by the bricklayers in the employ of the Trustees or the Board. The masons and bricklayers apparently had no base. They moved from job to job except when there was a want of work for them and then they were summarily discharged.

The question as to the effectiveness of a large direct labour force was aired again around 1883 during discussions about the cost of building double-storey transit sheds at Harrington Dock. The Dock Committee was chary of the relatively high price of the proposed sheds, and the members were seeking economies. They were persuaded eventually, however, that it would be safer in terms of quality control to allow the dock works to be undertaken by the Engineer than to have the work done by contract.[12]

The history of Coburg Dockyard in the 20th century was characterized by the disappearance of some trades and practices, the introduction of others and the generally ill-timed attempts to provide physical accommodation to match these changes. Up to 1939, various alterations and conversions were implemented to provide more space for the electricians, for example. It was suggested that all of the steam and gas plant should be replaced with electrical machinery and that the iron foundry and smiths' shops should be completely rebuilt. Before any substantial reconstruction could be realized, the outbreak of the Second World War put an end to all development proposals. During the war, the dockyard was slightly damaged by bombs, but the major strain was imposed by the need to deal under poor conditions with the vastly increased work load which was the result of enemy action elsewhere in the docks. Necessary dock repairs were not only unpredictable but also urgent. The Board's floating plant was more than ever in demand.

After the war, Coburg Dockyard was not high on the list of priorities for repair and modernization, so it was 1957 before the scheme accepted 20 years earlier began to be implemented. Progress was spasmodic and most of the agreed projects were never realized. Rather, conversion and adaptation continued to be the chosen solutions to problems of accommodation: the wheelwrights' shop became the painters' and plumbers' shops; sailmakers and leatherworkers were installed above the gate shed; wiresplicing machinery was fitted into part of the old shed on the north side of the Brunswick Half-tide Basin. A new millwrights' shop, by then properly a welding shop, was erected to the south of the boiler makers' shop in 1953, and in 1960 the old gate shed was demolished and replaced with a sawmill for gate and graving block fabrication and repair. The foundry was last used in 1969, and Coburg Dockyard, apart from the modern sawmill which is still operated by the Dock Company, was closed by 1976.

Dockyard wages and welfare

Around 1840, apart from the surveyor, his clerk and the storekeeper, all dockyard employees were paid weekly. Amongst the better paid in this latter group were the Foreman Carpenter (£3), the Principal Draughtsman (£2 10s), the Foreman Millwright (£2) and the Timber Measurer and Check Clerk of Masonry (£2). Carpenters were paid between 3s 6d and 5s 6d per day, and millwrights from 3s 6d to 7s 6d per day. The boy in the drawing office received 1s a day.[13] By 1919 foremen were paid £6 a week, rivetters £3 15s 6d, and holders up £3 9s 6d.

Despite imposing conditions of service which seem harsh when judged by today's standards, the Dock Trustees and Dock Board did make some provision for the welfare of their employees. Of those who worked in the dockyard, the Principal Clerk and the watchmen were entitled to houses rent free (until 1860, at least). The dining hall built on the waterfront on the west side of the dockyard as a works canteen for all must have provided an enviable outlook over the Mersey, and during G. F. Lyster's time as Engineer a library for the workers was provided in the dining room.

The origins of the Dockyard Workmen's Relief Fund are obscure, though generally thought to have been initiated by Hartley in the 1830s. Participants paid a proportion of their weekly wages (2d from 15s for example) into a fund which provided allowances to sick or disabled workmen in proportion to their years of service. From 1864 the fund was augmented by the amount of any unclaimed dockyard wages, that is, wages which would have been paid had no employees been absent from work. Weekly allowances ranged from about 7s to 10s for periods of between five and ten weeks. An employee disabled as the result of an industrial accident was entitled to receive 10s a week during the pleasure of the Engineer without reference to the duration of that workman's employment by the Board. A death grant of £3 was payable in 1870, £6 in 1900. The Dockyard Workmen's Relief Fund was run down between 1902 and 1907 and was replaced from 1911 by the general National Insurance scheme.

On the whole, employees' interests were not badly served. The records abound with instances of internal promotions, rewards for unusual industry and compensation for unusual misfortune. For much of its history, Coburg Dockyard was not only the hub of dock building in the port of Liverpool, but also a very unusual little community.

1 DCM 25.vii.1805; 23.xi.1807
2 DER 1835
3 Ib
4 MDHB Contracts Book, 3.iii.1826
5 DCM 21.v.1841
6 MDHB Sub-Committee of Works, 3.vii.1841
7 Ib
8 DER 1841
9 DCM 15.ii.1814
10 MDHB Sub-Committee of Works, 2.vii.1858
11 Letter from W. G. Armstrong & Co, Elswick Works, 5 October, 1877 to G. F. Lyster, Dock Office, Liverpool. MDHB Coll., drawer no. 377.
12 *Liverpool Mercury*, 9.ii.1883
13 MCM, MDHB misc papers 6/12 no 8, 1838
14 MCM, Unbound WUP Dockyard Workmen's Relief Fund 56.E..32

Dock engineers

Between 1710 and 1897 the water area of the docks in the port of Liverpool increased from around 4 acres to nearly 550 acres. This extension of the dock system was the work of the dock engineers Thomas Steers, Henry Berry, Thomas Morris, John Foster, Jesse Hartley, John Bernard Hartley and George Fosbery Lyster. With the possible exception of John Hartley whose Liverpool career was relatively short-lived, each of these seven men made very important contributions to dock construction on Merseyside and their careers warrant examination. Their job titles have changed a little over the centuries – Berry was Dock Engineer, Jesse Hartley was Dock Surveyor, George Fosbery Lyster was Engineer-in-Chief – and their overall responsibilities have altered somewhat too. As a microcosm of the development of the engineering profession, however, these men represent a dramatic progression from the amateur, through general canal and bridge engineer to specialized professional.

Thomas Steers (c1670–1750) Dock Engineer 1710–50

In the absence of definite information, Steers' main biographer Henry Peet postulated that the soldier Steers came to Britain from Holland with William of Orange.[1] Steers held a Commission in the 4th Regiment of Foot which was engaged at the Battle of the Boyne in 1690; the family papers which confirmed Steers' involvement also recorded that he 'started some Salt Works on the River Boyne'.[2] He probably remained in the army until the Peace of Ryswick in 1697 when his regiment was returned to Woolwich and reduced to half of its strength. By 1699 Steers was married and living in Rotherhithe and thought to have worked on the new dock being built there at the time: Steers' knowledge of hydraulic engineering gained by experience of it in the Netherlands combined with the 'salt works' evidence of his mechanical skills and interests would have made him a useful member of the construction team. It is unlikely that he would have been approached later by the Liverpool dock promoters if he had had no knowledge of dock construction.

Although Sorocold, an engineer of standing in the fields of textile mills and river works, was the first engineer to be consulted about building the original Liverpool dock, it was Steers who supplied the design adopted in 1710 and oversaw the ensuing construction work. In 1712 he was admitted to the freedom of the borough and thenceforward he became an increasingly prominent citizen. His public appointments included Dock Master (1717), Town Bailiff (1719), Dock Master and Water Bailiff (1724) and Mayor (1739), but these manifold civic responsibilities did not prevent his undertaking a variety of other projects. He worked on a scheme to supply water to Liverpool from Bootle, built St George's Church (rebuilt 1823), the Old Ropery Theatre and a number of houses, and he drew up plans for a new Exchange. During the Jacobite rebellion he was made responsible for strengthening the town's defences. His income from the Corporation was supplemented from 1718 by his anchor smithy in Steers Alley near Dock Quay, by speculative land purchase and development in the town of Liverpool and by remuneration for outside consultancies. In 1712 Steers surveyed the River Douglas and published his proposals for making the Mersey and Irwell navigable; and he was amongst the principal promoters of the Bills which became the Navigation Acts of 1720 and 1721 respectively. Between 1736 and 1741 Steers was retained by the Commissioners of the Newry Navigation to survey the River Boyne and build the Newry Canal, for which he was paid a total of £1651 17s 6d. During the same period Steers was also preparing plans for a second wet dock in Liverpool, but implementation of this scheme was so long delayed that he did not live to see it through.

Henry Berry (1719–1812) Dock Engineer 1750–89

When Thomas Steers died, the Town Council resolved that '. . . Henry Berry, late clerk to him, be continued to oversee the works till further notice'.[3] The following year Berry, who was born near St Helens, was made a Freeman of Liverpool under the designation Engineer to the Docks. At the time he was completing the construction of Salthouse Dock, but once the new dock was opened he was instructed to carry out a survey of the Sankey Brook. This he did with William Taylor during the summer of 1754, following which the Council resolved to lend £300 towards the payment of expenses incurred in obtaining an Act of Parliament to render it navigable; four of the five Liverpool merchants whose names appeared on the petition for the Act were prominent members of the Corporation of Liverpool. Berry was given leave to spend two days a week to make the new navigation, work began in 1755 and the first part of the Sankey Brook was opened to shipping two years later. The older Weaver Navigation now compared unfavourably to the Sankey and a meeting between the Weaver commissioners and certain merchants of Liverpool agreed in 1758 that Berry should undertake a survey of the Weaver with a view to its improvement.

Between 1756 and 1765 Berry constructed the three graving docks to the west of the old Dry Dock and in 1767 he started work on George's Dock which was opened in 1771. He was also responsible for building (to Grundy's design) the first dock at Hull, between 1774 and 1778. His final major work was the King's Dock in Liverpool which he completed in 1788 just before resigning his post the following year. He continued to live in his Duke Street house until his death in 1812.

Thomas Morris (dates unknown) Dock Engineer 1789–99

Morris was perhaps the least significant, in terms of his contribution to Liverpool, of the six engineers being considered in detail here. He was the only one, other than John Hartley, to leave to go on to work elsewhere and his departure, after only 10 years in office, seems not to have been on the best of terms. His early life is obscure but it seems likely that he was the son of Thomas Morris, one of James Brindley's assistants on the Bridgewater Canal, who first appears in Brindley's diaries in 1763. Despite being dismissed by one of Brindley's biographers as a 'practical carpenter', Morris attracted the following notice in the Coventry Mercury in 1767:

'... [in addition to Brindley] ... the Duke of Bridgewater has another ingenious Man, viz. Thomas Morris, who has improved on Mr Brindley, and is now raising a Valley to the Level by seven double Water Locks ...'[4]

The younger Morris's first known work was at Glasson, at the mouth of the River Lune, south of Lancaster. Work on a pier here had begun in 1780, but following a series of difficulties (in the course of which the Port Commissioners approached Henry Berry for assistance, though in vain) Morris was requested in October 1783 to 'take possession of the Commissioners' property' from a defaulting contractor.[5] Two months later Morris, apparently unsolicited, submitted a fresh scheme for completion of the pier and the construction of a wet dock. These plans having been accepted, he agreed to superintend these works though his remuneration was not regularized until March 1787 when he was paid retrospectively £100 per annum from Feb 1784. He was paid off in Dec 1787 as

'his attendance [was] no longer necessary'.[6] Morris was again consulted over proposed developments at Glasson Dock in 1795 and 1797.

He arrived in Liverpool, as Dock Surveyor in succession to Berry, in 1789 when work was in progress on the new Queen's Dock. He served the Dock Trustees until 1799 when he was discharged following an application to the Trustees for 'a very great increase' of salary.[7] Morris's salary at the time was 100 guineas p.a.; when in 1803 he took up the post of resident engineer under William Jessop at the West India Export Dock in London it was at a salary of £840 p.a. (Morris had, in fact, submitted plans for the West India Docks in 1799 but those by the consortium of Jessop, Dance and Walker were preferred.) During his incumbency at Liverpool, Morris was asked to advise on the dock extensions at Hull in 1793 and on the improvement of the River Mersey between Warrington and Runcorn in 1796. His period of office coincided exactly with the dramatic increase in responsibility of the post of Corporation Surveyor being achieved by John Foster. In stark contrast to that of Morris, Foster's salary in the period 1789 to 1799 rose from £150 p.a. to £400 p.a. The facts that Foster took over Morris's responsibilities upon his dismissal and that the Corporation had built graving docks and warehousing on the dock estate suggest an uneasy relationship between the two posts at this time.

Morris continued as resident engineer at the West India Docks until his retirement in 1811.

John Foster (1759–1827) Dock Engineer 1799–1824

John Foster was the only son of a John Foster, master joiner, whose name appears in Liverpool newspapers and directories from the middle of the 18th century.[8] By 1781 John Foster junior's name was appearing alongside that of his father in directories, and throughout the decade the firm did a great deal of work on Corporation projects. The father seems to have been a measurer of brickwork for the Corporation and in 1789 the son was appointed superintendent of the Corporation's public buildings. On the dismissal of Morris in 1799, Foster also took over the post of Dock Engineer and, in addition, in 1801 he became Surveyor of Streets. Throughout much of this period he also seems to have continued to operate the family joinery and building business.

His duties for the Corporation in the 1790s brought him into close contact with the docks and it is likely that he built the Chester Basin in 1795 and Graving Docks Nos 4 and 5 in 1796. He was also probably involved in the improvements by the Corporation to the facilities around the Manchester Basin in 1789 and possibly in the construction of the tobacco warehouse of 1790–93. He prepared plans for the improvement and extension of the docks as early as 1792 but it was not until the first two decades of the following century that any major dock building commenced after consultation with Jessop in 1800 and with Rennie in 1809. This period saw the addition of basins to Queen's Dock, the enlargement of Queen's Dock itself, the construction of Prince's Dock, the enlargement of George's Dock and the addition of gates to Manchester Basin to convert it into a wet dock. It also witnessed the rebuilding of the Goree warehouses after the disastrous fire of 1802, the construction of the vast new tobacco warehouse at King's Dock and the addition of numerous transit sheds around the docks, including the iron-framed shed at Queen's Dock. Foster had continued to be a principal in the building firm of Messrs Foster & Co whose financial affairs became illegally entangled via the Surveyor, with those of the Dock Trustees. Following the discovery of these irregularities, the Trustees resolved to appoint as deputy to Foster a civil engineer whose exclusive concern was to be the Liverpool docks. Two weeks after the appointment of the new engineer, Foster, his clerk and his measurer all resigned their Corporation jobs. John Foster succeeded his father as Corporation Surveyor and subsequently became a successful architect whose most famous building was the Custom House erected from 1826 on the site of the Old Dock.

During Foster's thirty-five years incumbency of various Corporation posts more than 20 acres of water space had been added to the dock estate and the town's dock frontage had been transformed by warehouse building. Although Foster also designed numerous residential terraces and several public buildings, including the Union Newsroom, the Theatre Royal and St Luke's Church, his real talent seems to have been that of a surveyor rather than either an architect or an engineer. He was at his best laying out improvement schemes, whether for dwellings, warehouses or docks, and seems to have had to collaborate with architects and engineers on the technical implementation of these schemes. Thus it was under Foster that the first attempts were made to regulate the construction of warehouses by introducing clauses into the tenancies on the Corporation estate: the Goree warehouses, built to Foster's designs, were the most impressive product of the desire for a unified warehouse frontage.

Foster died in 1827, leaving a considerable fortune, and described in his will as 'surveyor'.

Jesse Hartley (1780–1860) Dock Engineer 1824–60

Jesse Hartley, claimed *The Times* obituarist in 1860, '... as a dock engineer ... is admitted to have occupied a high, if not indeed the highest, position of any man who has lived within the present century'.[9] The claim is questionable, but it was a tribute that would have been supported by everyone in Liverpool. Among the pall bearers at his funeral were the Chairman of the Dock Board, Charles Turner; the Chairman of the Dock Committee, John Bramley-Moore; John Bibby, a great shipowner; and James Walker, a past president of the Institution of Civil Engineers.

Jesse Hartley was born in Pontefract in 1780 and trained as a mason, probably under his father, Bernard Hartley, who was appointed Surveyor of Bridges to the West Riding in 1797. Jesse's first known work was on the bridge at Ferrybridge, built by his father in 1804 to John Carr's designs, while in 1805–8 father and son collaborated – the elder as designer, the younger as contractor – on the bridge at Castleford which bears plaques giving the names of both.

Soon afterwards Jesse Hartley was in Ireland. He probably worked with the architect William Atkinson for the Duke of Devonshire at Lismore Castle in around 1811, and Atkinson's design for a 5-arched bridge over the River Colligan at Dungarvan, Co Waterford, was superseded by a single-arched design by Hartley. He may also have been responsible for the building of the Market Square at Dungarvan. He married Ellenor Penney, daughter of a Dungarvan innkeeper, in 1809, and his last mention in the Lismore papers at the National Library of Ireland is in 1818, when he returned to England to take up the post of bridgemaster for the Hundred of Salford.

In 1824 he was chosen from a list of 14 candidates as Deputy Surveyor of the Liverpool Docks;[10] eight months later he was promoted to Surveyor. He was an indefatigable worker, and in addition to his Liverpool work he accepted consultancies on Littlehampton Harbour (1825), the Grosvenor Bridge, Chester (1826), the Liverpool and Manchester Railway (1827), the Manchester, Bolton, and Bury Canal (1832), the Carlisle Canal (1835) and the original, privately promoted Harrington Dock (1840). He was careful never to be absent from the docks at spring tides, but after 1840 he was asked, nevertheless, to confine his attention to the estate of the Dock Trustees.

Hartley's most obvious achievement was in the immense expansion of the Liverpool docks which was carried out under his superintendence – from 45 acres to over 210. But no less significant – and essential if his ambitious engineering works were to be realized – were his organizational innovations and reforms. He introduced the practice of making an annual report of his department's progress and expenditure. He established a formal dockyard. He initiated the rental of a quarry devoted solely to the Liverpool dock works, and the building and maintenance of a fleet of work boats for the purposes of the docks. He brought railways onto the estate, and introduced hydraulic power. Picton described how:

'... for thirty-six years [he] guided with a despotic sway the construction of some of the mightiest works of the kind ever erected. Personally he was a man of large build and powerful frame, rough in manner, and occasionally even rude, using expletives which the angel of mercy would not like to record; sometimes capricious and tyrannical, but occasionally, when he was attached, a firm and unswerving friend. Professionally he had grand ideas, and carried them into execution with a strength, solidity and skill that have never been exceeded ... For a man of his undoubted mental power he was singularly slow of speech. Examination before a Parliamentary committee was his dread. He had as much difficulty in making himself understood as his contemporary, George Stephenson. In this respect he differed materially from his son, associated with him in the latter part of his career, who was one of the clearest professional witnesses who ever stood the fire of cross-examination, and could baffle a counsel by retiring into a thicket of mathematics where it was impossible to follow him.'[11]

The Times' obituary added words that now seem prophetic: '... in the design and construction of the numerous docks of Liverpool he has left monuments of his skill as an engineer which will endure at least as long as the fame and commercial prosperity of the port'.[12]

63   Thomas Steers.

64   George Fosbery Lyster.

His son John, who had worked with Jesse Hartley in later years and had himself been retained as consultant engineer for the Hull docks in the 1840s, continued in the employment of the Mersey Docks and Harbour Board for a year after his father's death. Thereafter, though retired on account of ill health, he was retained as consulting engineer for several more years before his death in 1871. Jesse Hartley's elder brother, Bernard, succeeded their father in 1837 as Bridge Surveyor to the West Riding of Yorkshire.

George Fosbery Lyster (1821–99) Dock Engineer 1861–97

G. F. Lyster was born in Ireland and educated at King William's College, Isle of Man, before becoming a pupil of J. M. Rendel, perhaps working at Birkenhead where Rendel was engineer to the Birkenhead Dock Company in the 1840s. He began his professional career when he was appointed as assistant resident engineer on the works for the improvement of the River Shannon. His next major job was as assistant resident engineer on the Holyhead refuge harbour works where he worked for 7 years under J. C. Dobson. Then he was appointed resident engineer for new harbour works at Guernsey before being selected from amongst 70 applicants for the post of Engineer-in-Chief to the Mersey Docks and Harbour Board. He also became engineer to the Wallasey Embankment Commissioners.

Lyster's major contributions to the development and extension of the port of Liverpool included building most of the Birkenhead docks and new docks at the north end of the Liverpool Estate, the construction of the Herculaneum and new Harrington and Toxteth Docks at the south end, the erection of grain warehouses on both

65 Jesse Hartley (by M. Noble).

66 John Bernard Hartley (by M. Noble).

sides of the river and the introduction of impounding systems to increase the depth of available water in various parts of the dock estate. From 1889 Lyster was aided by his son Anthony, who was subsequently appointed Engineer-in-Chief to the Board upon his father's retirement.

Anthony George Lyster (1852–1920) Dock Engineer 1897–1913

A. G. Lyster was born at Holyhead and educated at Harrow School and at Bonn, Germany; he entered the Engineer's Department as a pupil under his father in 1872 and then spent several months at Armstrong's Elswick works before returning to Liverpool to work on the construction authorized by the 1873 Dock Act. He was responsible for the reconstruction of docks at both ends of the Liverpool estate under the 1898 Act and his career culminated in the construction of the Gladstone Graving Dock.

Dock Engineers 1913–72

After the completion of the major rebuilding of the King's, Queen's and Brunswick Docks in the early 20th century, the engineers' responsibilities in the South Docks were limited to maintenance and repair. By this time, too, harbour engineering had become a professional discipline largely unaffected by the personalities and particular interests of the individuals who practised it. Below are listed the names of the men who were the engineers-in-chief until the closure of the South Docks: Thomas Monk Newell (1863–1932) Dock Engineer 1913–28, Thomas Lord Norfolk (1875–1962) Dock Engineer 1928–41, Leopold Leighton (1884–1964) Dock Engineer 1941–49, Adrian B. Porter (1899–1958) Dock Engineer 1949–58, John Donald Jameson Saner (1895–1962) Dock Engineer 1958–60, Norman Alastair Matheson (1908–1966) Dock Engineer 1960–66, Martin Agar (*b* 1913) Dock Engineer 1966–73.

1 Peet, 1930, 72
2 Ib
3 LTB 7.xi.1750
4 *Jopson's Coventry Mercury*, 28.ix.1767, quoted in Boucher, C. T. G., *James Brindley, Engineer, 1716–1772*, 1968, 54–5
5 Lancashire RO, Minutes of Commissioners of the Port of Lancaster, 16.x.1783
6 Ib xii.1787
7 LTB 19.ii.1799
8 J. Longmore, *The Liverpool Corporation Estate*, unpublished thesis, University of Reading, 1982
9 *The Times*, 25.viii.1860
10 The other candidates were Henry Austin, Liverpool; J. H. Bartholomew, Bradford; John Boorer, Pentonville; William Buck; B. R. Dodd; William Cranston, Sheerness; John Hall, Bangor; H. Jessop, Bridgewater; Albinus Martin, Pentridge; Kenneth Mathieson, H. W. Reveley, London; G. C. Scott, Edinburgh; J. W. Hemingway, Devonport
11 Picton, 1873, 652–3
12 *The Times*, loc cit

TECHNICAL AND MECHANICAL ASPECTS

67   Reconstruction of Brunswick Dock showing the former Brunswick
graving dock at left, 1907

68   Reconstruction of Canning River Entrance, 1983.

Piling technology and dock wall construction in the South Docks

A fundamental requirement of dock construction is the building of dock walls that can withstand pressures from three directions: first, the weight of the walls themselves on their foundations; second, the pressure of the water within the dock; and third, the strongest of these forces, the pressure of the backing behind the dock walls, threatening always to push them forward into the dock itself. Dock walls tend to fail in one of four ways: by overturning, by settlement on their foundations, by sliding bodily forward, and by sheer along the lines of masonry courses. The means of overcoming these potential failures were by sound foundations, by spreading the load upon them, by the choice of profile adopted for the dock walls, by increasing the walls' mass, or by tying the face of the wall into the material of the backing. All of these means were adopted by the engineers to the Liverpool docks over the course of time, at the same time as they sought improvements in the mortar or cement binding the masonry of the walls in order to achieve a harder and speedier setting during construction in wet conditions.

In the 18th century, the Liverpool engineers were faced, for the first time, with building docks of sufficient depth to accommodate laden vessels, and the problems of dock wall construction were exaggerated beyond contemporary engineering experience. That they were not entirely successful is shown by frequent reports of the dock walls being 'liable to sink and in other respects to give way'.[1] The river walls gave the most trouble, sometimes collapsing so dramatically that at high tide small craft could sail directly into the docks through the gaps. The walls of the Old Dock were apparently from time to time partly demolished by shipbuilders, in order that they might launch their ships into it. Failures were due in part to the changes in pressure exerted on dock walls caused by their drying at low tide or when it was necessary to drain a dock for cleaning. Failure was also due to the want of proper foundations, though little is known of the foundations provided for the 18th-century dock walls. The eastern sides of most of the early docks lay along the shoreline where the sandstone bedrock is relatively close to the surface and overlain with marl. To the west, however, the sandstone dips gently deeper below ground level and is variously overlain with gravels, sand and silt.

The Old Dock walls were of brick with a rubble backing, set in lime mortar, and with a curved profile to buttress the backing and which was of no disadvantage to contemporary ships with hulls of a rounded section. The brick facing was probably tied to the backing by through stones. Salthouse, George's, King's and Queen's Docks had walls almost entirely of sandstone, with ashlar faces in regular blocks bound by through stones to the rubble masonry behind. The original walls of the Duke's Dock were built in the same manner, using stone from the Runcorn area. These last are the only 18th-century dock walls still extant in Liverpool, and are straight with a slight batter. The choice of a straight profile may have been due to the relative shallowness of the dock; it is uncertain how long a curved dock wall profile continued to be employed for deeper docks.

No documentary reference to the binding agents used in the Liverpool dock walls has yet been found dating from earlier than the 1790s. The lime mortar used in the Old Dock had very little resistance to wet, but it could be strengthened by the addition of some siliceous material such as volcanic ash or burnt clay, which also increased its water resistance and allowed it to set in damp conditions. The granite and Portland stone blocks of Smeaton's 1756 Eddystone lighthouse were bonded with tarras mortar, a mixture of pozzolana and slaked blue lias lime, though it was not until 1793 that the Liverpool Dock Trustees, proposing to experiment with the use of pozzolana, consulted John Rennie as to its application.[2] It is clear that the Trustees cautiously instigated practical trials before committing themselves, as they subsequently did, to the use of a new building material.

A persistent problem in the late 18th and early 19th centuries was the want of adequate supplies of suitable backfill. In 1805 the Surveyor was authorized to proceed with the enlargement of King's Dock 'in order to obtain earth from the excavation of the said enlargement for backing the wall now building to the front of the river . . . on the west side of that dock'.[3] In 1810 the Surveyor reported that he had been unable to obtain sufficient earth, ballast or rubbish and that the walls he was then building at George's Dock and the Dry Dock 'were constantly suffering great loss and injury from being forced down and damaged for want of backing'.[4] The main cause of the difficulty was the Trustees' reluctance to pay for fill at a time when they were chronically short of money, and their only solution lay in a policy of trying to supply the Surveyor's needs in one place from his own excavations in another. He effected additional economies by re-using old materials wherever possible.

It is not known when dock walls of straight profile were generally introduced in Liverpool, but they seem to have been general by the beginning of the 19th century. It is possible that improvements in dock cleaning, requiring less frequent draining with the consequent strain thrown on dock walls, made it possible to build walls of a more upright form. Such a form was in any case essential for the ships of the 19th century with deeper, more straight-sided hulls than their predecessors. A further

improvement in the 19th century, probably due to Jesse Hartley, was the introduction of limestone and granite in preference to the softer sandstone that seems to have been generally employed in the earlier docks.

The walls for both the Brunswick and George's Dock Basins were made mostly of Aberthaw Limestone supplied by John Hughes, though some of the backing consisted of old stones, cleaned and re-laid. The rubble backing was coursed and set in mortar. The ashlar facing-stones were chisel-draughted. The backing and facing were built up together, bound by through stones at intervals not greater than 15ft laid above one another in every other course. Counterforts were built into the walls at intervals to resist

69   Pile driving, Brunswick Dock reconstruction, 1906.

70   (*opposite*) Albert river wall steps.

the tendency of the masonry to slip downwards and backwards; at Brunswick Basin the counterforts were constructed around brick pillars, cruciform in section and 45ft apart.

In 1858, Robert Rawlinson, who had been associated with Hartley since the 1820s, described the normal form of dock wall built in the Liverpool docks during that time:[5]

'[*Hartley*] *carried piers down to the level of the general foundations, leaving in masses of rock, and then threw over flat relieving arches. The general dimensions of most of the Liverpool dock walls were 12ft at the foundations and 6ft at the capping, and 36ft vertical height, with a face batter of 1in to the vertical. The counterforts were generally 6ft square and 12ft apart, bonded with the main wall, and in bad ground additional strength was given ... Latterly, all the Liverpool dock and river walls had been constructed of rubble ... The face was of granite rubble, and the back of sound stone rubble. The mortar was composed of Halkin Mountain lime, engine ground, with sea-sand and ashes, the proportions being 1 of slaked lime, 1 of sand, and ½ of furnace ashes, ground twenty minutes, mixed fresh from the kiln, and used the same day. The result was that the walls never exhibited signs of weakness.*'

This account is confirmed by Hartley's surviving work. The Albert Dock river wall is of necessarily massive construction, faced with granite (above LWONT) and sandstone and backed with courses of sandstone rubble. The front of the wall rises nearly vertically 29ft above the level of the Old Dock Sill from a projecting toe consisting of one deep course surmounted by four steps. The back of the wall rises vertically from its 14ft wide base up to ODS where its section diminishes by a series of steps to the floor level of the warehouse vaults from which point it again rises nearly vertically. On the face of the wall huge granite coping stones (every third one is 6ft deep by 2ft 6in wide) and headers are surrounded by granite rubble set in minimal amounts of lime mortar, but the area of the face where the exposed masonry is rubble is comparatively small. The section and profile of the dock wall are very similar to those of the river wall though the facing of the upper part of the dock wall is mostly granite rubble and the very large coping stones and headers are distributed less regularly. From the bottom of the dock to within 10ft of the water line, the facing masonry is red sandstone ashlar with the narrowest possible joints and beds.

The Duke's river entrance, built by Hartley in conjunction with the Albert Dock development, was also a composite structure: the northern dock wall was built of red sandstone ashlar blocks for the first few courses of this face, whilst the rest of the facing and the backing were made of granite rubble. The square quoin at the entrance was of granite and the hollow quoin limestone. The base of the river wall at Duke's entrance was 14ft 6in wide and founded upon wooden framing supported by rows of eight circular section piles. The toe of the wall was formed by three steps rising to a height of 6ft whence the face battered 1in per ft to its maximum height of 37ft above the foundation. The back of the wall rose in narrow steps, five of which were each 6ft high, below one of 4ft high and a top step of 3ft. At coping level the wall thickness was 3ft 9in.

Lyster's problems at Herculaneum were the opposite of Hartley's at Albert. On the Herculaneum site, the rock was not only exposed, but also rose sharply towards the east to form a hill some 70ft above the intended level of the quays. Worse, the rock was neither soft enough to provide useful backfill nor hard enough to make sound rubble masonry. It was also well-fissured and permeable, so that it had to be faced either with Runcorn sandstone or with concrete. The short (126ft) stretch of west wall to the half-tide dock was composed of rubble backing and sandstone ashlar facing, but most of the rest of the dry and wet docks at Herculaneum made use of the bedrock for their foundations and walls. The pier heads of the original graving docks and the river entrance were fashioned in granite rubble with ashlar after the style of Hartley.

At Herculaneum, Lyster introduced a technique he described as veneering:

'*The rock was cut down to a nearly vertical face at a distance of 2 to 4 feet behind the face line of the stonework, with which it was to be veneered. At distances of about 20 feet apart along the line of the wall, excavations were made from coping to foundation levels in the form of counterforts. They were 5 feet in width, 4 feet in depth and were dovetail in shape from top to bottom. Into these were inserted large blocks of ashlar, also cut dovetail, so as to fit the excavated chamber, and shaped dovetail outwardly to interlock the masonry panels which intervened between the counterfort stones.*'[6]

This system could not be applied to the stepped walls of the first two graving docks which were faced with ashlar in the traditional manner and coped with limestone. Graving Docks Nos 3 (1881) and 4 (1905) were constructed almost entirely of concrete except where granite was used on points of wear such as copings, slides and floor blocks at the bases of the slides. The heartings of the walls and floors were in 8:1 concrete dovetailed to stepped excavations in the sandstone, and the facings were in 6:1 concrete.

The borings for Brunswick river entrance works indicated that the bedrock lay at a depth of 30ft whereas it was actually found at 68ft, an uncertainty which was probably typical of dock construction in Liverpool from the beginning. Also typical of Liverpool practice was the use of existing masonry walls to which were bonded, as far as practicable, new faces. At the Brunswick river wall, facing concrete 2ft thick was fixed to the old wall by means of dovetailed pockets cut in the old stone. The general cross section of the new walls here, founded on the west side on compacted gravel and on the east on the rock (there at the anticipated depth), was 30ft wide at the base rising plumb to a level of 4ft below ODS where the back began to rise in steps each 2ft high by 9ft wide until this wall thickness became 8ft 6in; it continued to rise

vertically from this point to the coping at 26ft 6in above ODS.

With the exceptions of the river wall and the gate recesses, the whole of the new work above mean tide level was faced with 1ft of 6:1 granolithic concrete in which were set granite headers each not less than 2ft deep. Internal bonding was by means of irregular hard stone displacers which the resident engineer referred to as 'plums' and which had the additional virtue of effecting a saving on the cost of cement. The backing concrete was 8:1, as were the lock floors. The concrete used for the Brunswick project was made with Portland cement and with aggregate from Piel Island (near Barrow-in-Furness) which contained granite pebbles and a good quality of clean, angular sand. The granite from which the copings, hollow quoins, sills and clough jambs were made came from the same quarry at Kirkmabreck which had been

71 Granite masonry in Albert river wall.

supplying this material for the Liverpool dock works since 1830.

While dock walls were becoming more massive as docks became deeper, and as massive construction appeared to contemporaries the surest way of resisting any pressures that might lead to their collapse, so it was essential for foundations to be of adequate strength to carry their weight. The specifications and contracts for the rebuilding of George's Dock basin and for Brunswick Basin in 1825 survive to provide a clear account of practice during Hartley's first five years as Surveyor.

The Brunswick Basin north quay was founded on rock and so needed no piling. The George's Basin walls were to be founded upon the heads of square section timber piles (oak, beech, or other) with mid-point section no less than 8in and no greater than 12in. The three front rows of piles, which were battered so as to be aligned tangentially to the foot of the wall, were driven 'by means of a ram and punch' to a depth of 22ft and those for the counterforts were driven to a depth of 28ft. Sections, 10yds in length, of the driven bearing piles were encircled by an iron sheet pile cofferdam which was secured by timber framing. Once the surplus water was removed from inside the dam, the earth around the pile heads was excavated to a depth of 1ft and the pile tops were adzed so as to form a 1:7 incline from the front to the back of the wall. The spaces between pile heads were filled with gauged and axed stones laid on a strong bed of mortar, with the upper-most layer forming an even surface elevated about $\frac{1}{2}$in above the tops of the piles. All joints were filled with grout and clean chippings. After this had set, a course of hard stone ashlar was laid on top ready to receive the masonry of the wall.

In 1840 Hartley took a series of borings on the Albert Dock site which ranged in depth and substrata respectively from 12ft (hard gravel) to 52ft (sand and gravel); most of the trial holes were around 30ft deep. In 1841 he was authorized to order three or four thousand beech or elm trees for piling at a cost not to exceed 1s 7d per foot, and modern investigations have revealed the use of both timbers. The circular section piles now appear to have been lightly charred, as a form of preservative treatment. In 1844 John Hartley described current pile-driving practice: '. . . at the Liverpool docks he generally used a ram of 13cwt to 14cwt, falling through a distance of 30 to 40ft, upon beech piles with wrought iron shoes . . . he had sometimes used a ram weighing 20cwt'.[7] Jesse Hartley stipulated that the piles be driven no more than half an inch at a blow.

An 1842 order for cast-iron sheeting piles and connecting cramps indicates that the subsequent work on the dock and river wall piles after driving was similar to that described for the walls of George's Dock Basin, although it is not known whether or not the masonry of the walls was founded directly on a single ashlar course. Sheet piles – both iron and timber – also formed part of the permanent substructure. The north and west sides of the Canning Half-tide Basin were 'secured by sheeting piles closely driven upwards of 12ft in depth below [the bottom of the dock]; and the whole of the west end of its bottom [was] laid with a thick puddle of marl etc rendered necessary by the soft and varying nature of its substratum'.[8] That part of the river entrance enclosing the gate recesses, sills and apron was pinned in position by 15ft iron sheet piles. The toe of the south wing wall was also secured by similar piles positioned so as to prevent the escape of sand from beneath the wall. Wooden sheet piles were driven beneath the north and south walls of the basin, bearing on the rock under the walls but not reaching it under the counterforts.

The north, south and west stacks of the Albert Dock warehouses were piled beneath the basement columns and the external walls. The column foundation consisted of a 1ft-thick triangular stone pile cap supporting a triangular course of brickwork upon which were laid two circular courses of bricks surmounted by a 1ft 3in-thick circular stone slab into which the base of the column was let. The configuration of piles was one directly below the column and one at each of the three corners of the cap. The piles beneath the external walls were laid in staggered rows of three; in the north stack these walls were piled to a depth of about 34ft with the pile heads at a depth of 13ft. There the pile caps consisted of 1ft thick stone slabs upon which the sandstone and brick footings of the warehouses were erected. The two stacks of warehouses on the east side of the dock were built on a sort of raft of inverted brick arches (see p146) and were not piled.

1 eg DCM 10.i.1800
2 MCM, MDHB misc papers, unclassified
3 DCM 15.iv.1805
4 DCM 4.i.1810
5 Min Proc Inst Civil Engineers, 1858, 552
6 Lyster, A. G., *Dock Extension in the Port of Liverpool*, Min Proc Inst Civil Engineers, 1890
7 Milne, J. *Description of the Piling Machine used at Montrose Harbour Works*. Min Proc Inst Civil Engineers, 1844
8 DER 1843

Dock wall sections

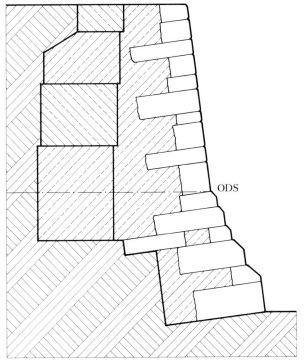

Cross Section through West Wall, Brunswick Dock, 1830.

Cross Section through East Wall, Brunswick Dock, 1830.

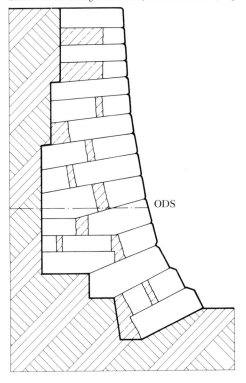

Plan of Counterforts, West Wall,
Brunswick Dock, 1830.

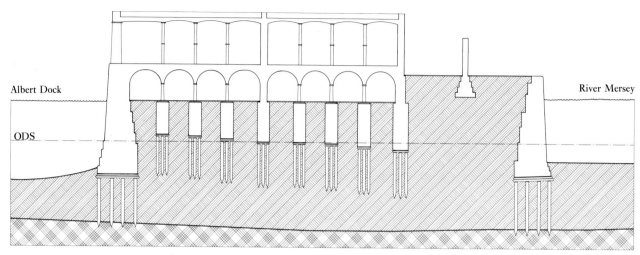

Cross Section through West Wall, West Stack Albert Warehouses and Albert River Wall, 1845.

Cross Section, Albert River Wall, 1845.

Cross Section, West Wall, Albert Dock, 1845.

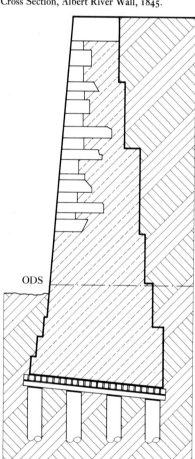

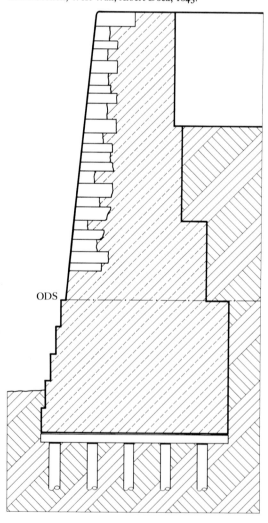

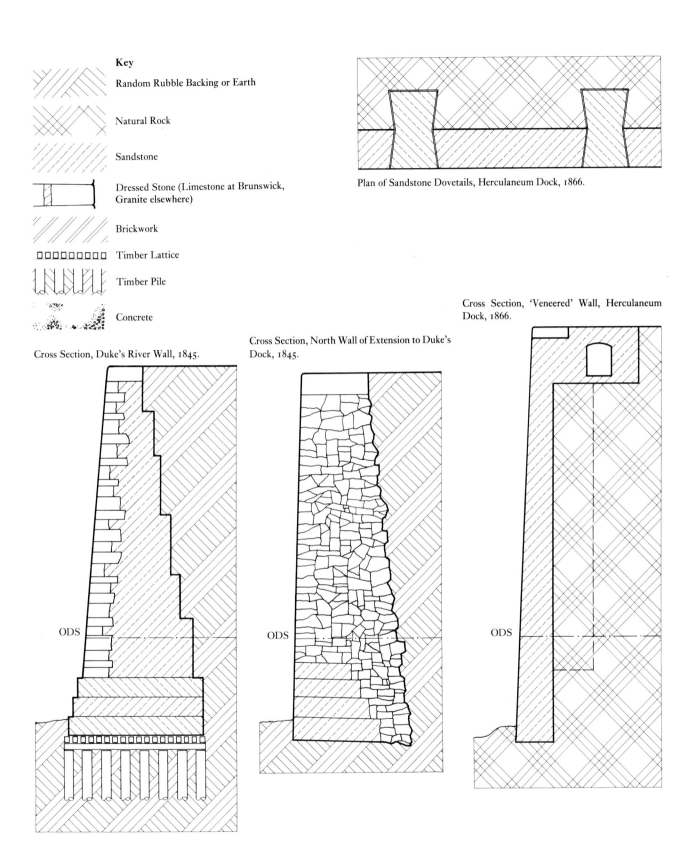

Key

Random Rubble Backing or Earth

Natural Rock

Sandstone

Dressed Stone (Limestone at Brunswick, Granite elsewhere)

Brickwork

Timber Lattice

Timber Pile

Concrete

Plan of Sandstone Dovetails, Herculaneum Dock, 1866.

Cross Section, 'Veneered' Wall, Herculaneum Dock, 1866.

Cross Section, North Wall of Extension to Duke's Dock, 1845.

Cross Section, Duke's River Wall, 1845.

ODS

ODS

ODS

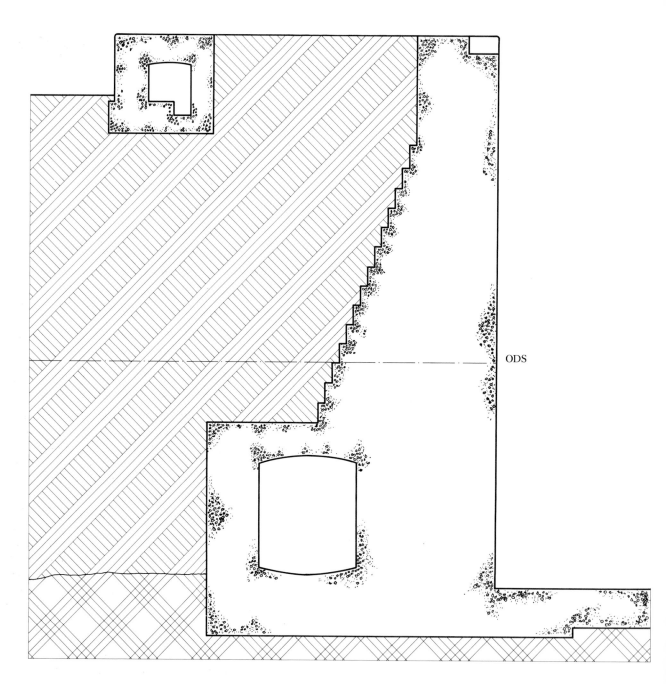

ODS

Cross Section, West Wall of 80′ Lock, Brunswick River Entrance, 1905.

The general character of the water regime in the Liverpool docks has been described: the development of a system of wet docks approached by tidal basins into one in which tidal basins were replaced first by half-tide docks and later by locks. Information on the physical means of containing water within the docks, however, is scanty before the 19th century. There is some evidence that certain docks were provided with double pairs of gates opening in opposite directions to make possible both the normal retention of water within the dock when the basin outside was dry at low tide, and, conversely, the exclusion of water from the dock when the water outside was high. The latter arrangement made it possible to repair dock walls and to remove accumulated silt. Double gates also made it possible to maintain different water levels in connecting wet docks.

Gates

Little is known of the form of early dock gates, but some at least were provided with sluices which could be opened to level the water within and without the dock. The George's Dock gates of 1771 had sluices at the top and bottom, operated by devices described as 'machinery contrived for that purpose',[1] but perhaps no more than leadscrews. The Queen's Basin around 1800 with the gates into the dock itself beyond is illustrated (figure 1); the gate sluices are open, presumably to lower the water within the dock to meet the level of the rising tide so as to enable ships to leave and enter the dock. Such information as exists suggests that sluices in gates may have been normal practice. In 1805 the Surveyor was ordered to fix new cast-iron sluices into the King's Dock gates. It remained common for sluices to be incorporated in dock gates, though in some cases (for instance, Langton Dock of 1879) the gate sluices were never used because the wall culverts were adequate.

No details of the materials or methods of construction of 18th-century Liverpool dock gates have been uncovered. In the early 19th century the practice in Liverpool was for the main-frames and ribs to be made of English or European oak and planked with oak or pitch pine. The heavy structural members consisted of squared balks morticed and bolted together and stiffened with wrought-iron flitch plates at the joints. The heelposts were made up using a number of long logs strapped together at overlapping joints and secured with gun-metal coach bolts. In addition to oak, the timbers known to have been purchased up to 1824 for gate construction were softwoods from the Baltic (Prince's Dock) and hardwoods from Africa (Queen's Half-tide, or Union Dock). All of the 18th-century gates appear to have been manually operated by ropes.

The opening in 1840 of the 70ft-entrance to Coburg Dock marked the beginning of the construction of gates considerably larger than those built for the 45ft-entrances which hitherto were the 19th-century norm in Liverpool. (Peet[2] gives the dimensions of the Old Dock gates as being 34ft wide and 23ft high.) Hartley searched in person for adequate supplies of suitable scantlings, particularly oak, but he was not always successful. Increased gate sizes also posed design problems.

From the middle of the 19th century, greenheart became the most usual timber with which to build the heelposts, frames and ribs of dock gates, because it was obtainable in long lengths of great girth and also superior to oak in terms of hardness, density and resistance to shock loads and boring worm damage. Planking and decking, too, were generally greenheart, with pitch pine fenders. The development of galvanizing as a common industrial process made it possible to reduce the corrosion of straps, collars, flitches and other fixtures and fastenings. Lock gates of the 19th century in Liverpool met at a very shallow angle, with a 'rise' (the proportion between the span of the opening and the distance between the apex and the base of the triangle formed by the closed gates) of only 1:6. At this rise, the strains on a lock gate are considerably greater than if they meet at a sharper angle (elsewhere a rise of 1:4 or 1:5 was more generally used) and its successful employment in Liverpool is evidence of the soundness of the timber construction of the dock and lock gates in the port. The reason for the adoption of so shallow a rise is not known; it may have been an inheritance from the smaller gates of the early docks.

In the 19th century the operating cable in use in the Liverpool docks was chain, but the gates were still opened and closed manually by means of winches. They turned on a pivot-bearing which consisted of a cast-iron socket let into a large block of granite to receive a brass pivot with a gun-metal ball in the top; the top of the pivot with the ball entered a brass casting let into the heel post. The gate turned on the ball bearing. A subsequent design consisted of a solid steel pivot, bolted to the granite platform, which entered a socket fixed to the heel of the gate. The movement of gates was additionally eased by means of rollers fixed to the bottom of metal spears and placed between the heel and the mitre on the base of the leaf. The iron rollers ran in channels set in granite blocks, and cast with openings in them to admit flushing water which washed away mud and other obstructions.

The application of hydraulic power to the dock gates in Liverpool was not introduced until the 1860s and it did not become common until the 1880s. Some of the gates in the South Docks, notably at Canning River Entrance, Albert north passage and Duke's Dock, were never converted from manual operation.

In the 20th century, the size of new lock and dock gates in general outgrew the dimensions for which it was possible to evolve a satisfactory and economical design in timber construction. In the port of Liverpool, however, only at Gladstone Dock did an entrance exceed the dimensions (100ft) which Hartley had managed at Canada Dock. Furthermore, the presence of sea water polluted by sewage rendered the conditions particularly unfavourable for iron or steel. Coincidentally, the pollution also rendered the estuary environment unsuitable for healthy colonies of *teredo navalis*. Very few of the South Docks were fitted with steel gates, as is shown by the list (opposite) of the fabric of the gates in the 1950s.

72   Coburg Dock 70ft gates, *c*1840, front elevation.

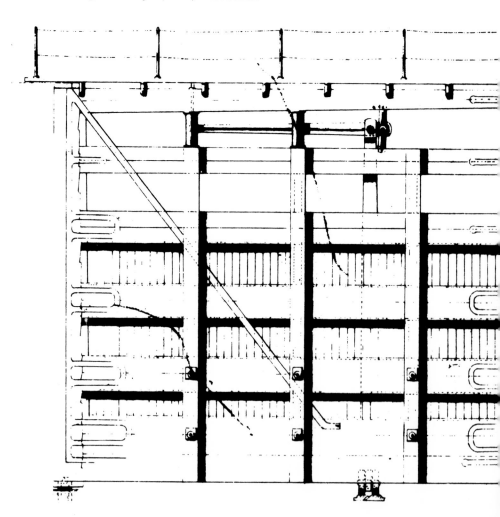

GREENHEART

Canning Graving Docks
Canning River Entrance
Albert Dock
Coburg Dock
Brunswick Half-tide Dock
Brunswick River Entrances
Toxteth–Harrington passage
Herculaneum River Entrances
Herculaneum Graving Docks, Nos. 1 & 4

OAK

Salthouse–Wapping passage
Wapping–Duke's passage

TIMBER–UNSPECIFIED

Herculaneum Graving Docks Nos 2 & 3
Wapping Basin–Wapping Dock passage

STEEL

Queen's Graving Dock

Brunswick–Toxteth passage

(Herculaneum 80ft entrance converted to steel gates 1967)

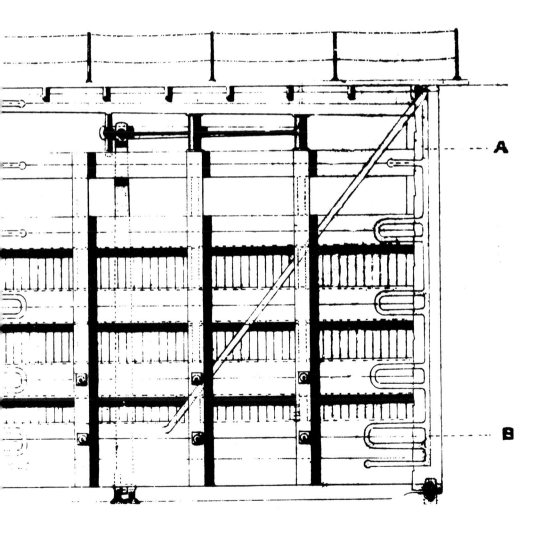

Sluices and culverts

Culverts formed a means of control over water levels additional to that obtainable by gates and sluices. Whereas sluices do no more than connect the water lying immediately on either side of a barrier, by means of culverts water can be carried over a distance independently of what may lie between its extremities. Culverts were constructed within the walls of the first Liverpool dock, though their presence was not part of any sophisticated scheme of water regulation. The municipal sewers emptied into the Old Dock, and the feeder stream from off the Mossbank Fields continued to flow into the dock for some years, causing flooding that the culverts provided were largely inadequate to prevent.

Another function of a culvert network was to scour accumulated silt from the dock floor or the river bed by the sudden release of water pent up elsewhere to form an artificial current. Before the introduction of dredgers, there was no other means save manual digging to rid the docks of the silt that was carried in on every tide. In 1810 such

73   Gate leaf with cloughs and details of heel post.

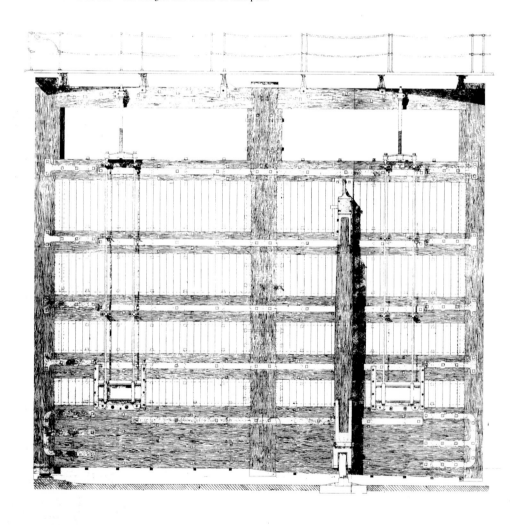

scouring culverts were described as a novelty, though they had been in use in the Liverpool docks for at least a quarter of a century before:

'... *large tunnels are laid from one dock to another, through which the water employed in cleaning the docks is conveyed. When any dock is to be cleaned, it is permitted to become dry, the tunnels are then opened in several directions, the water from which, forming into rivulets, sweeps away the mud which is thrown into them by men prepared for the purpose. This is a new, a very cheap, and very expeditious method, as the operation of cleaning a single dock is generally completed in twelve or fourteen days.*'[3]

The Dock Committee did not agree that this method was acceptable;[4] the members must have greatly regretted the inconvenience, apart from reduced dock revenues, caused by the closure of one of the only five docks available at that time.

Later in the 19th century more elaborate systems of sluicing culverts were built as supplements to rather than substitutes for dredging. The Pluckington Bank, which extends the whole length of the waterfront from the modern Pier Head to Herculaneum Dock, consistently thwarted the engineers' attempts to maintain fairways across it. The rebuilding of Brunswick Dock and the construction of two new entrance locks were occasioned by

74   Duke's Dock 40ft gates, 1862.

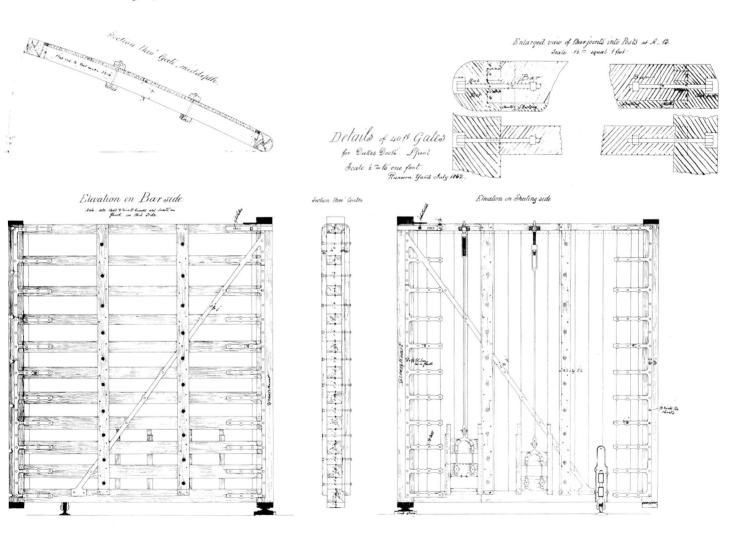

the pressing need for deep water access to the docks behind Pluckington Bank. At Brunswick and Herculaneum Docks '. . . a special arrangement of sluices was designed and carried out, passing along and incorporated with the wing walls and pier heads of the entrances . . . continuing along timber piers [supporting sluice pipes] . . .'.[5] Concrete blocks laid in the river bed at the outfall of the sluices prevented scour in these positions and rendered the sluicing effective over a far greater area.

The flow of water through culverts is regulated by means of sluice gates, or clough paddles which when lowered into position along vertical cast-iron rails effectively block the mouths of the culverts. Such paddles were generally made of oak or greenheart and hung by eye bolts from lifting rods connected to quay-level winding machinery (activated manually or, after about 1865 in Liverpool, by means of hydraulic power). When in position the paddles were seated between jambs of granite (Canning River Entrances) or greenheart (Brunswick River Entrances) with the pressure of water forcing the paddle hard against the seating and thereby forming an efficacious seal.

Pumps

At first, pumps were only used to de-water graving docks and to keep them dry; pumping to increase the depth of water in wet docks was not introduced in Liverpool until near the end of the 19th century. The earliest graving docks were emptied by running off through culverts the water above tide level and using lift pumps to remove the residue. The first pumps so employed must have been manually or horse driven chain pumps. Steam driven machinery was installed relatively late in the graving docks in the South Docks: the Queen's Docks Nos 4 & 5 were not provided with steam pumping engines until 1846–47, a surprising fact in the light of the knowledge that by 1850 consideration was being given to building an hydraulic power centre at Queen's Dock. Even so, it took six to eight hours to drain a graving dock of average early 19th-century size (that is, some 400ft in length). Efficiency increased progressively with the development of compound engines of various types, and in 1875 the introduction of the horizontal centrifugal pump made it possible to de-water a graving dock, with a ship in it, in one hour. After de-watering, pumping continued to remove water which entered the dock by percolation through the walls and by seepage up through the floor and through the gates.

Occasionally, when a vessel was to occupy part of a graving dock for an extended period, a temporary stank, or dam, would be erected between the end of the ship and the dock gates. This procedure allowed use of the remainder of the dock and full employment of scarce and valuable graving dock space. It also imposed a need for more pumps and more complicated systems for running them.

Just after the turn of the 20th century the graving docks in the South Docks comprised Canning Nos 1 & 2, Queen's and Herculaneum Nos 1, 2, 3 & 4. Of these only the Canning Graving Docks, dating from the 18th century, were of any antiquity. Records of the pumping machinery installed at Canning before the 20th century have not been found. In 1947 two Gwynne vertical spindle single-entry centrifugal pumps, driven by two Mawdsley DC motors and capable of handling 2,500 gallons of water per minute were brought into commission at the Canning Graving Dock station. At the new Queen's Graving Dock, completed in 1905, the pumping station housed the following:

2 main pumping engines (Crossley Bros, 1905)
2 horizontal gas-engine-driven centrifugal pumps, IHP 500
1 drainage engine (Tangye)
1 horizontal gas-engine-driven twin centrifugal pump, IHP 157
1 priming engine (Tangye)
1 horizontal gas-engine-driven pump, IHP 20
1 air compressor (Crossley Bros) and 1 ventilating engine (Tangye).

The dock (634ft long) could be pumped out in $4\frac{3}{4}$hrs (with a ship in it) or $5\frac{1}{2}$hrs (without a ship in it), through culverts up to 7ft 6 ins in diameter.

The first pumping machinery to be installed at the Herculaneum Graving Docks was supplied by Messrs W. G. Armstrong in 1864, to de-water graving docks. The graving dock pumping engine was replaced in 1885 by a locomotive engine used as a stationary steam engine. In 1893 a new engine was put in to work the graving dock pumping machinery and a turbine pump 'of large capacity'[6] was fixed in the southern well in place of one of the chain pumps. The need for still more powerful pumps was met by two compound jet-condensing steam centrifugal pumps supplied in 1898 by Messrs W. H. Allen, Sons & Co of Bedford, and three steel Lancashire boilers supplied the following year. The engine and boiler houses underwent extensive alterations in order to receive the new plant. All of the Herculaneum Graving Dock pumps together consumed a daily average of 13 tons of coal, and they could de-water the docks (with ships in them) within $2\frac{1}{2}$ to $3\frac{1}{2}$hrs, depending on the size of the dock.

Impounding

During the latter part of the 19th century more and more ships, owing to the increase in their draughts, were unable to enter the older Mersey docks on neap tides. The six Sandon Graving Docks, opened in 1851, were the first whose depth over sill could be artificially increased using an impounding by pumping installation designed by G. F. Lyster in around 1885. The success of this experiment in the North Docks was such that it was repeated in the south where it was applied to the Brunswick–George's group. These docks, built between 1771 and 1855, were not available, on neap tides, to vessels of more than 16ft draught until after the implementation of Lyster's impounding scheme. After 1890 water in the South Docks was impounded at a level which provided ample draught to all ships so long as they passed between river and docks

75 Section through Coburg impounding station, showing pump and culverts.

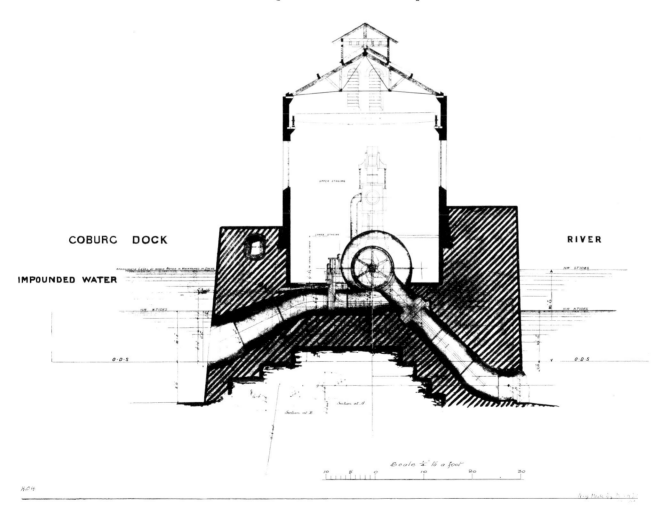

COBURG PUMPING STATION

COBURG DOCK

IMPOUNDED WATER

RIVER

by way of the deep-water river entrances to Herculaneum and, after 1905, Brunswick Docks.

The pumps at the Coburg Dock impounding station had to do all of their work quickly at or about high water and so needed to be extremely powerful. Their capacity was 1200 tons of water per minute, and they raised the water level over some 80 acres of dock. The pumps had suction and delivery pipes of 54in diameter and they were driven by vertical compound surface condensing engines with cylinders 22in and 40in diameter by 30in stroke. Both pumps and steam engines were supplied in 1887 by Messrs J. & H. Gwynne of Hammersmith. Joseph Foster and Sons supplied five Lancashire boilers and an economizer was ordered from E. Green & Sons. After 1911, the Coburg pumps were used additionally to push extra water through the sluices at the Brunswick and Herculaneum River Entrances in order to maintain the navigability of the passages.

1 Moss, 1796, 48
2 Peet, 1930, 187n
3 Troughton, 1810, 278
4 DCM 25.iv.1809
5 Lyster, 1896, 14
6 DER 1893

Hydraulic power was first introduced to the Liverpool docks at Albert Dock in 1848, though the new dock was not provided with a complete cargo- or dock-operating system; Stanley and Wapping docks in the late 1850s were the first to be provided with a comprehensive range of hydraulic cargo-handling equipment. It was not until the 1860s that hydraulic power was applied to dock gates and bridges. In the period 1880–1920, however, hydraulic power on the docks became widespread and virtually indispensable.

There are several possible explanations for the slow movement from manual (and to a small extent, steam) to hydraulic power. In the days of sailing ships, ship-owning and merchanting were less capital intensive than with the advent of steam, and quick turn-round and efficient

76 Hydraulic jigger with operating chain in position, Albert Warehouses, 1983.

discharging and loading were of less financial significance. Manpower was readily available and cheap; it took very many man hours at a few shillings a week to equal the several thousand pounds' cost of an hydraulic power centre. Both ships and packages were smaller and more manageable.

The greater cost of steamships, however, and the greater capital cost of their huge cargoes, meant that time spent unnecessarily in port represented a greater loss than it did to the owner of a small sailing ship. With their demand for coal, steamships also created a new demand for bulk cargo that was met by the construction in the 1850s of the high level coal railway at Bramley-Moore Dock, with hydraulic loading appliances, and by the erection of the huge coaling cranes and hoist at Herculaneum Dock in the 1890s. The increasing bulk of other cargoes also called for power handling. The first hydraulic crane at Queen's Dock was installed in 1852, to handle great logs of mahogany, and as the export of heavy machinery grew, so manual cranes were increasingly inadequate for the weights involved.

The first hydraulic dockside crane was designed and built by W. G. Armstrong and installed at the upper end of Newcastle Quay in 1846. Having dismissed at first the idea of a 'water crane', Hartley travelled to Newcastle to see Armstrong's device for himself and was greatly impressed with it. He reported back to the Sub-committee of Works:

'. . . although I have heard a great deal in favour of this crane, it surpassed my expectations and I think it one of the most important acquisitions which can be given to warehouses and docks.'[1]

When the new Albert Dock and its warehouses were nearing completion Hartley ordered two hydraulic lifts and two hydraulic cranes for the warehouses. Armstrong supplied two 5-ton lifts or hoists, works numbers 13 and 14, in 1848. Hartley's annual report for 1849 recorded the fixing of two hydraulic cranes on the Albert Dock quay in the following year, but all evidence for their place of installation has disappeared. These first installations drew their water from the Corporation mains water supply, via pipes originally of 7ins diameter but which were replaced by 12ins pipes in 1850.

The principle of the operation of these early cranes was

the same as that of all subsequent hydraulic installations in the Liverpool docks. Power was provided by a head of water, and movement by an hydraulic ram, normally used in the form known as an hydraulic jigger. The ram consists in essence of a hollow cylinder, closed at one end, and in the other end a sliding piston which is forced to move when water under pressure is admitted into the cylinder. A jigger comprises a ram with a set of pulleys or sheaves at either end of the ram assembly, round which passes a chain. The chain is fixed at one end, while the free end is attached to whatever it is desired to move. The movement of the piston is transferred to the chain, and the distance of the piston's travel is multiplied by the number of pulleys around which the chain passes. The photograph at figure 76 makes clear the general appearance and arrangement of an hydraulic jigger.

77   Toxteth Hydraulic Power Centre, 1889. Elevations and section
     through accumulator tower.

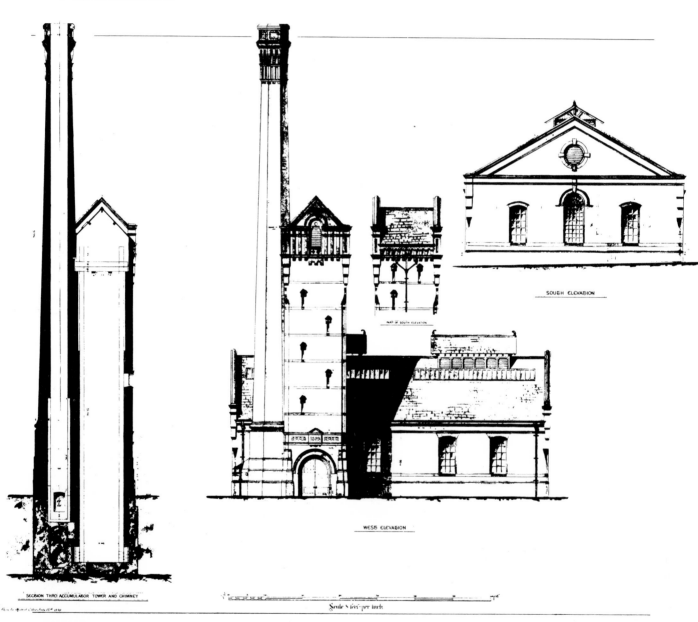

Hydraulic accumulators

Variations in pressure and practical limits on the head of water which could be obtained were two disadvantages of using the town water supply. One solution to such problems was the construction, in 1849, of the Grimsby Dock water tower to support a 33,000-gallon water tank 200ft above the quay; the tower provided an independent head of low pressure (around 86 psi), but it was such an enormous structure that to found similar ones on most other sites was not feasible. By 1850 Armstrong had developed the weight-loaded accumulator (into which water was pumped by a steam engine), which could provide a constant supply of water at a constant high pressure (over 600psi). The hydraulic accumulator effectively stored power against demand and so was particularly useful in meeting intermittent demands and in ironing out cyclical variations in pressure from pumps.

Armstrong supplied his first accumulator to the Manchester, Sheffield and Lincolnshire Railway Company for its dock installation at New Holland on the Humber in 1850. Shortly thereafter Armstrong accumulators and their associated machinery were installed in the Liverpool

78   Albert Hydraulic Power Centre, 1878. Section through boiler house, engine house and accumulator tower.

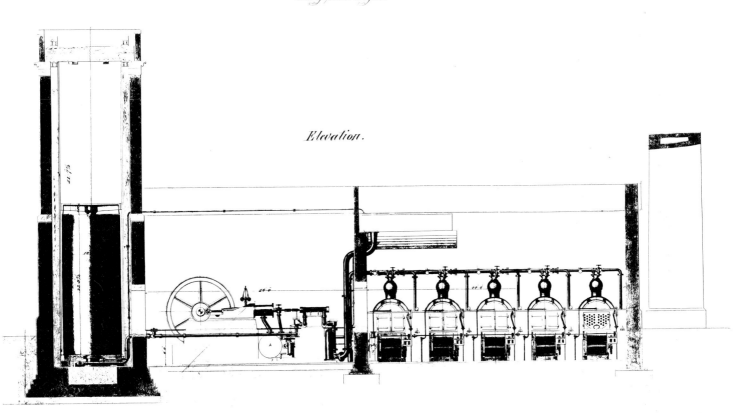

bert Dock. Liverpool.

Design of arrangement of steam engines, boilers, accumulator, pipes, &c.

Scale of 1/4 inch to 1 foot.

Elevation.

Sir W.G. Armstrong & Co
ELSWICK ENGINE WORKS
NEWCASTLE-UN-TYNE.

docks, to power cranes to be used for shipping coals at the Queen's and Stanley Docks. Armstrong's first estimates were submitted in March 1851. For Queen's Dock, he offered to supply a 7-ton crane, a 12-horsepower high pressure engine, accumulating reservoir including the weight-case and load, cast-iron pressure pipes, one 5,000 gallon capacity water cistern and '... miscellaneous apparatus consisting of a wrought iron cradle for containing the coal waggons ...'[2] at a cost of £1,660. He also quoted for a second crane: '... one 15 ton hydraulic

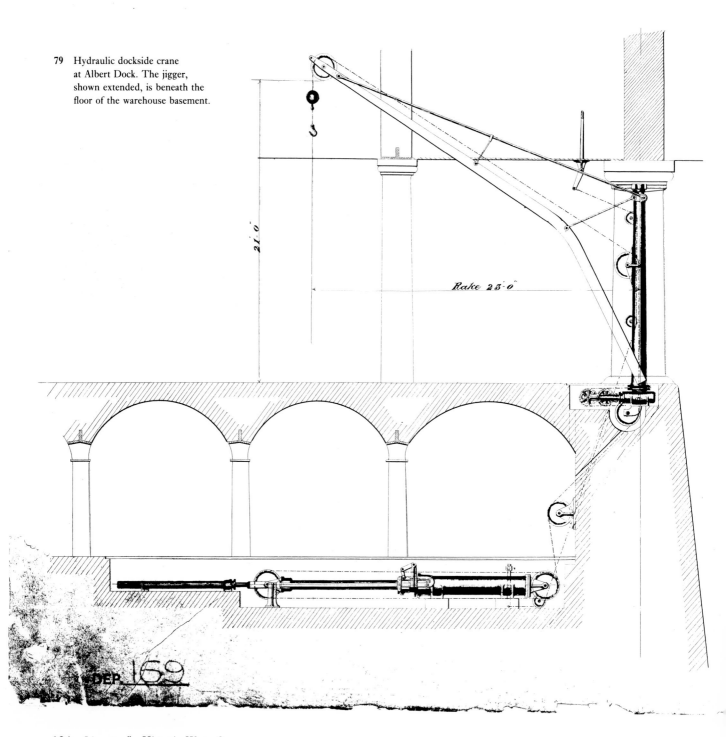

79 Hydraulic dockside crane
    at Albert Dock. The jigger,
    shown extended, is beneath the
    floor of the warehouse basement.

21'.0"

Rake 25'.0"

DEP. 169

crane adapted to stand upon a pedestal – radius of jib 26ft 6in – height from ground to centre of top sheave 35ft – 3 cylinders for variable powers and turning apparatus – including the chain and the foundation plates and holding bolts £840'.[3] The machinery at Stanley Dock was to include a 'hoisting machine with vibrating jib for raising coal boxes out of barges and delivering them into ships lying outside of the same'.[4] By March, 1852, an hydraulic crane was in operation at the north-east corner of the Queen's Dock. In April 1853, tenders were sought once again for providing hydraulic apparatus for the Stanley Dock warehouses. Two accumulators were installed at Stanley Dock by 1854 and one of these still survives. The precise locations of the two Armstrong cranes Nos 51 (1850, 20 tons) and 128 (1851, 10 tons) which had operating pressures of 600 psi and 700 psi respectively and so could only have worked with water supplied via an accumulator, have not been identified.

Hydraulic power centres in the South Docks

Much of the history of hydraulic power in the Liverpool docks prior to 1856 is a matter for speculation. On 2 July, 1856, the Wapping Dock hydraulic power station was brought into commission. Subsequent centres became operational at Herculaneum Dock in 1864, Albert Dock in 1878 and Toxteth in 1890. The original plant and machinery for all of these hydraulic power stations were supplied by W. G. Armstrong. By 1901 a new hydraulic mains pipeline had been constructed along the South Docks, between the Albert Dock centre and the Herculaneum Dock centre, where additional pumping machinery was installed. More engine and boiler power were provided at the Toxteth station and a new accumulator to work in conjunction with Toxteth was erected at the south east corner of Harrington Dock. In 1906 the machinery in the Albert and Wapping centres was dismantled, and thenceforward all of the hydraulic engines in the South Docks worked off the pressure water supplied from Toxteth and Herculaneum.

Hydraulic machinery: cranes and hoists

The development of warehouse and quayside hydraulic cranes began with cranes slewed by hand and was followed by wall cranes with hydraulic slewing as well as lifting, roof cranes and moveable cranes. The cranes installed in the Albert Warehouses in 1878–79 were little different from those installed at Wapping early in the 1850s, but this kind of wall crane was specific to multi-storey warehouses. At Harrington and Toxteth Docks the double-storey transit sheds were surmounted by hydraulic

roof cranes to serve the upper storeys while the lower floors were served simultaneously by shipboard machinery. None the less, in 1896 nine ordinary manual hoists were fixed in the upper storey of the east quay shed, Harrington Dock, in lieu of the hydraulic jiggers which were removed. However, since ships of great size could not enter the South Docks, there was no need to develop cargo-handling gear beyond that installed in the Toxteth and Harrington and later (around 1905) the King's and Queen's transit sheds.

80　Moveable jigger ('elephant'), Albert Dock. Water from the hydraulic power system was supplied through rigid pipes with flexible joints and exhausted through a hose.

Although hydraulic cranes generally could not be made self-propelling, two notable types of moveable cranes, for which Armstrong had devised a special, high pressure flexible joint, were employed on the South Docks. The earlier of these was a jigger on wheels known in Liverpool as an 'elephant' and in London as a 'devil'. In these 'elephants', chains driven by an hydraulic ram drove a barrel and so turned a large wheel carrying the rope fall. At first the fall was simply led up over a fixed cat-head at the top of the building, thus enabling goods to be hoisted only to doors under the cat-head. The later introduction of a sheave which travelled on a wire span running along the top of the dockside warehouse wall permitted greater flexibility of working. Both Albert and Wapping Dock warehouses were fitted with such wire spans on their dockside elevations, and in 1906 there were eleven one-ton 'portable jiggers' (presumably elephants) in use on the quays of the Albert Dock.

The second type of moveable crane used in the South Docks was the large coaling appliance. One of these was supplied by Sir W. G. Armstrong, Whitworth & Co

(£4,990) and another by the Hydraulic Engineering Co (£4,195) and they were erected in 1896 and 1898 respectively on the east quay of Herculaneum Dock. Railway trucks, hauled to position by hydraulic capstans, were loaded on to a cradle sitting on the rails; the truck was secured by a pair of hooks engaging one of the axles, lifted and tipped (by means of an additional hydraulic cylinder fitted to the coaling appliance) into the ship's hold. Bunker coal (steamship fuel) and cargo coal both were handled in this way and demand for the Herculaneum coaling cranes peaked during the First World War. Thereafter the coal trade declined in importance, but the cranes continued to be extensively used for heavy lifts and bulk cargoes, such as limestone, for the duration of the active life of the Herculaneum Dock. Another hydraulic coaling appliance installed at Herculaneum by C. & A. Musker & Co in 1907 was a 25-ton coal hoist which lifted loaded trucks, on a cradle, by means of a direct-acting hydraulic cylinder beneath the cradle. The contents of the truck were tipped down an adjustable shoot by the action of an oscillating hydraulic cylinder which up-ended the wagon. Both the cranes and the hoist handled only end-door trucks.

Hydraulic machinery: gate engines

In spite of the fact that hydraulic power has not yet been bettered for the operation of dock and lock gates, this kind of power was very slowly introduced for gate operation in the Liverpool docks. Neither Stanley nor Wapping Dock was originally furnished with hydraulic gate machinery, though both of these dock developments incorporated hydraulic power centres. Herculaneum was the first of the South Docks to be provided with hydraulically operated gates, in 1864. In 1877 the Queen's Half-tide Dock river entrance was converted to hydraulic power, as was the Coburg–Brunswick passage in 1890. The gate engines installed in the new Harrington (opened 1883) and Toxteth (opened 1888) Docks were either manual machines converted to hydraulic operation or hydraulic machines whose components were the same as those in a manual-to-hydraulic conversion. Between the building of Herculaneum (1866) and the reconstruction of Brunswick, King's and Queen's (1906) the installation of improved gate machinery was desultory, and the north passage of the Albert Dock, and the Canning River Entrance were never transformed from manual operation.

All of the hydraulic gate engines in the South Docks were worked by means of chains wound either round a winch drum or round the multiple sheaves of a jigger. Those which worked by means of winding drums were

generally examples of manual winches which had been converted to hydraulic operation by fixing Armstrong reciprocating engines to the gearing mechanisms of the winches. These engines consisted either of three in-line oscillating pistons which drove cranks at 120°, or of two cylinders with cranks at 90°. Such engines were installed, for instance, in the South Docks at Herculaneum Dock, and in the north at Salisbury and Nelson Docks (where they were still operational in 1982). At the 100ft lock, Brunswick River Entrance, the gate leaves were worked by jiggers – one 9ft long opening jigger and one 13ft 4ins long closing jigger for each leaf. The operating chains passed from the jigger down chases in the lock walls to the level at which they were attached to the gate. From here the chains would tend to remain stretched some 20ft above the lock floor when the gates were shut. Thus each gate-closing jigger was fitted with an auxiliary jigger which pulled the main ram back to its fully retracted position, allowing the gate chain to slacken and fall by its own weight to the bottom of the lock. The gate-closing jigger had to be longer than the opening one because it had to draw in the slack chain before winding the gate leaves shut. All of the above gate operating systems are of the type known as 'direct chain'. The Toxteth and Harrington dock gates were also operated by chains wound around jiggers. In these cases, however, the opening and closing chains were led from a jigger along the top of the gate to a point near the mitre whence they passed over sheaves and down either side of the gate leaf to submerged sheaves below. From here they were led to rings fixed in the dock walls at the same level as the submerged sheaves on the gate. In this system, known as the over-gate chain system, the operating machines were installed on the same side of the passage as the gate leaf they worked.

Hydraulic machinery: capstans

Armstrong developed his first hydraulic capstans using the same arrangement of multiple in-line oscillating pistons that he had devised for the conversion of manual winch gear to hydraulic operation. He subsequently invented a capstan engine which worked off direct acting radial pistons situated beneath the winding drum; this arrangement was more efficient and more compact. In the South Docks, capstans were used extensively to haul both ships and railway trucks. The capstans first installed at Herculaneum Dock in 1864 to facilitate the movement of vessels to and from the graving docks were operated by three in-line pistons. Following the introduction of the two 25-ton coaling cranes on the east side of the Herculaneum branch dock, additional capstans were installed there to haul the cranes as well as the railway wagons. Also during the 1880s and 1890s 11-ton hydraulic capstans with in-line pistons were installed at the south east pier of the Canning Half-tide Basin and on the island between the two river entrances at the Queen's Half-tide Dock. Capstans with radial pistons were installed at Toxteth and Harrington Docks during the same period. Most of this machinery was supplied by the Armstrong Company, but important contracts were also awarded later on to Tannett Walker & Co, Leeds and C. & A. Musker and Ogden & Barnes, both of Liverpool. The Dock Board supplied hyraulic power for capstans, and maintained and repaired them but non-Dock Board users had to supply their own labour, ropes, gear and tackle for working them.

Hydraulic machinery: swing bridges

Swing bridges, too, were converted from manual to hydraulic operation by the fitment of in-line pistons to their winding gear. The more modern, post-1870 bridges, were opened and closed by large jiggers, which were always paired and set horizontally in the bridge pits: as one jigger was set to inlet, the other was set to exhaust, with the extension of one causing the retraction of the other by means of a cable passing between them. The bridge was swung by the cable wrapped around its slewing drum. Francis Morton & Co, Tannett Walker & Company, and W. G. Armstrong were suppliers of hydraulic bridge gear (at Wapping and Coburg Docks, Brunswick/Toxteth and Herculaneum/Harrington passages respectively).

Hydraulic installations: manufacturers, operation and maintenance

During the early history of the Mersey Docks, the provision of manually operated dock gates, winding gear and lifting tackle was within the competence of the local shipwrights and millwrights whose labour was available to the managers of the dock estate. With the increasing sophistication of mechanical and hydraulic engineering knowledge and practice grew the need to rely on contractors to provide the necessary expertise and machinery. The first, and best known contractor to supply hydraulic machinery for the Liverpool docks was W. G. Armstrong, who monopolized the supply of hydraulic installations in Liverpool until the early 1880s, when the propriety of approaching Armstrong alone for tenders was questioned with increasing indignation and publicity. The Hydraulic Engineering Company Ltd of Chester followed by Tannett Walker, Ogden & Barnes, Morton's and others, then began to win orders from the Dock Board. However,

as much work as possible was undertaken by the Dock Engineer's expanding direct labour force. By far the greatest part of this work was dock and building construction, but it also included such fairly simple fabrication as fashioning water tanks for hydraulic power centres.

A common element of most traditional dock machinery, regardless of its motive power, was cable. During the 18th century this was usually natural fibre rope; for most of the 19th century it was wrought-iron chain; and this in turn was generally superseded by steel wire ropes. In 1830 the Corporation of Liverpool invested £603 12s 8d in a chain proving machine and a chain testing works was established at the King's Dock, north of the tobacco warehouse. From at least 1865, there was also a chain testing works on the dock estate in Birkenhead. Under the superintendence of a Corporation official based at the works, chains were tested for soundness and strength and annealed regularly to restore the ductility lost through 'work hardening' (a brittleness caused by repeated passage over pulleys).

81 25-ton hydraulic coaling crane at Herculaneum Dock. The crane jib is hidden behind the tower.

Apart from the first few years in the late 1840s, when water to operate hydraulic dock machinery was drawn from the Corporation mains water supply, the provision of hydraulic power on the estate was autonomous. The Engineer's Department of the Dock Board was responsible for the provision of plant and accommodation for pumping and power stations; it was the Traffic Department's responsibility to collect the rates payable by the vessels using the quayside cranes. The cost of using a crane was determined by the duration of time during which exclusive use of the crane was allowed plus a charge per lift rising from £3 for a lift of less than 10 tons to

£25 for a lift of more than 70 tons in 1858. The charges for warehouse cranes and cranes included in tenancies were calculated on different bases.

In response to pressure from shipowners using the South Docks, the Works Committee of the Dock Board recommended acceptance of Armstrong's offer to provide a 100-ton floating crane. It was parenthetically observed that such a crane could also be used by the Dock Engineer to remove heavy gates. The proposed new floating crane was not ordered, though stationary quay cranes of 20 and 25 tons were erected at Queen's and Coburg Docks respectively. The policy governing provision of hydraulic appliances does seem to have been ill-defined. Despite the undoubted utility of hydraulic power, it was not generally adopted on the dock estate for a long time. In 1884 the lifting machinery on the estate comprised 15 hydraulic cranes (27 to 100 tons, presumably exclusive of wall cranes), 78 hand cranes, 3 steam cranes (7, 50 and 60 tons) and one 27cwt hydraulic salt crane. By 1906 the number of hydraulic cranes (10cwt to 100 tons, presumably inclusive of wall cranes) had risen to 191, the number of hand cranes (30cwt to 25 tons) had dropped to 32 and the number of steam cranes (5, 7, 8, 9, 20 and 87 tons) had doubled. In addition to these last were 29 (20cwt) hydraulic roof cranes and 4 moveable hydraulic cranes (25, 30, 30 and 40 tons) on the dock estate in 1906. The provision of machinery in 1927 was 192 hydraulic cranes (10cwt to 40 tons), 39 electric cranes (20cwt to 5 tons), 4 steam cranes (5 to 87 tons), one 15 ton steam crane, 27 hand cranes (20cwt to 25 tons) and 2 coaling cranes (25 and 30 tons).

The use of hydraulic power for cargo handling thereafter was not long-lived except on the docks which were in decline. By the 1920s multi-stage centrifugal pumps driven by high-speed steam turbines or electric motors were readily available to replace cumbersome reciprocating steam engines; small, cheap to run and requiring no accumulator, this type of pump was installed at Tilbury Docks in the Port of London in 1923. The system was not adopted for the South Docks in Liverpool; for a number of reasons, most of which related to the impact of the First World War on the whole port, the Board's working capital was severely strained and available resources were concentrated on the Gladstone system in the north. By the 1930s electric power had supplanted hydraulic power in most places and for most applications in modern docks, largely because the electric power consumed was proportional to the work done and so electric power showed a cost advantage over hydraulic power. In Liverpool's South Docks the hydraulic power systems were never universally superseded by any other type, although a few electric cranes were installed, notably at Albert Dock (quayside) and King's and Queen's Dock (some transit shed roofs). The full-scale re-development which would have rendered hydraulic cargo handling machinery obsolete never occurred in the South Docks.

1 MDHB Works Sub-Committee, 10.vii.1847
2 Ex Inf J. D. Fryer
3 Ib
4 Ib

BUILDINGS AND COMMUNICATIONS

82 The Liverpool waterfront in the late 19th century.

83 Interior of Albert Dock office, 1982.

84 View up stairwell, Albert Warehouses, 1982.

85 Iron fire door, Albert Warehouses, 1982.

86 Quay level, south-west corner, Albert Warehouses, 1982.

Sheds and warehouses

The functions of sheds and warehouses are distinct, sheds forming a simple protection from the weather for the sorting and checking of inward and outward bound cargo, and warehouses providing longer term and secure storage. Whereas sheds were built on the quaysides, and had no use elsewhere, most warehouses were away from the immediate margins of the dock. A few dockside warehouses were built to enable goods to be discharged directly inside, when it was necessary to handle bulk cargoes (as at Duke's Dock grain warehouse) or to ensure the security of goods of high value or in bond (as at the Albert Dock warehouses).

During the 18th century the Corporation provided some open sheds on the quays, while the provision of

warehouses was generally left to private merchants. The tobacco warehouses in the South Docks were built by the Corporation in 1793 and 1811, as were the contemporary first and second Goree warehouses. From the 1790s the Corporation tried to promote warehouse construction by means of covenants inserted in leases and deeds relating to their property near the docks, since they no doubt felt that a plentiful supply of warehousing would increase the docks' attractiveness. The Dock Trustees did not build any warehouses of their own until the 1840s, when the Albert Dock warehouses were constructed to store a variety of goods under bond. Later, changes in cargo-handling methods and in modes of distribution made multi-storey warehouses less useful and attractive for general use than

87   Iron transit shed, 1818, Queen's Dock. Drawn 1868.

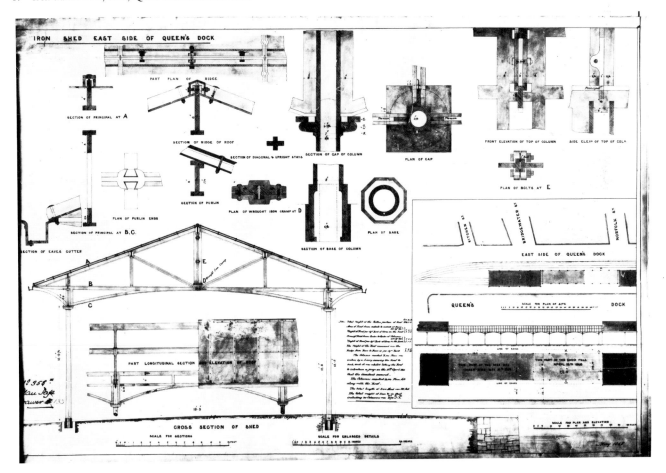

large transit sheds, and after the 1860s the only new dockside warehouses were those purpose built for tobacco or grain.

The versatility of the transit shed was increased from the late 19th century by the building of sheds of two and three storeys, able to receive cargo off-loaded at speed by steam and hydraulic machinery. There was nevertheless a tendency, strengthened by the re-use of certain standardized components, to perpetuate the designs of utilitarian structures of this sort, and transit sheds in particular did not change their overall form over a considerable period of time.

Sheds

The simplest and probably the earliest type of dockside shed recorded comprised ranks of timber columns carrying wooden ties and a king-post roof covered in slates. Such

sheds were typically 20 to 30ft wide and 50 to 100ft long. The first iron shed seems to have been built in 1818, some three or four years later than Rickman's use of cast iron in the churches of St Paul, Toxteth and St Michael le Hamlet, both in Liverpool. Foster was the Dock Trustees' engineer at the time, but the degree of his own design responsibility for the use of what was still a novel material in this shed is not known: he is not otherwise recorded as an exponent of iron construction, and like Rickman he may have had the material suggested to him by others.

The 1818 shed, at Queen's Dock, was destroyed following an accident in 1868, but it was fully recorded with measurements at the time.[1] It had a span of 30ft, and comprised nine 19ft 3in bays. Cast-iron columns carried a roof of fairly shallow pitch formed of mirror pairs of castings bolted and strapped at the centre line to form a species of king post truss, and with curving braces rising

88   Transit shed, *c*1840, King's Dock. The standard form of open-sided transit shed with iron columns and a timber roof braced by iron ties. Section.

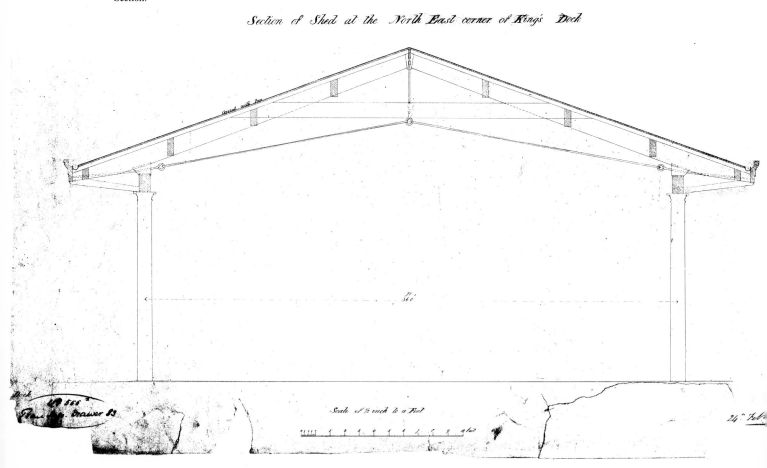

Section of Shed at the North East corner of King's Dock

Scale of ½ inch to a Foot

from the capitals and cast integrally with the truss members. Cast girders, similarly braced, spanned the bays. The covering was of sheet iron on cast iron purlins. The shed is illustrated at figure 87.

While this shed introduced into the docks elements that were to be repeated in later buildings, it seems not to have been widely imitated immediately. An alternative form of shed, using more traditional materials, seems to have been introduced by Hartley soon after his appointment as Dock Engineer in 1824, and widely adopted throughout the docks. A typical example is at figure 88.[2] This comprises columns of cast iron, carrying timber principals joined by a timber collar and purlins. A wrought-iron hanger descends from the apex of the roof through the collar and terminates in an eye, whence a pair of wrought-iron tie rods extends to the feet of the principals. The roofs of these sheds were boarded, and covered in slates or iron, and as the practice slowly developed of enclosing sheds, so it became common to provide roofs with skylights and ventilators.

89 Transit shed spanning 90ft, between King's and Wapping Docks, 1857. Section.

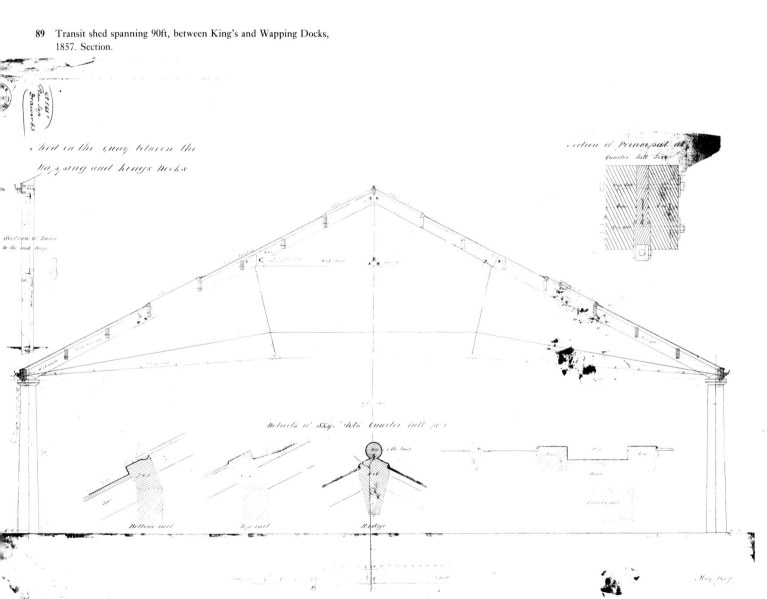

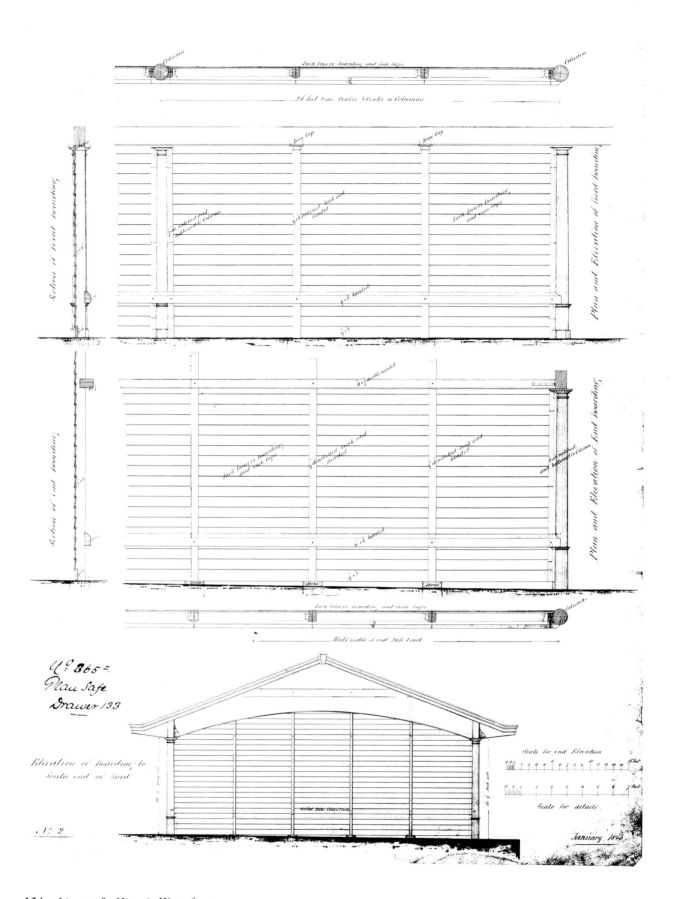

The structure of these sheds was capable with only modest alteration of application to sheds of much greater size. Figure 89 is the section of a shed of 1857 between Wapping and King's Docks.[3] This inherits the principals and collar of its smaller predecessors, but with the difference that all timber members are doubled, and that the wrought-iron tie rods are in three parts, suspended by hangers from purpose cast mountings at the junction of collar and principals. In addition, the lower parts of the principals and the collar itself are strengthened by bracing rods, placed between the paired timbers. The whole was carried on columns 19ft 6in high with a 5ft splay below quay level where they rested on mass concrete foundations capped in stone. The span of the shed was 90ft.

While earlier sheds were generally open on all sides with canvas and wooden screens against the weather, it

90 (*opposite*) Transit shed, 1853, Queen's Dock. A typical boarded shed. Elevations.

91 Transit shed, 1846, Coburg Dock. The standard form of masonry shed. Plan, section and elevation.

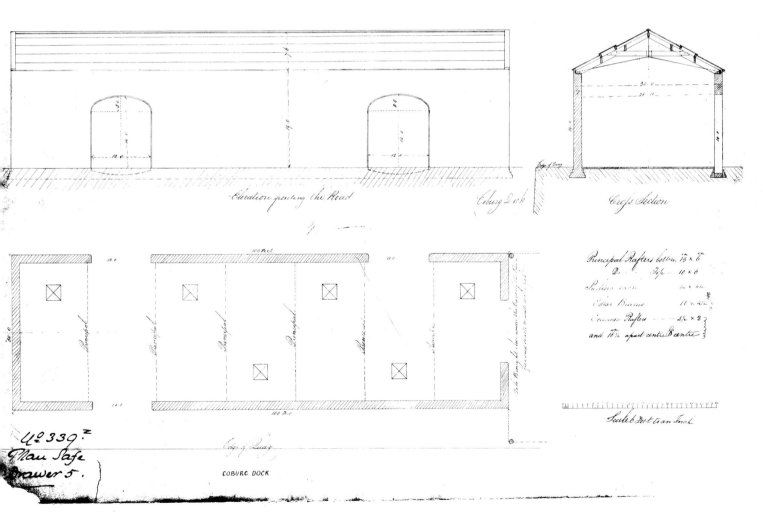

became increasingly normal to build them with masonry gables, to provide an element of longitudinal support as well as of enclosure, and with pierced masonry walls to quay and road side, to give better protection from the weather to the goods within. This type of partly-enclosed, masonry-walled shed was probably another innovation of Hartley's, and as a type was ubiquitous and long-lived; the last to be built in the South Docks was a 30ft × 315ft shed erected in 1912 on the south-west quay of Salthouse Dock, with a continuous line of sliding doors along the dockside.

The first double-storey transit shed – a form also to become typical by the early 20th century – seems to have been the Great Western shed at Duke's Dock, built in about 1857, and provided with a double-span kingpost roof that overhung the dock by 14ft to provide a covered loading area for barges. Advanced in conception in the context of the Liverpool docks, it was traditional in execution, with its conventional timber trusses and non-fireproof construction. Walls were of masonry, supporting the outer ends of the landward truss and the centre point

of the dockside truss. The landward truss was supported also at an intermediate point by superimposed pairs of iron columns on the centre line of the enclosed portion of the shed. The dockside truss was additionally braced with wrought iron rods from the apex of the roof to the outer end of the tie, while floor beams were also braced with wrought-iron rods to carry heavy loads. Figure 92 illustrates the section of this shed.[4]

Another illustration of the need to adapt standard forms of transit shed to the demands of cargo handling is provided by a shed erected in 1853 at the north end of Salthouse Dock. This was basically a shed of a normal, open form, with the typical braced collar roof of other Hartley sheds. However, the quayside elevation was adapted to accommodate a crane. The truss aligned with this crane was curtailed at the junction of collar and principal, and carried at that point on an elongated column. The bays either side of the crane were cut back to accommodate the swing of the crane's jib, and faced in a plate (described as a breast beam) that extended to meet the truss either side at the point of its upper purlin. The

92   Great Western shed, 1857, Duke's Dock. Section.

93   (*opposite*) Transit shed, 1853, Salthouse Dock, with part of roof cut away to form crane bay. Plan, section and elevation.

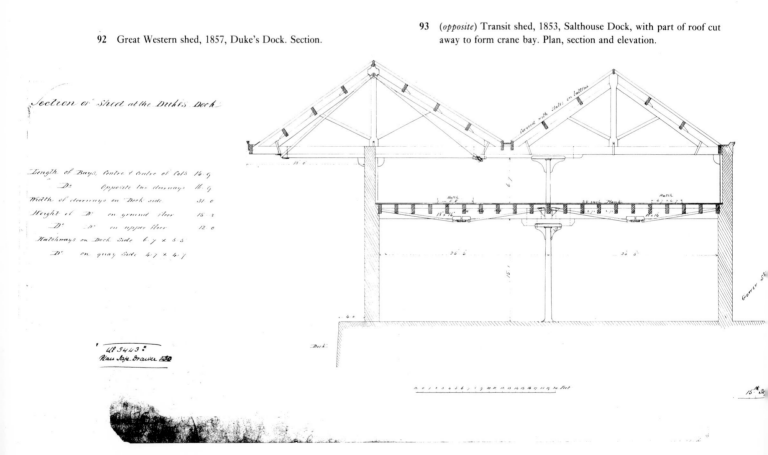

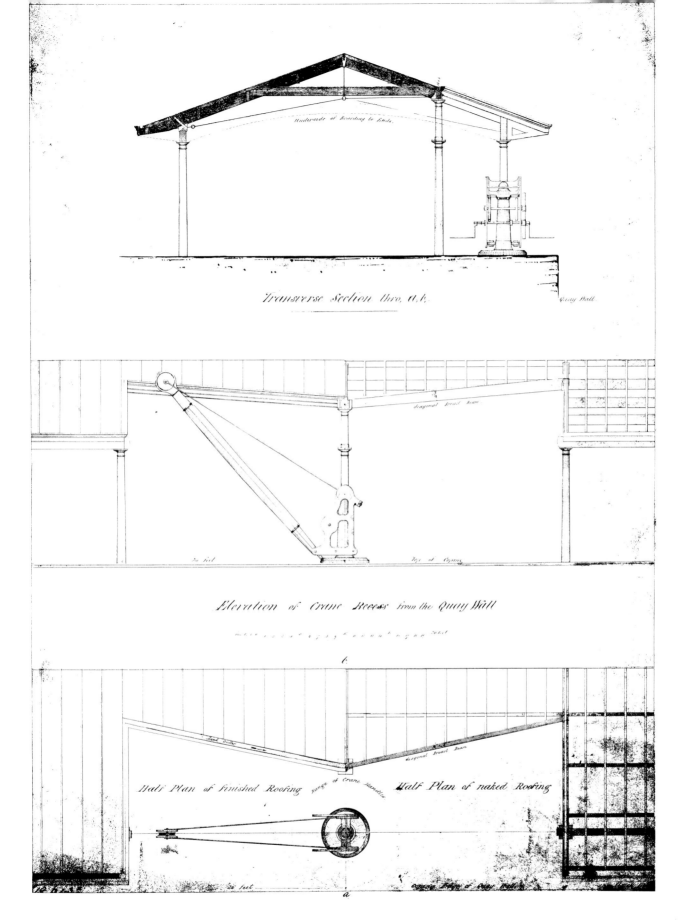

Transverse Section thro. a, b.

Quay Wall.

Elevation of Crane Recess from the Quay Wall

Half Plan of finished Roofing   Half Plan of naked Roofing

installation is shown in figure 93.[5] The arrangement is the equivalent, for the transit shed, of the tall, deep, crane bays that had made their appearance in the Albert Dock warehouses of 1843–49, and illustrates well the kind of compromise that became increasingly necessary as traditional dockside facilities required adaption to the requirements of modern handling devices. In a transit shed of 1872 on the north-east side of Queen's Dock, three of the five dockside columns also served as crane posts, which called for reinforcement of foundations and for a stronger roof construction in order to resist the movement on the columns.[6] Columns were often cast with an annulus for a crane seating, but there is no evidence that sheds incorporating such columns were normally reinforced otherwise. Where overhead travelling cranes were installed, as in the Toxteth Dock mahogany shed of 1851, masonry or timber piers were normally built to carry the rails.

94 Double storey sheds, King's Docks Nos 1 and 2, 1906. Section.

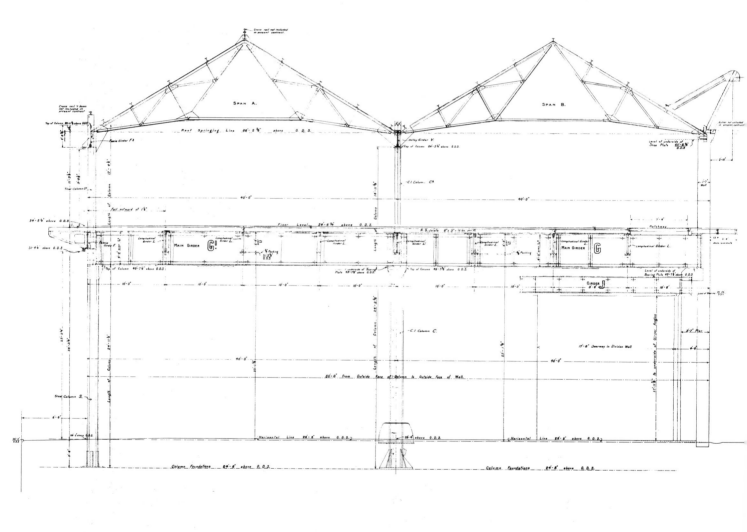

LIVERPOOL DOCKS.

CROSS SECTION OF DOUBLE STOREY SHEDS. 80 FT WIDE.

The first large double-storey transit sheds were built by Lyster in the early 1880s, along the east quay of Harrington Dock. In their construction, partially of steel, as well as in their form they marked a fresh stage of development. They retained cast-iron internal columns and brick external walls, but floors were carried on built-up steel plate girders, while roofs were also of steel and built up of rivetted angles and rolled joists. At Harrington Dock brick piers at ground level and rivetted steel columns on the first floor took the place of the earlier cast-iron columns.

95 Transit sheds, 1906, between King's and Queen's Docks.

Designed to receive cargoes discharged as fast as ship-board steam winches could handle them, these Harrington Dock sheds had continuous quayside openings on the first floor with steel sliding doors and irregularly spaced single and double doors with cast-iron windows in the walls between at quay level; on the road side were loading bays to the first floor, and double doors and windows to the ground floor.

The transit sheds on the west sides of Toxteth and of Harrington Docks were both brick-built, single-storey, double-span sheds with timber and steel composite roof trusses, and intended primarily to receive goods by road or rail for export. They featured continuous openings on the dock side and large arched entrances on the roadside. Cross walls were carried up above roof level to form a coped parapet to resist the spread of fire. All major new transit sheds built under the provisions of the 1898 Southern Works Act at Brunswick, King's and Queen's Docks were modelled on these examples already built at Harrington and Toxteth Docks, the differences between them being limited to details of column sections,

fireproofing, disposition of openings and types of cargo handling machinery. Figure 94 illustrates a shed of this type.[7]

All dockside buildings were liable to damage from the collision of vehicles and of carelessly handled cargo; the 1818 Queen's Dock shed had collapsed after a lorry collided with one of its iron columns in 1868. An early precaution was to dispense with downspouts and to channel rainwater down through columns, a system which continued to be used into the 20th century. Later on the columns themselves were afforded a measure of protection by wheel guards around their bases. Hartley, in particular, used granite dressings on buildings at potential collision and wear points, and loading bays were often provided with iron or steel sills and heads as well.

96 Interior of double storey transit shed King's Dock, 1982.

Warehouses

Although the Corporation owned nearly all the land around the dock basins, its development, on building leases, was left to private individuals. The areas around Nova Scotia, Salthouse Dock and King's and Queen's Docks were built upon in a haphazard manner from the beginning, with buildings that included multi-storey warehouses. Typical of this kind of building, though built on the Duke of Bridgewater's land rather than the Corporation's, was an eight-storey brick warehouse some 93ft long by 45ft deep (and probably shown in the distance in the photograph of Salthouse Dock at figure 13) put up at the north-east corner of Duke's Dock between 1780 and 1783. This warehouse is thought to have been of conventional construction, as were the thirteen-storey Goree warehouses built by the Corporation in 1793 on the

east side of George's Dock. The great height of these warehouses was apparently not exclusive by local standards; Aiken in 1795 wrote:

'On the sides of the docks are warehouses of uncommon size and strength, far surpassing in these respects the warehouses of London. To their different floors, often ten or eleven in number, goods are carried up with great facility.'[8]

These first Goree warehouses were destroyed by fire in 1802 and rebuilt, probably to the original design, six storeys high in 1810. It is possible that the Corporation Surveyor, John Foster, was responsible for designing these warehouses which were used as a model for Liverpool warehouses erected on Corporation land for the next fifty years. In the hope of regularizing building on the waterfront, clauses included in Corporation leases governed height, building lines, the duration and materials of construction and the provision of arcades at ground level for the protection of pedestrians. The Goree arcade (figure 97) survived along with the warehouses until destroyed by enemy action during the Second World War, but it remained the exception rather than the rule of late

97 1810 Goree Warehouses, photographed in 1942 after war damage.

98 Duke's Grain Warehouse, part north elevation.

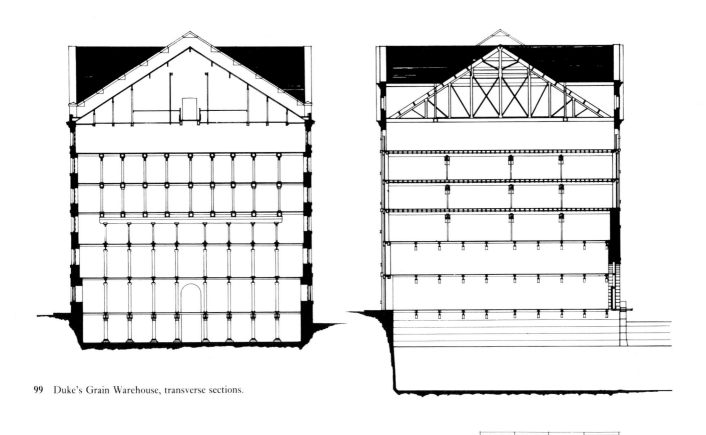

99 Duke's Grain Warehouse, transverse sections.

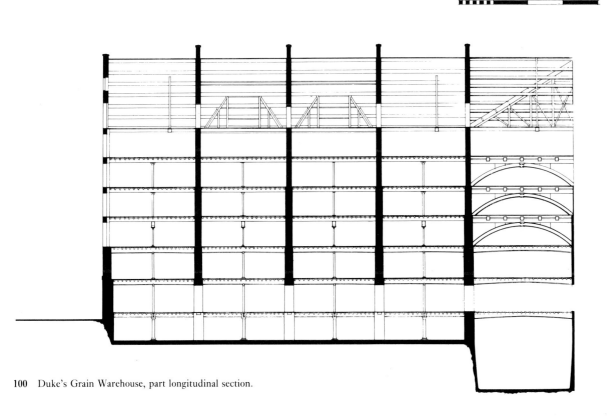

100 Duke's Grain Warehouse, part longitudinal section.

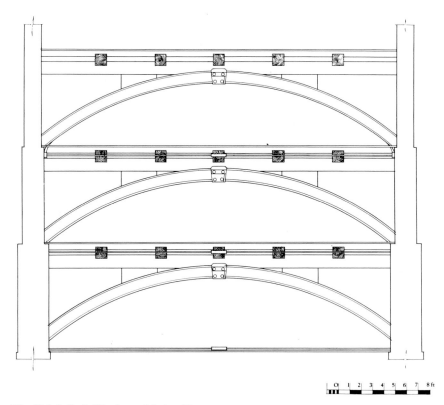

101   Duke's Grain Warehouse, 'elephant' beams.

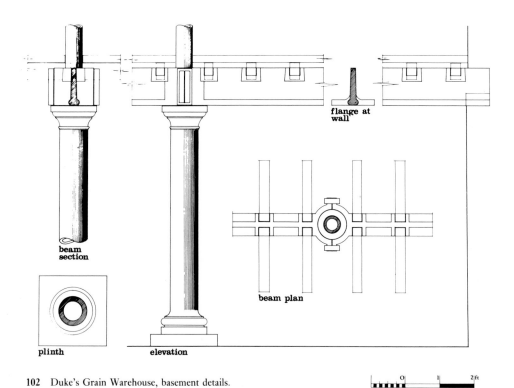

flange at
wall

beam
section

plinth   elevation

beam plan

102   Duke's Grain Warehouse, basement details.

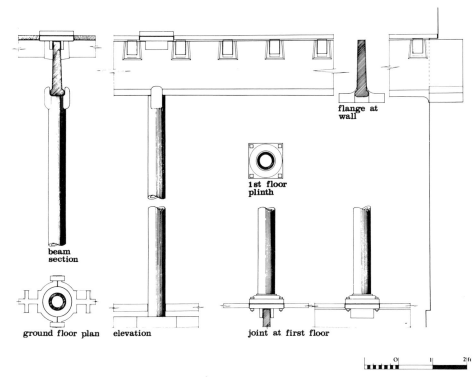

flange at
wall

1st floor
plinth

beam
section

ground floor plan   elevation   joint at first floor

O   1   2|ft

103   Duke's Grain Warehouse, details, ground and first floor.

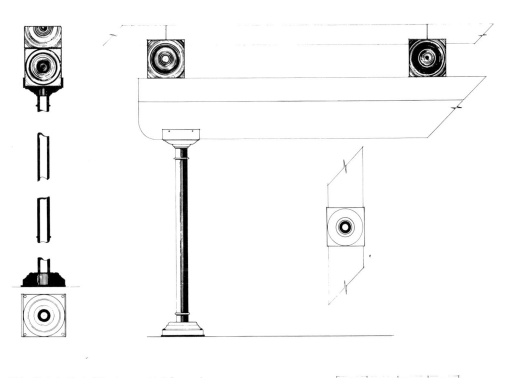

104   Duke's Grain Warehouse, third floor columns.

18th and early 19th century dockside building. Complaints recorded about the additional expense of erecting arcades seem to explain developers' reluctance to build warehouses incorporating a feature which had no direct commercial value.

The grain warehouse at Duke's Dock, erected in 1811 and now known primarily from detailed drawings of it made prior to its demolition in 1960,[9] incorporated a substantial amount of iron in its construction besides other features that make the structure remarkable. It was divided by masonry walls into ten bays, of which the central two spanned a pair of barge holes for the discharge of cargoes under cover directly into the warehouse. Warehouses which made provision for the direct discharge of goods from boats were commonplace on canals, but they never became the norm in the Liverpool docks. The barge holes were spanned on the three lower floors by cast-iron beams of I section, and on the upper three floors by so-called 'elephant beams', cast-iron arches spreading the load of the floors they carried on to the masonry walls of the bay division. The outer bays, the four either side of the barge holes, had each a line of cast-iron columns from front to back. In the basement and two lower floors, these carried iron beams and probably wooden joists. On these

105   1811 Tobacco Warehouse, west side King's Dock. Plan and section showing extensions.

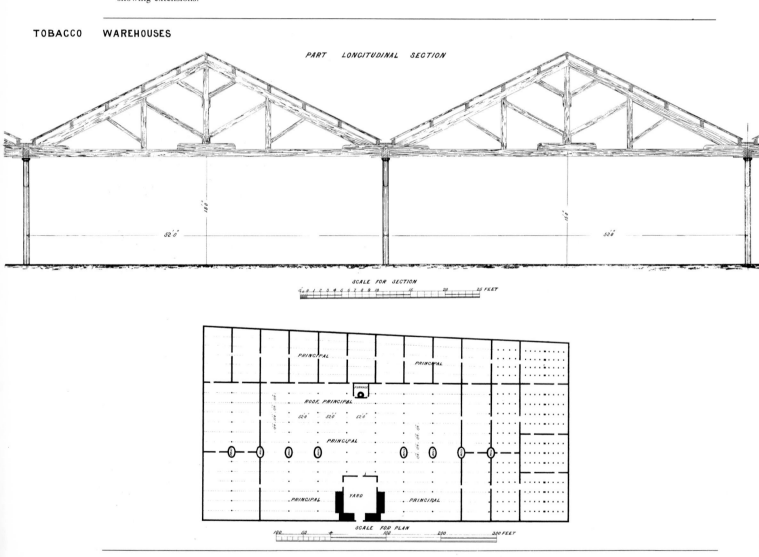

106 Albert Dock, looking south-west from the east quay, 1982.

end bays at each of the north and south ends of the warehouse, the entire internal space was open. The roof was a king-post truss of conventional form, trusses spanning 52ft with bays of 17ft, and carried on columns probably of iron. The only concession to the great span of the roof was the provision of a pad at the base of the king post to spread the load above the tie, and similar reinforcement above the columns beneath the valleys. The warehouse was remarkable for its similarity in plan to the tobacco warehouse built off the Western Dock, London Dock, in 1814, which had bays 53ft by 18ft. The reason for this similarity must be connected with the size of hogsheads of tobacco or the method of calculating duty on them in bond, though the precise explanation has not appeared. The construction of the London warehouse was in other respects very different from that of the Liverpool example. The Liverpool warehouse is illustrated at figure 105.[10]

108 Basement, Albert Warehouses. Longitudinal view, 1982.

107 Basement, Albert Warehouses. Transverse view, 1982.

lower floors, there were eight columns in each rank, but on the upper floors their number was increased to nine, and a system of additional beams on the second floor served to redistribute the weight of the upper rank of columns on to the lower. The section at figure 99 makes clear this odd arrangement, whose purpose is far from obvious and which in any event will have introduced constructional difficulties that must have outweighed any theoretical advantage to be gained from it. The building seems to represent a stage in the development of the iron-framed warehouse in which the potential of the material was as yet imperfectly understood.

More conventional in construction, though not in overall form, was the tobacco warehouse built by the Corporation on the west side of the King's Dock, between 1811 and 1814, to supplement and eventually replace the earlier warehouse on the eastern side. This was a single storey building covering an area some 577ft × 241ft, with classical detail to the outer walls and a formal entrance into a 60ft square internal courtyard. Apart from the two

109 Quay level, Albert Warehouses, 1982.

111 Interior. Roof level, Albert Warehouses, 1982.

110 Detail of junction of column, transverse beam and truss, Albert Warehouses, 1982.

The Dock Trustees' first dock warehouses were opened around the Albert Dock from 1846. As originally constructed, these brick and iron buildings surrounded the dock and were interconnected at basement level except where the north and east dock passages intervened. From ground level the warehouses rose in five separate stacks to five storeys above the quay; above-ground infill of the gaps between stacks in the south east and south west angles of the dock, and the construction of mezzanines between the quay and first floors slightly altered this overall pattern. On plan, the warehouses fronted the dock on one side and a roadway on the other; on the roadside large loading bays were incorporated at varying intervals. Although built up of modules about 18ft by 12ft, the

warehouses also varied in layout and number of bays on the roadside of the spine walls.

The walls are of brick, diminishing from 4ft at ground level to 2ft at fourth floor level, reducing by half a brick in each floor. Internal spine and cross walls reduce similarly in thickness, and rise through the roof to form fire resisting parapets. The dockside elevation comprises lines of cast iron, Greek Doric columns at the edge of the quay behind which the warehouses were originally open on the ground floor; at the rear the masonry wall is pierced by cart openings and other doors. This open elevation is broken at intervals above the colonnade by a broad, eliptical arch which formed a bay for the operation of the crane fixed to one of the quayside columns.

In the foundations of the north-east and south-east stacks of the warehouse, inverted arches extend lengthwise from column to column of the basement, and from column to column of the quayside elevation within the dock walls. (This would appear to have been a modification to the original form of foundation proposed by Hartley, and incorporated at the urging of Hardwick.) A cast-iron plate beneath each basement column sheds the load on to the springing of the inverted arches. In the other stacks, the buildings bear on piles (see p108). The basement itself comprises brick or stone barrel vaults carried on iron columns, running axially the length of the warehouses and springing from cambered iron beams spanning the columns.

Above basement level, the internal structure comprises iron columns and beams carrying jack arches. Superimposed columns are connected by a socket and spigot, and the beams are an inverted-Y or -V section. The layout of these arches is such that the central bays are spanned laterally, and are buttressed by ranks of axial arches in the outer bays. The thrust of the central bays is further resisted by iron ties at 4 or 5 foot intervals, strained between pairs of beams and staggered alternately to allow for the fixing of their ends. In addition, further iron ties pass from the front to the back of the building within the masonry of the floors above the arches. Skewback beams are incorporated into the outer walls to provide a bearing for the jack arches and for the beams that carry them. Bond bars 3in or 4in wide and a $\frac{1}{4}$in to $\frac{3}{4}$in thick are introduced within the walls to resist any tendency to uneven settlement, though it is doubtful whether, in view of the great mass of the buildings, they would have provided effective stiffening had any serious settlement threatened.

The roof of the Albert Dock warehouses is of wrought iron covered in sheets of galvanized iron, and hidden behind a parapet. Trusses comprise T-section top chords with a two-part tie rod passing through the eyes of hangers which are bolted on to alternate sides of the vertical web of the upper chord. The hipped sections of

112   Albert Warehouses, roof, 1982.

the roof are constructed of incomplete or modified trusses in which elements have been omitted, cut back or bent. The span of the trusses varies, however. It seems likely that the adoption of an essentially simple form of roof

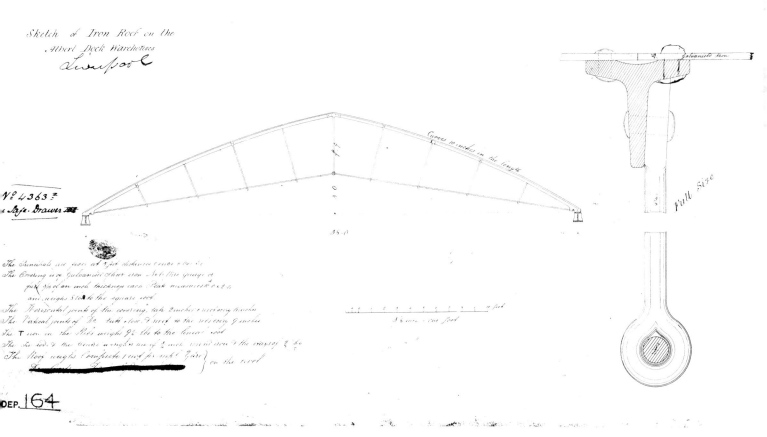

Structure of the Albert Dock warehouses

Key

1   Galvanised wrought iron slates, 6ft × 2ft 6ins × $\frac{1}{4}$in, riveted together and to the trusses.
2   Wrought iron roof trusses, at 5ft centres, spanning up to 50ft; top chord 'T' section, $2\frac{3}{8}$ins × $3\frac{1}{8}$ins, bottom tie and struts $\frac{3}{4}$in in diameter. There is no cross-bracing.
3   Stone upstand, 1ft 2ins thick.
4   Lead lined secret gutter.
5   Stone cornice.
6   Water cistern.
7   External brick walls, 3ft 2ins thick from basement to first floor; reducing by $\frac{1}{2}$-brick thickness at 1st, 2nd, 3rd and 4th floors to 1ft 7ins thick on the 4th floor.
8   Staircase wall, 2ft 6ins thick.
9   Stone stair treads cantilevered from walls.
10   Wrought iron balustrade.
11   Brick pier.
12   Floor tiles, $1\frac{1}{2}$ins thick.
13   Mortar bed, $\frac{3}{4}$in thick.
14   Broken brick, concrete and ash fill.
15   Brick arch, $4\frac{1}{2}$ins thick, spanning 11–12ft between inverted 'Y' beams.
16   Soffit of arch.
17   Base of brick arch and edge of 'Y' beam.
18   Wrought iron tie bar, $1\frac{1}{2}$ins diameter, at approximately 5ft centres, spanning between inverted 'Y' beams and angled plate.
19   Wrought iron main tie bar, $2\frac{1}{4}$ins diameter, adjacent to columns, within floor thickness spanning between external walls.
20   Third floor cast-iron column, maximum diameter $8\frac{3}{4}$ins, thickness 1in, floor to head height 8ft 11ins.
21   Second floor cast-iron column, maximum diameter $9\frac{1}{2}$ins, thickness 1in, floor to head height 9ft 11ins.
22   First floor cast-iron column, maximum diameter $10\frac{3}{4}$ins, thickness 1in, floor to head height 9ft 11ins.
23   Quay level mezzanine column, diameter 1ft $0\frac{1}{4}$in, thickness $1\frac{3}{4}$ins, quay to underside first floor height 15ft 7ins.
24   Basement cast-iron columns, maximum diameter 1ft 2ins, thickness $2\frac{1}{4}$ins, height 5ft 5ins.
25   External dock side cast-iron column, maximum diameter 4ft, thickness 1in, height 15ft 7ins.
26   Internal cast-iron column behind main arch, maximum diameter 2ft 4ins, thickness $1\frac{1}{4}$ins, height 15ft 7ins.
27   Brick arch, $13\frac{1}{2}$ins thick, spanning 11–12ft between inverted 'Y' beams.
28   Broken brick concrete.
29   Ash fill.
30   Sandstone masonry.
31   Cast-iron collar.
32   Circular sandstone column base.
33   Three course brickwork.
34   Triangular sandstone pile cap.
35   Beech timber piles, 4 per column base, diameter 1ft to 1ft 3ins, length between 26ft and 31ft.
36   Brick spine wall, 3ft 2ins thick up to 1st floor, reducing by $\frac{1}{2}$-brick thickness at 1st, 2nd, 3rd and 4th floors to 1ft 7ins on 4th floor.
37   Rectangular masonry pier, 3ft 2ins × 4ft 6ins.
38   Brick wall, 1ft 6ins thick, enclosing main dock basin side arch recess.
39   Main arch.
40   Floor trap with cast iron sides.
41   Hoist doors.
42   Basement cast iron inverted 'Y' beam, maximum size at mid-span 2ft 1in × 1ft 7ins and $1\frac{1}{4}$ins thick with $1\frac{1}{4}$ins thick webs at 3ft 6ins centres, spanning 17ft 9ins between columns.
43   Main cast iron inverted 'Y' beam, maximum size 1ft $0\frac{1}{8}$in × 1ft $6\frac{1}{2}$ins and $1\frac{1}{4}$ins thick with webs and thickening at the position of tie bars and spanning 17ft 9ins between columns.
44   Secondary cast iron inverted 'Y' beam, maximum size at mid-span $9\frac{1}{2}$ins × 1ft $1\frac{1}{4}$ins and $1\frac{1}{4}$ins thick, spanning 16ft between columns and dock side external wall.
45   Secondary cast iron inverted 'V' beam, maximum size at mid-span $9\frac{1}{2}$ins × $8\frac{3}{8}$ins and $1\frac{1}{4}$ins thick, with tie rod passing through beam invert and spanning 16ft between main inverted 'Y' beam and dock side external wall.
46   Cast iron skewback angle wall plate, 9ins × $10\frac{3}{4}$ins and 1in thick.
47   Cast iron beam spanning 18ft 10ins between dock side larger diameter external columns, maximum size at mid-span 3ft 2ins × $10\frac{1}{4}$ins out of $1\frac{1}{2}$ins thick sections.
48   Cast iron inverted 'T' beam supporting wall enclosing dock basin side arch recess, 1ft 7ins × $10\frac{1}{2}$ins × $1\frac{1}{2}$ins thick.
49   Cast iron bond bar.
50   Wrought iron tie bars between secondary inverted 'Y' and 'V' beams and angle plate.

Notes

A   Internal columns are joined one above another with spigot and socket joints.
B   Main inverted 'Y' beams bear on to lead sheet on column heads and are shaped to fit around columns without fixings.
C   Secondary inverted 'Y' beams are shaped to fit around column heads without fixings.
D   Secondary inverted 'V' beams are shaped to fit main inverted 'Y' beams and skew back angle wall plates without fixings.
E   Tie rods to main inverted 'Y' beams are staggered and fixed in beams with wedges.
F   Roof trusses are built into walls and rest on an iron wall plate without fixings.
G   Brick arches are stiffened at main inverted 'Y' beam support with brickwork ribs.

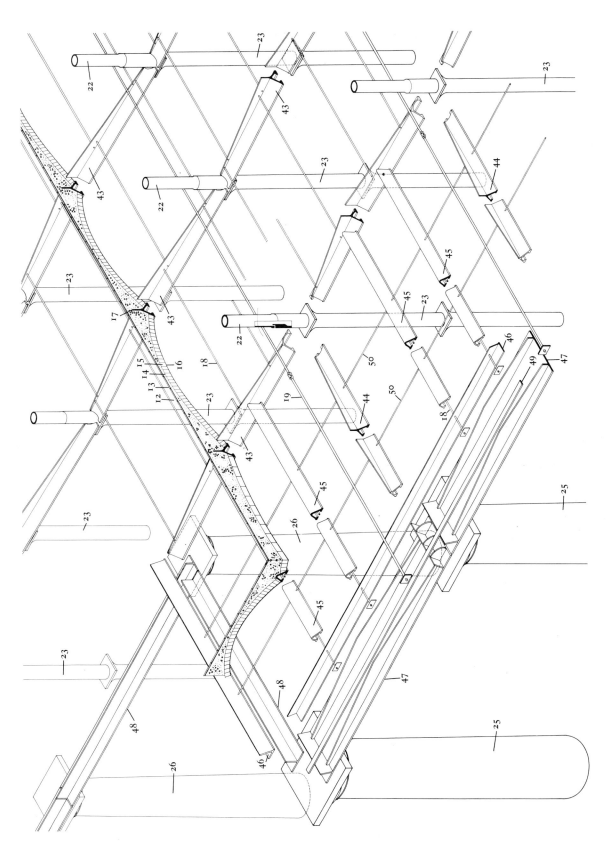

Isometric projection of structural elements

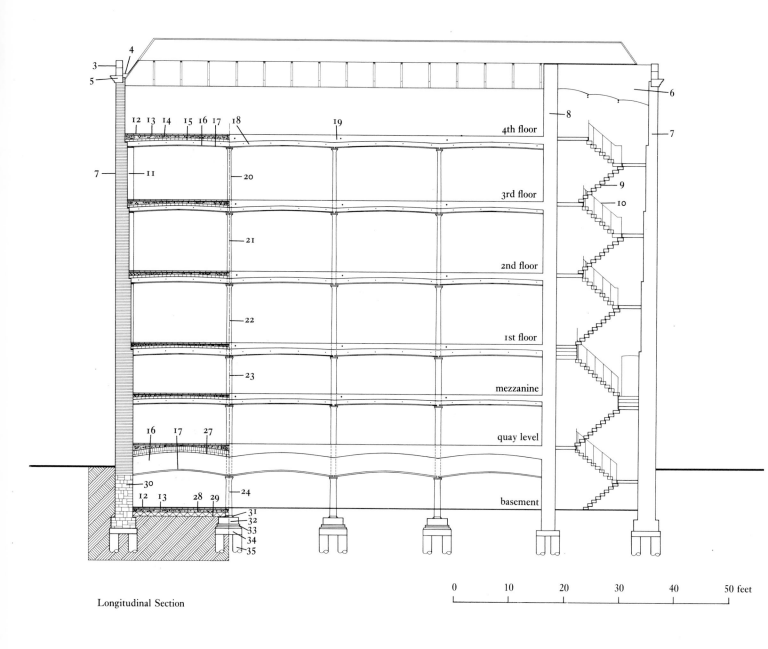

Longitudinal Section

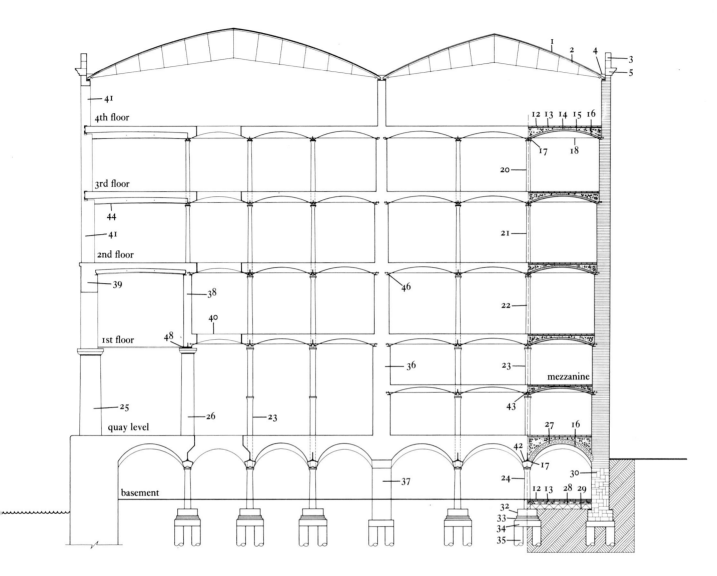

4th floor

3rd floor

2nd floor

1st floor

quay level

basement

mezzanine

Transverse Section

truss that could readily be modified may have been prompted by the necessity of varying the bays with slight irregularities of the site; nevertheless the frequent changes in the roof's alignment seem to introduce a further and perhaps needless factor making difficult the standardization of parts.

The iron sheets to the roof are generally 10ft by 2ft 6in, and $\frac{3}{16}$in thick. They are supported by trusses at 5ft centres but fixed at their edges only. Joints are filled with putty, and staggered. Sheets of iron are butt jointed and rivetted where they meet at a truss, lapped and rivetted where they meet elsewhere. Gutters are formed in the iron sheets, and at parapets lead flashing covers the junction between roof covering and masonry. Special iron sheets are laid over stair wells, where they serve not only to cover the well but also to form open water cisterns, filled from the valley gutters and discharging by down pipes. These serve to flush closets in cast iron cubicles bolted into the corners of the cart bays on the landward elevations.

The Wapping Dock warehouse repeats many of the features of the Albert Dock warehouses: the construction of the intermediate floors at the Wapping warehouse is almost identical. The basement storey, however, is arranged differently in that brick piers encasing cruciform iron cores take the place of the cylindrical iron columns at Albert Dock, and the vaults of the basement are all turned in brick rather than in stone. The quayside columns are slightly splayed at the base, and form a less elegant profile. The overall layout differs somewhat, in that the rear elevation has no cart recesses but opens on to a cart way the length of the building and which appears from the first to have been provided with a line of railway. Within the building also is a railway line, entering it at either end.

The roof is not dissimilar to that of the Albert Dock warehouses, differing mainly in the method of fixing its main elements (the two are illustrated in figures 111 and 117), and in its covering which is of wood rather than galvanized iron. It is possible that the heat of the upper storey in summer, beneath the iron roof, was too great a disadvantage to set against its fire resistance.

The irregularities in the roof of the Albert Dock warehouses have already been remarked upon. It is equally remarkable of the Wapping Warehouse how little duplication of elements there is; how, given the opportunity to design a building whose uniformity could make possible the maximum standardization of parts, Hartley – who cannot have been unaware of the advantages in trouble and expense in reducing the variety

of parts – deliberately ignored it. The forms of beams to the roof, illustrated in figure 117, show this well: how by spacing internal columns at a distance that was dissonant from the spacing of the roof trusses, a different casting was required for each of the beams that rested on the former and carried the latter. Figure 119[11] illustrates the range of door sills and door heads employed in the Wapping Dock warehouses. It is difficult to know whether this variety represents Hartley's search for the most mechanically satisfactory solution, or whether as with his architecture it is a deliberate mannerism: a sort of architectural contrariness. (There are 15 different types of window in the north stack of the Albert Dock warehouses alone.)

114 Basement, Wapping Warehouse, transverse view, 1982.

115 Basement, Wapping Warehouse, longitudinal view, 1982.

In 1867 Lyster proposed to build a series of warehouses, along the east quays of Coburg and Queen's Docks, which apart from the fact that they were to have had transit sheds along their westward sides, were very like the Wapping and Albert Dock warehouses in general concept. By that time, however, the increasing size of ships and packages of cargoes, the increasing mechanization of unloading equipment and the extension on the docks of railways for the rapid removal of goods from the quays were making the provision of dockside warehouses not only unnecessary but also undesirable. Quay room was needed for the removal of cargo, not for its long-term storage, and no more general warehouses were built in the South Docks. Subsequent warehousing in the docks was limited to such specialized developments as Lyster's huge tobacco warehouse opened in Stanley Dock in 1900 and the great granaries of the early 20th century.

1 Drawing 178/2/1; 178/3/27, MDHS microfiche
2 181/4/1, MDHS microfiche
3 179/29/26/2a, MDHS microfiche
4 324/D96, MDHS microfiche
5 164/6, MDHS microfiche
6 178/3/30–32, MDHS microfiche
7 18681, MDHS microfiche
8 Aitken, 1795, 142
9 Measured and drawn by John Cottam and J. H. G. Williams, Liverpool University School of Architecture, 1959
10 179/3/2 MDHS microfiche
11 Folio, Drawer 285, MCM, MDHB, Maritime House

118 Detail of junction of column, transverse beam and truss, Wapping Warehouse, 1982.

116 Ground floor, Wapping Warehouse, 1982.

117 Interior Roof level, Wapping Warehouse, 1982.

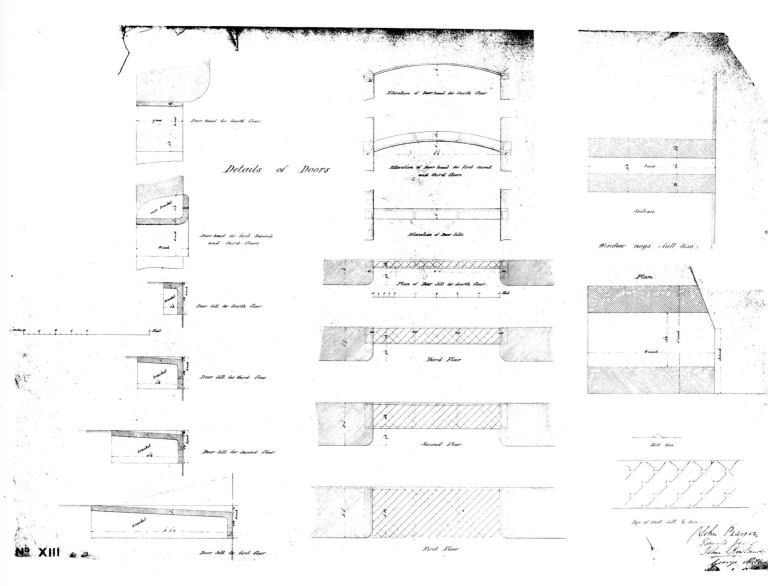

119 Wapping Warehouse, *c*1855, details of doors.

Dock architecture

The landscape of the docks has greatly changed over the last 20 years. Far more buildings have been demolished since the Second World War than were destroyed during its course. The great majority of the buildings in the docks, however, have been structures of little or no architectural pretension: sheds and warehouses whose principal constructional claims to interest have been described already. Early sheds doubtless had wooden columns, though none survived. In the 19th century, iron columns were normal, generally with a slight taper and a capital at the head; their forms made some slight concession to classical precedent but were primarily determined by the nature of the material and the function of the member. Warehouses were for the most part buildings of a type that, by 1800, was widespread: masonry walled, with a timber internal structure and with plain openings for hoists and windows arranged on a regular and functional grid.

The Corporation, perhaps at the instance of the elder John Foster (see p96) tried to regularize warehouse building. The Goree warehouses, destroyed in 1942, were the only substantial evidence for Foster's success, though some similarly arcaded but isolated warehouses close to the docks appear in 19th-century views. The arcades of the Goree warehouses (known as the 'Goree Piazzas') comprised arches, alternately large and small, and gave on to a covered walk with shops and offices behind. The arcade appears to have been of stone, with curious incised rustication.

Few other early warehouses had any architectural pretensions. The tobacco warehouse of 1792 at the King's Dock, however, had a two-storey facade with slightly projecting centre and end bays on the west front, each forming a rusticated centrepiece flanked by plain walls with bulls-eye windows in the upper part. There was a central pediment and a small cupola, the whole (which appears in figure 26) forming an extraordinarily conservative design for the date. If the elder Foster was its architect this attribution lacks documentary support.

The most striking architecture in the docks is that of Jesse Hartley. Hartley arrived in Liverpool with his architectural style already partly formed, perhaps by his own apprenticeship as a stonemason and by his association with William Atkinson whose work tended to a heavy-handed mediaevalism. Hartley's own earliest Liverpool work is loosely, however broadly, classical rather than mediaeval. A design of his for a dockmaster's house at Brunswick Dock in 1831 is circular at ground floor level but octagonal above, a mannerism already giving a foretaste of the idiosyncrasy of his later work. The architecture of E. B. Lamb provides perhaps the closest well-known parallel to Hartley's in his similarly free use of precedent and his deliberate coarsening of detail. The origins of the style of both are pre-Victorian; Hartley, though, achieved by the 1850s a symbolic appropriateness of form and of detail that would have been apparent to contemporaries. While there has been a tendency in the present century to condemn Hartley's medieval clock towers and pumping stations and to praise the functional monumentality of his warehouses, it is worth recalling that the near-contemporary James Picton, who had been writing about Liverpool buildings since the 1850s, singled out the latter for criticism on account of their lack of architectural ornament.

Essentially, the fortress style developed by Hartley for major building in the docks seems to symbolize defiance of the elements and expresses the security of the closed dock system. (The former may be paralleled elsewhere, as in the Tower of Refuge in Douglas harbour, IOM; the latter is obvious, as it was to the many designers of castellated gaols in the 1840s and 1850s.) The most striking examples of the style are (or were) in the North Docks, but the accumulator tower, engine house and gate-keeper's house at Wapping are the outstanding examples in the south. The accumulator tower is battlemented and machicolated while the engine house has random masonry walls composed of massive granite blocks; both are expressive not only of the safety of the harbour but also of the power of the machinery within and of the strength of the buildings necessary to contain it. The gate keeper's hut expresses the security of the system by its massive construction, by its tiny loop-hole windows and even by its internal, vaulted roof. That all these details are exaggerated far beyond any medieval precedent merely heightens the rhetorical effect. The massive granite of which the buildings and dock walls are constructed was equally expressive of permanence and strength, while at the same time it was functional in that it provided bonding for smaller blocks, resistance to abrasion in dock walls, and sound arrises for dock walls and for manholes

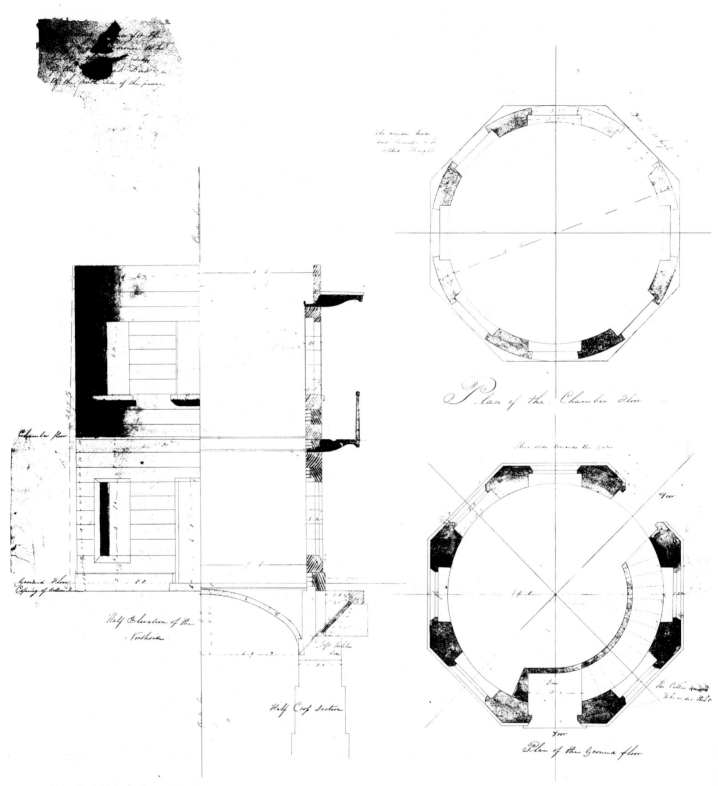

Plan of the Chamber Floor

This side towards the gate

Plan of the Ground floor

Chamber floor

Ground Floor
Copying of bottom store

Half Elevation of the
Northside

Half Cross Section

120 Dock Master's House, 1831, Brunswick Dock. Plans, half section, half elevation.

121 Gate piers, south-east corner of boundary wall, Albert Warehouses.

123 Canning Island gatemen's hut, 1982.

122 Wapping Dock, gatekeeper's hut, 1982.

124 Masonry patterns on Canning Island.

and hatches in the surface of the quay. The random masonry of small structures used up smaller fragments of granite, which was for the most part shipped in large blocks and dressed on site.

Certain forms adopted by Hartley were already established in Liverpool. The polygonal gatemen's huts that remain at the Canning river entrance, formerly with counterparts at Brunswick, Herculaneum, Queen's and Duke's Dock river entrances, were the adaptation of a hut of similar plan that had been the approved form for such buildings for many years. It allows observation through a full circle. The deep eaves were functional in providing protection from rain and from glare, and lent themselves to construction out of the huge blocks of masonry that Hartley preferred. The two-storeyed Brunswick dock-master's house was one of a number of houses broadly similar but, like the gatemen's huts, different in detail; it was probably circular for a similar reason. The dock master was expected to be on duty 24 hours a day and the provision of a chamber floor probably enabled him to take some rest, knowing that he could, when roused, immediately see what was going on.

125
Dock Traffic Office,
Albert Dock, 1982

The house was probably not intended for permanent occupation; it has few amenities. The provision of residential accommodation for Dock Trust employees had been debated in the early 1840s when the Trust doubtless felt it could better ensure constant attendance of its employees round the clock by building them houses close to their place of work. Drawings for employees' houses of the 1850s, however, show them as unremarkable in any way, and entirely typical of housing of their class and period. As dwelling houses, they appear to have been superimposed on the docks, without any of Hartley's fortress-like treatment which would surely have been inappropriate.

126 Superintendent's House, 1880, Herculaneum Dock. Plans, elevations.

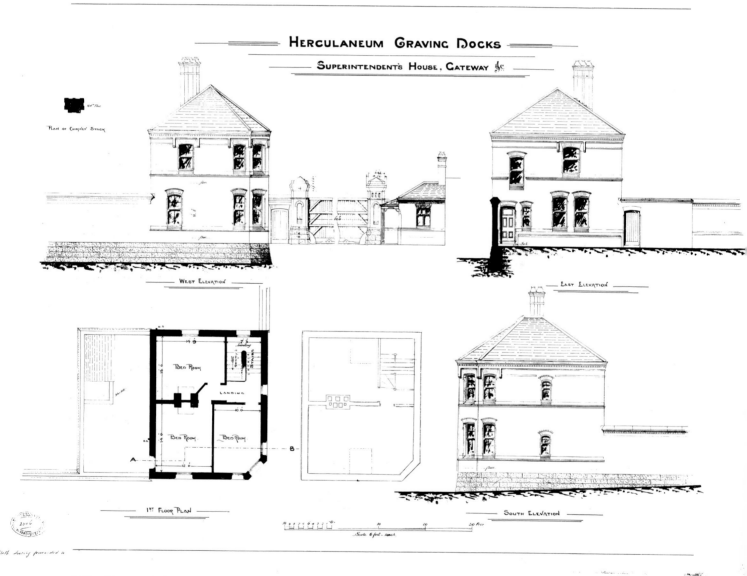

The precise division of responsibility between Hartley and Philip Hardwick over the form of the Albert Dock warehouses and of the associated structures is uncertain. Most details of their construction are almost certainly Hartley's, though Hardwick was consulted a good deal (for instance, over the detail of the substructure) at the planning stage. Early designs show the ranks of columns along the quayside but not the crane bays which, though introduced for practical purposes, articulate the otherwise monolothic façade and give a visual interest that would otherwise be lacking. The north-east block was surmounted by a classical clock tower, damaged during the Second World War and later demolished; it was both visually and structurally completely unrelated to the warehouse below. It is not known why Hardwick came to design this part of the building, since Hartley would have been perfectly capable, on existing evidence, of designing such a thing himself.

The Dock Office at the north-east corner of the Albert Dock was also designed by Hardwick; it is possible, though unlikely, that Hartley mistrusted himself in the classical manner. From the building itself, it appears that Hartley deepened the portico, strengthened the cornice between first and second floors, and subsequently built on

127   Customs Depot, 1890, Toxteth Dock. Plans, section, elevations.

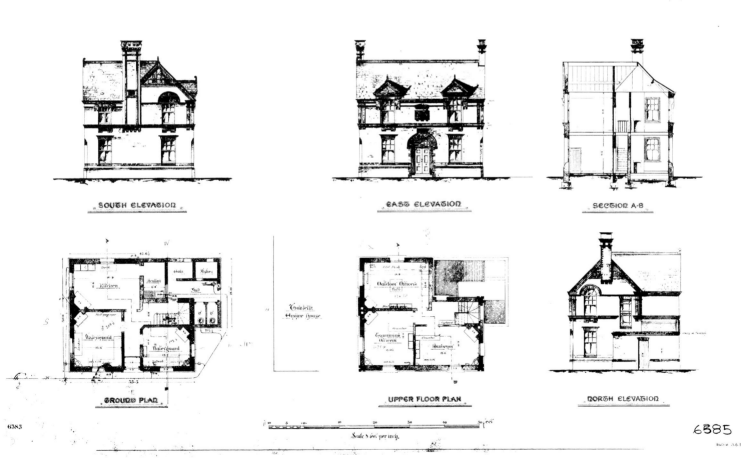

an upper (second) floor to provide residential accommodation. The whole certainly acquired a heaviness of feel absent from Hardwick's original drawing. Within, a two-storey public hall with a balcony gives on to offices at both levels.

A group of dwellings on the Albert pierhead was another joint Hartley and Hardwick construction. Hardwick designed three-storey houses for the dock master and for the chief superintendent of the warehouses, while Hartley produced accommodation for lesser staff and a dock-master's office and a cooperage. The reason for the division of work between the two is not clear. That

Hardwick should be consulted on the technical design of the warehouses was natural, given the similarity of the Liverpool scheme to that at St Katharine's Dock, but all else that he provided was within the capacity of Hartley and his staff. It is possible that Hardwick was employed simply for the prestige of his name and reputation, though it is not easy to see these as decisive influences with the cost-conscious Dock Trustees.

The architectural work of G. F. Lyster, Hartley's successor, is very much less remarkable. There is little evidence for the housing provided by the engineer's department before the 1880s, though the increase in the

128 Pilotage Buildings, 1883, Canning Half-tide Basin. Details.

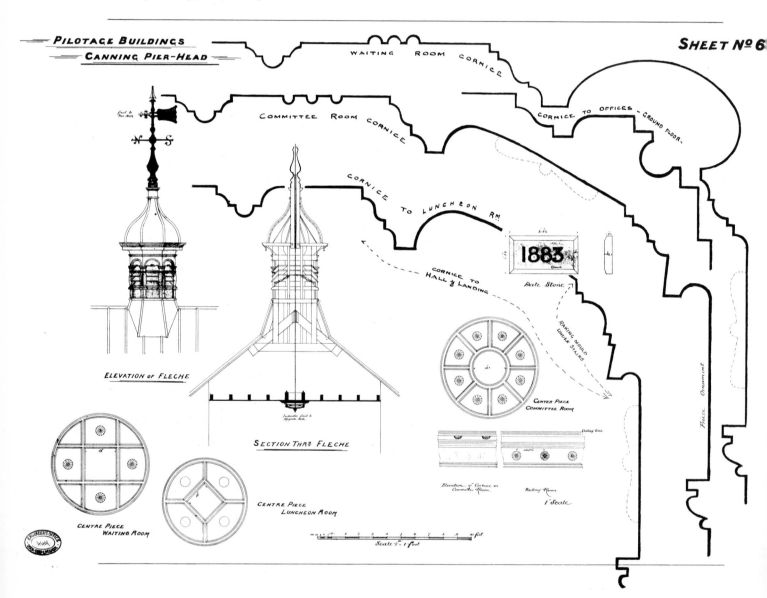

provision of accommodation for employees, static plant and offices meant that under Lyster the engineer's department was called on for considerably more architectural work than it had been under Hartley. The superintendent's house at Herculaneum of 1880 (figure 126) is an entirely straightforward brick house with terracotta dressings, not unlike the Customs depot for Toxteth Dock of ten years later (figure 127); both indicate the modest character of dock architecture of the period. The latter building, however, incorporates elements of the Queen Anne style, with the sort of detail already apparent at least as early as the Pilotage Buildings at Canning pier head of 1883 (figure 128, and visible also in a photograph at figure 30). This becomes pronounced in the Brunswick Dock dwellings of 1891 (figures 129 and 131). In these last, advantage was taken of the comparatively large scale

of the composition and of the hierarchy of housing for a greater degree of architectural display than on smaller buildings: a central block of flats for gatemen is given a central balcony and is flanked on one side by quite a commodious house for the dock master and on the other by a smaller house for the north-east pier master.

The result, however, is not very satisfactory; the tensions between a symmetrical composition and a desire to differentiate between the two flanking houses is not well resolved. Lyster probably used the Queen Anne style since its details could be applied with a minimum of expense to otherwise functional buildings; but by the time of his patronage the style had ceased to be a novelty.

Lyster's major installations received an architectural treatment that was minimal. The brick detailing of the Albert Dock pumping station of 1878, for example, is in

129 Houses for Dock Master, Dock Gatemen and Pier Master, Brunswick Dock.

RESIDENCES NORTH END OF BRUNSWICK BRANCH DOCK

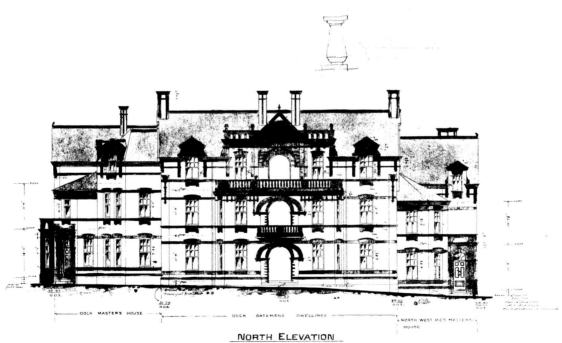

DOCK MASTERS HOUSE — DOCK GATEMENS DWELLINGS — NORTH WEST PIER MASTERS HOUSE

NORTH ELEVATION

SCALE 8 FEET PER INCH

13. 7. 91

(*left*) Hydraulic Power Centre, 1878, Albert Dock.

the vernacular of late 19th-century industrial brickwork, and the faintly machicolated chimney no different from the treatment of numerous other chimneys of the time. The pointed window to the engine house, by being incorporated into very workaday brick masonry, has entirely lost the symbolic power that mediaeval detail has in Hartley's work. Nevertheless, its preservation is valuable, providing the Albert Dock and Canning pierhead with important surviving examples of almost all the architectural styles of the docks' two major 19th-century engineers when so much else has been destroyed.

1 Picton, 1873, 1, 660

12

131 Gatemen's dwellings, Brunswick Dock, 1891.
Front elevation, detail of upper floor.

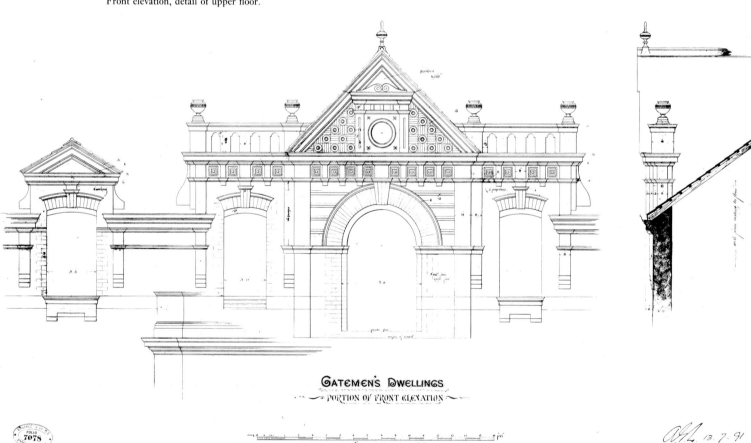

GATEMEN'S DWELLINGS
~ PORTION OF FRONT ELEVATION ~

Communications

Efficient internal communications and links with its hinterland are crucial to successful port operation. The first internal links to be built in the port of Liverpool were the roads adjoining the quays and the bridges spanning the dock entrances. These were followed by roads built inside the expanding dock estate and then by branch lines of the national railway network (from 1833) and the construction of the dock lines of railway (from 1842). Of equal significance were the canal connections, some direct to the docks and some indirect. Duke's Dock was built in 1773 as the Liverpool terminal of the Bridgewater Canal; Egerton Dock was built around 1838 as an extension of the Bridgewater enterprise; and in 1848 the Leeds and Liverpool Canal joined the east end of the new Stanley Dock. In response to the need to move people as well as goods, a horse-drawn omnibus service was initiated in 1859. The Liverpool Overhead (electric) Railway was opened in 1893, and at the peak of its operations it carried 8,000,000 passengers a year between Dingle at the south end of the dock estate and Seaforth Sands in the north.

The canal undertakers were ultimately unable to compete with the railways. The Bridgewater and Mersey & Irwell Navigation Companies' interests were allied with railway companies, bringing Duke's, Egerton and Manchester Docks within the orbits of the respective new partners. The docks and quays were also affected by developments culminating in the dominance of road haulage for internal distribution: the old narrow quays lined with transit sheds have become obsolete in an era of bulk cargoes, containers and roll-on roll-off traffic.

Roads and bridges

The quays around the Old Dock were built and used both as thoroughfares and landing wharfs. Dwellings, shops and warehouses extended to within feet of the edge of the dock, and the strip of land between these buildings and the dock was used variously for shipbuilding, trading, loading and unloading of cargo and for the passage of pedestrians and vehicles. At the seaward end of the Old Dock was a narrow wooden drawbridge which caused traffic jams even when lowered and long diversions when raised, and the impediment posed to town communications by this bridge was one of the reasons cited in favour of closing the Old Dock altogether. The other 18th-century

docks were no better served by roadways or bridges, but since Salthouse, George's, Duke's, King's and Queen's Docks were all built along the foreshore their inadequacies were not as obtrusive as they would have been in the town centre.

Safer, more convenient pedestrian ways were provided by street level arcades built beneath or along the fronts of dockside warehouses. By the end of the 18th century it had become common practice for the leases and sales of Corporation property near the docks to include covenants for the erection of arcades. These were built at the expense of the Dock Trustees and then maintained by the warehouse owners. Sometimes the arcades alone were erected: 'Warehouses have been erected on both sides of Orford Street, to the front of the dock; but the two remaining lots, adjoining Salthouse Lane, are still unbuilt, except as regards the arcades, which have been built by the Dock Trustees.'[1] Nevertheless, the 1811 Dock Act confirmed the Trustees' powers to build arcades and the practice is assumed to have continued until the mid-19th century when most of the dock estate was closed to the public.

In 1808 the Surveyor was directed to obtain plans and estimates for a cast-iron swing bridge to replace the oak drawbridge across the Queen's Dock passage.[2] Three years earlier, following a report that the principal timbers supporting the balance beams of the old bridge were considerably out of perpendicular, the bridge had been shored and by 1808 it was in a '. . . rapid state of decay'.[3] A plan was obtained from the Hull Dock Company, but it was not until 1809, after a man had been killed by the failure of one of the balance beams, that the Dock Committee authorized the Surveyor to contract with Aydon & Elwell of Bradford for the supply of an iron bridge like that at Hull. Since Aydon & Elwell had supplied ironwork for the first phase of the London Dock (1801–05) where a double-leaf iron swing bridge by Rennie was installed across the Wapping entrance lock, it is not unlikely that the bridge supplied to Liverpol was based on Rennie's design.[4] Certainly the iron swing bridges erected in Liverpool by Hartley (post 1824) were very similar to the London Dock example, and there is no evidence that he departed from an established tradition. Nor did he change the pattern subsequently. The only surviving example in the South Docks of this once pervasive type spans the Albert Dock north passage; this one was cast at the Haigh Foundry near Wigan. Earlier bridges (1820s) were cast by William Hazledine following Aydon & Elwell's failure to fulfil their contracts for bridges at George's and Prince's Docks. The Low Moor Foundry also supplied cast-iron bridges to the Trustees.

Some dock passages were provided with pedestrian bridges only, particularly after the dock estate's internal road system had begun to take shape, or where there was especially heavy traffic. In 1822 a design for a footbridge was obtained from Marc Brunel and the bridge was installed, but its features were not recorded.[5] In 1845, having been instructed to erect a 'fly' bridge over the west entrance of Canning Dock for the convenience of pedestrians with business at the Canning Graving Docks, Hartley designed a double-leaf timber and iron, stayed counterbalanced footbridge which still survives, and installed it for £200. A number of wheeled pedestrian bridges built on the same principle as ships' gangplanks were also provided at various positions on the estate throughout the 19th and early 20th centuries. Ferry passengers wanting to cross the bridges at George's Dock were particularly impatient. At tide time the bridge at the north end of the dock was to be closed five minutes before the hour and half hour; when on the 19 August, 1863, the bridge was three minutes late in closing, a complaint was lodged which elicited the following defence: the bridge was opened at 12.40pm (immediately after the first opening of the dock gates) when the dock master commenced to pass the brig *Arcaty* out; the wind was north, north-west, blowing fresh, and notwithstanding the exertions of 6 men at the vessel's winch assisted by the dock gatemen with lines to both shore capstans, the ship was not clear of the bridge until 12.58pm.[6]

The actual extent of paving on most of the dock quays and roadways is unknown, although it was apparently 1824 before the quay and street between the Goree Piazza and George's Dock were paved. In the 1820s, paving stones from Dublin at 8*s* per ton were recommended for general use, while Scotch stones of superior quality at 10*s* or 12*s* per ton were required for particular situations. With the small paving stones unfit for use on the surface, the Surveyor made hardcore for building cart roads '. . . upon the principle and manner adopted by Thomas Telford'.[7] By 1850, the internal road system on the dock estate was of a good standard, with surfaces made of large, rectangular granite setts bedded in tar and laid on hard packed sand. In the latter part of the 19th century, granite cube setts were adopted to pave the new streets or parts of the dock estate such as Harrington and Toxteth Docks

where there were wide roadways behind the transit sheds. The layout of the later warehouses and transit sheds included cartways and loading bays to facilitate inland distribution by road vehicle. Dotted about the whole dock estate were cart stands, some 21 in 1847, which could accommodate 420 carts. However, since there were said to be nearly ten times this number with business on the docks, the provision was woefully inadequate and complaints from carters and non-carters alike were numerous. Carters loaded so much cotton, for instance, that the bales projected three or four feet beyond the wheels on each side, rendering the whole dangerous to other carts and carriages and to foot passengers, especially when crossing the dock bridges.

The installation of hydraulically-operated bridges dates from the last quarter of the 19th century. The only hydraulic bascule bridge erected in the South Docks was supplied by W. G. Armstrong in 1878 for the entrance to the Brunswick Branch Dock. It failed in 1885 and no bridges of a similar type were used again. Thenceforward, hydraulic swing girder bridges were supplied either complete from the manufacturer (single-leaf bridge for Coburg–Brunswick passage, Francis Morton & Company, 1900) or made in the Coburg Dockyard and fitted with hydraulic machinery supplied by a contractor (Union–Toxteth passage, Hydraulic Engineering Company Ltd, 1889). New single-leaf hydraulic bridges were installed at the Wapping Dock – Wapping Basin and the Salthouse–Canning passages in 1962 by Morton of Garston; in 1972 they became redundant; in 1983 the Salthouse–Canning bridge was demolished to make way for a new causeway to the Albert Dock site then being re-developed.

Dock lines of railway
The attitude of the Dock Committee towards the possibility of developing a rail link between Liverpool and Manchester was summarized in their resolution of 15 March, 1825:

'That the Solicitor be directed to watch the said Bill and see that provision be made to prevent the railway being brought upon any of the dock quays; that the tunnels or sewers made by the Dock Trustees be not interfered with . . . and in the event of the promoters . . . not acceding to such provisions, that the Chairman be authorised to affix the Seal to a petition to the House of Commons against the Bill . . .'[8]

They wished to prevent the introduction of the railway upon the dock quays absolutely and without limitation. Their objections were not recorded but may have been based on fears of added congestion, on worries about ceding some operational control to another authority or perhaps on the idea that a rival service could be introduced by the Trustees themselves. It was fortunate that the railway promoters had the foresight to plan from the outset a branch goods line from Edge Hill to Wapping and a goods depot opposite the Queen's Dock. The man appointed to be Inspecting Engineer and Arbitrator for the Wapping tunnel was Jesse Hartley.

The goods line and depot were operational by 1829 and 1830 respectively, and by 1833 a line of rails had been laid from the depot across Wapping and Ironmonger Lane to the coal yard established by the railway company on the east side of King's Dock. The Dock Committee appropriated a quay berth to the Company for the use of vessels carrying cargo to and from the railway, with proviso that should the railway become an inconvenience the line should be taken up and the pavement replaced.[9] In 1835 the Committee sanctioned the laying of track from the goods station, along the east side of Queen's Dock to the timber wharf at Brunswick Dock,[10] but revoked permission four years later. In 1841 the Dock Trustees obtained an Act of Parliament to give them powers to make tramroads or railways on the dock quays.

The development of a railway network on the docks was initially inspired not by visions of more efficient cargo handling, but by the hope of accelerated dock construction. The Surveyor reported in March, 1842,[11]

133   Pedestrian arcade, Goree Warehouses, 1942.

132   Fly bridge *c*1845 across the Canning Dock entrance.

that with the exception of the excavations, the works at Canning Dock (in conjunction with the building of Albert Dock) had made satisfactory progress; the excavations had been held up by inclement weather which had prevented the flats from carrying away the spoil as quickly as was hoped. In consequence, early in April the Surveyor suggested that a railway be laid from Salthouse Dock to the north of Beacon's Gutter,[12] and by the end of the month he had accepted the tender of the Chillington Iron Works to supply 250 to 300 tons of iron rails at £7 10s 0d per ton, 25 tons to be delivered within 10 days and the remainder in daily deliveries within a fortnight. In July the Trustees paid their first compensation to the owner of a horse which had caught its foot in the new railway. Two years later the Trustees applied to the Commissioners of Highways for permission to lay railways across the public streets adjoining the dock quays, and by 1851 the railway along the south division of docks (old Toxteth to Queen's) was connected to the London and North Western Railway Co depot in Wapping, complete with the necessary 'turn outs'.

An extension of the main line of dock railway was built by 1853 along the new Wapping Street from the north end of the Queen's Dock to the south end of Canning, but the use of this section was restricted for several years to the purposes of the dock works (Wapping improvements) and it was not available for the haulage of cargo. During the next twenty years a number of branch lines were laid, including track at the south-east corner of Brunswick Dock for the mahogany trade in 1852, into the Wapping Warehouse by 1857, to the east end of Duke's Dock in 1863, at Canning Dock in 1866 to connect with the 10-ton crane and at Harrington Dock in 1873 for the timber yards. The turntables and rails in Wapping Warehouse were removed in 1878–80. In addition to the goods station built originally at Wapping in 1829 by the Liverpool & Manchester Railway Co, and later absorbed by the London and North Western Railway Co, two other goods depots were developed by the Cheshire Lines Committee from 1864, on the eastern side of Sefton Street, near Brunswick Dock, and by the Lancashire and Yorkshire Railway near Canning Place.

The Port Authority was the only body allowed to lay railways on the dock estate. All track-laying, maintenance and repair were carried out by the Dock Board which was subsequently reimbursed, where appropriate, by the company on whose behalf the whole had been done. The Board was authorized under the Mersey Docks and Harbour Board (Consolidation) Act of 1858 to make reasonable charges for the use of the railways under its control. On the Liverpool side of the estate, the Board was also responsible for haulage between dock and goods station, though at Birkenhead individual railway companies operated right to the quays. The Dock Board was also responsible for the day to day working of the dock lines of railway and to this end bye-laws were adopted in 1856. All trains were horse drawn and consisted of a maximum of six wagons proceeding at no more than walking pace, with five-minute intervals between trains. Steam locomotives were not permitted on the dock lines until 1872 when the London and North Western Railway Co was given leave to draw wagons between Canada Dock goods station and the timber grounds to the north of Battery Street. In 1876 Thomas Monk, the contractor excavating at Herculaneum Dock, was permitted to use a small steam locomotive to draw wagons full of spoil to the North End, mostly during the night.[13] Locomotive drawn goods trains began to run along the South Docks in 1886, but it was not until 1895 that the use of locomotives was allowed under a bye-law.

The introduction of locomotives necessitated new rules and bye-laws, including the directives that locomotives should not exceed 3mph and that any locomotive should be preceded by a man carrying a red warning flag at a distance of not more than 15ft in front of the engine.[14] The Board was rightly concerned about the hazards of intermingling pedestrians, carts, horse-drawn trains and steam trains, but with the increase in the number of wagons allowed per train (up to 30 by 1924) pedestrians tended to be more impatient than cautious and to run across the line between the red flag bearer and the oncoming locomotive. A promoter of a scheme for an elevated railway said that '. . . the dock railway had been constructed for the special purpose of forwarding the designs of the Dock Committee, and removing the earthwork from one part to another . . . it was a most serious obstruction to the thoroughfares, and tended to retard, rather than to promote business'.[15]

As late as 1885 it was remarked that '. . . lines on the quays are not extensively used owing to the great proportion of carting that takes place to and from the private warehouses in the city; and therefore railway accommodation has not been largely developed'.[16] By the end of the nineteenth century, however, the principal railway on the Liverpool dock estate consisted of a double line of rails of ordinary gauge running along the whole of the eastern margin and connected, on the east side, by branches across the public highways to the stations of various railway companies, and on the west side, by branches on the estate to the docks and quays. In 1929 there were 70 miles of dock lines of railway in Liverpool. By then the Board had 20 saddle-tank locomotives, mostly built by Avonside Engineering Co Ltd of Bristol. The two locomotives used in the oil yards (Herculaneum Dock) were of the Caledonia Fireless type, built by Andrew Barclay, Sons & Co Ltd of Kilmarnock; diesel locomotives were introduced in 1930. By 1960, the Dock Board was operating 16 diesel, fireless and steam locomotives on 80 miles of track in Liverpool and on 60 miles of track in Birkenhead.

Once the absolute amount of traffic handled in the port of Liverpool had declined, and an increasing proportion of that which remained was distributed inland by road, large parts of the dock railway system became redundant. Wapping goods station and the tunnel to Edge Hill were closed in 1965. In 1971 the railway lines on the south docks were also closed and in 1980 the rails along the dock road were removed during construction of the Liverpool inner ring road. Most of the branch lines at the south end were subsequently excavated or buried during redevelopment of the old docks there.

134 Loading a train on the dock railway.

Liverpool Overhead Railway

The idea of an elevated railway was first discussed in Liverpool in 1853 when it was inspired by the frustration and delays occasioned by the volume of traffic passing along the docks. The original proposal was for a goods and passenger railway which would utilize the only remaining undeveloped open space between the docks and the city, the area above the dock railway.[17] The practical obstacles to the construction of a high-level railway for cargoes included the fact that there was no suitable way to transfer wagons and goods between quay/ground level and an elevated railway. Passengers were another matter.

The Dock Board considered building an overhead passenger railway, but later decided to lease the undertaking to the newly incorporated Liverpool Overhead Railway Co which then built and operated the railway.

The Liverpool Overhead Railway was based on an original design by the Lysters, detailed by Sir Douglas Fox and James Henry Greathead and built by the engineering firm of C. D. Fox and F. Fox on land leased to the LOR by the Dock Board. Opened in 1893 and extended in 1896, the LOR ultimately extended just over seven miles between Dingle and Seaforth Sands, with 14 intermediate stations. It ran on an iron viaduct carried on iron columns; the main, longitudinal girders were placed at 22ft centres to provide adequate space for the two lines of standard gauge dock railway to run below. The normal span between columns was 50ft, but this was altered in certain places to avoid interference with existing railway lines, roadways and gates and in many instances it was necessary to embed the columns in warehouse and boundary walls. Hydraulically operated tilting spans were installed at Langton, Sandon, and Brunswick Docks to permit the passage of high loads.

135 Iron swing bridge by the Haigh Foundry Company, *c*1845, across
north passage, Albert Dock.

In 1954 the structure of the LOR was inspected by
consultant engineers who reported that the decking should
be renewed within the next five years – at an estimated
cost of more than £2,000,000, a sum far beyond the
Company's resources.[18] The Liverpool Overhead Railway
Act 1956 relieved the Company of its statutory obligation
to operate the railway which was finally closed on the 30
December, 1956, and the cost of a workman's return fare
from Dingle to Pier Head went up overnight from 8*d* on
the railway to 1*s* on the bus.

Although the Dock Board had never operated passenger
services, it exercised stringent controls over their operation
by the LOR, largely by means of leases due for renewal
every seven years. The Board also protected its own goods
transport interests by inserting clauses in the enabling
legislation to control the weight of parcels carried on the
LOR and by blocking the Company's attempt to join the
Lancashire and Yorkshire Railway at Seaforth in order to
convey coal to Herculaneum Dock. Though the Board had
declined to build a passenger railway in the 1850s, in 1856
it did build the Liverpool High-Level Coal Railway along
the east quays of the Bramley-Moore and Wellington
Docks. The Board's failure to develop, or later rescue, the
Overhead Railway was due to its determination to restrict
its activities to the direct purposes of the docks.

1 LRO *Report of the Committee of Finance of the Town Council . . . on the
   Subject of Docks and Warehouses on the Dock Quays*, 1839, 45
2 DCM 14.iii.1808
3 Ib
4 Skempton, A. W. *Engineering in the Port of London, 1789–1808*,
   Trans Newcomen Soc, vol 50, 97, 108
5 DCM 23.viii.1822
6 MDHB Docks & Quays Sub-Committee, 26.viii.1863
7 DCM 18.viii.1824
8 DCM 15.iii.1825
9 DCM 19.iv.1834
10 DCM 2.vi.1835
11 MDHB Sub-Committee of Works, 23.iii.1842
12 Ib 2.iv.1842
13 MDHB WUP Dock line of railway, 1
14 Ib
15 Grantham, J., *Improved Plan for working the Docks*, Trans Liverpool
   Polytechnic Soc, 1853, 26
16 Vernon-Harcourt, op cit, 508
17 Grantham, op cit
18 MDHB WUP Overhead Railway v, 10.viii.1955

Appendix 1

Dates of opening and general dimensions of the principal docks in the Port of Liverpool

Note: (S) = Liverpool South Docks
      (N) = Liverpool North Docks
      (B) = Birkenhead Docks

Date of opening	Name	Original position of sill below Old Dock Sill (feet)*	Approx. original superficial area (acres)	Notes
1715	Old Dock (S)		$3\frac{1}{2}$	Old Dock Sill was the datum throughout the eighteenth and nineteenth centuries.
1753	Salthouse Dock (S)		$4\frac{3}{4}$	Original sill level not recorded; Salthouse sill deepened to 5ft below ODS in 1840.
1771	George's Dock (at George's Dock passage) (S)	4ft 6ins	5	
1773	Duke's Dock (S)	4ft 2ins	$2\frac{1}{2}$	
1785	Manchester Dock (S)		$\frac{1}{10}$	Sill 3ins above ODS
1788	King's Dock (S)	5ft	$5\frac{1}{4}$	
1796	Queen's Dock (S)	5ft	$7\frac{1}{4}$	Sill at Queen's Half-tide river entrance (1856) 6ft 9ins below ODS.
1821	Prince's Dock (N)		$11\frac{3}{4}$	
1829	Canning Dock (S)		4	
1830	Clarence Dock (N)	3ft 2ins	6	Clarence Half-tide sill was 5ft below ODS at river entrance.
1832	Brunswick Dock (at west passage) (S)	5ft 6ins	$12\frac{1}{2}$	
1832	Brunswick Half-tide Basin (S)	6ft	$1\frac{3}{4}$	
1834	Waterloo Dock (N)	7ft 8ins	$6\frac{1}{4}$	
1836	Victoria Dock (N)	6ft 6ins	$5\frac{3}{4}$	
1836	Trafalgar Dock (N)	6ft 4ins	$6\frac{1}{2}$	
1840	Coburg Dock (S)	6ft	$4\frac{1}{2}$	
1844	Canning Half-tide Basin (S)	6ft 2ins	$2\frac{1}{2}$	
1845	Albert Dock (S)	5ft 5ins	$7\frac{3}{4}$	
1847	Morpeth Dock (B)	5ft 2ins	$3\frac{1}{4}$	
1847	Egerton Dock (B)	7ft 4ins	$3\frac{3}{4}$	
1848	Salisbury Dock (N)	6ft 7ins	$3\frac{1}{2}$	
1848	Collingwood Dock (N)	6ft 3ins	5	
1848	Stanley Dock (N)	5ft 6ins	7	
1848	Nelson Dock (N)	6ft 1in	8	
1848	Bramley-Moore Dock (N)	5ft 6ins	$9\frac{1}{2}$	
1850	Wellington Dock (N)	6ft 2ins	$7\frac{3}{4}$	
1850	Wellington Half-tide Basin (N)	6ft 9ins	$3\frac{1}{10}$	
1851	Sandon Dock (N)	6ft 6ins	10	
1852	Huskisson Dock (N)		$14\frac{3}{4}$	
1855	Wapping Dock (S)	5ft 4ins	$5\frac{1}{10}$	
1855	Wapping Basin (S)	5ft 4ins	$1\frac{1}{2}$	
1858	Canada Dock (N)	6ft 6ins	$17\frac{3}{4}$	
1866	Herculaneum Dock (S)	8ft	$3\frac{1}{2}$	River entrance sills relaid at 12ft below ODS in 1883.

* See note on tidal datum on page xii

table continued overleaf

Date of opening	Name	Original position of sill below Old Dock Sill (feet)*	Approx. original superficial area (acres)	Notes
1866	Alfred Dock (at river entrances) (B)	12ft	$8\frac{1}{2}$	
1877	Wallasey Dock (B)		$12\frac{3}{4}$	
1878	Brunswick Branch Dock (S)	1ft	$1\frac{1}{2}$	
1879	Langton Dock (N)	9ft	18	Lock sill was 12ft below ODS.
1880	Alexandra Dock (N)	12ft	$17\frac{3}{4}$	
	Alexandra Branch No. 3		$7\frac{3}{4}$	
	Alexandra Branch No. 2		$9\frac{1}{2}$	
	Alexandra Branch No. 1		9	
1883	Harrington Dock (S)	11ft 3ins	9	
1884	Hornby Dock (N)	12ft	17	
1888	Toxteth Dock (S)	11ft 2ins	$11\frac{1}{2}$	
1905	Brunswick Entrance Locks (S)	19ft	$1\frac{1}{4}$	
1909	Vittoria Dock (B)		12	
1927	Gladstone Dock (N)	25ft	49	Gladstone lock, entrance to Gladstone and Seaforth, is 29ft 7ins below ODS.
1933	Bidston Dock (B)		$10\frac{1}{2}$	
1972	Royal Seaforth Dock (N)		$85\frac{1}{2}$	

* See note on tidal datum on page xii

Graving docks in the Port of Liverpool, 1882 and 1917

Names	Position and width of entrance		Sill below datum	Coping at hollow quoins above datum	Length of floor

1882

Liverpool Graving Docks

Names	Position and width of entrance		Sill below datum	Coping at hollow quoins above datum	Length of floor
		ft in	ft in	ft in	ft in
Langton No. 1	S. Outer	60 0	6 0	27 0	448 0
	S. Inner	60 0	6 0	27 0	500 0
No. 2	N. Outer	60 0	6 0	27 0	500 0
	N. Inner	60 0	6 0	27 0	448 0
Huskisson Lock as a Graving Dock		80 0	6 6	26 0	395 0
Sandon No. 1	East	60 0	3 6	26 0	565 0
No. 2	East	70 0	3 6	26 0	565 0
No. 3	East	60 0	3 6	26 0	565 0
No. 4	East	70 0	3 6	26 0	565 0
No. 5	East	45 0	3 6	26 0	565 0
No. 6	West	45 0	3 6	26 0	565 0
Clarence No. 1	N. Outer	45 0	3 0	26 6	451 0
	N. Inner	45 0	0 6	18 0	289 0
No. 2	S. Outer	45 0	3 0	26 6	454 0
	S. Inner	32 10	0 6	18 0	286 0
Prince's		45 0	5 9	28 2	277 4
Canning No. 1	North	35 9	1 8½ (above)	23 3	436 0
No. 2	South	35 9	0 0½	23 3½	482 0
Queen's No. 1	East	42 0	1 8¼	27 7¾	465 0
No. 2	West	70 0	3 6	27 5	467 0
Brunswick No. 1	East	41 0	2 6	26 6	460 0
No. 2	West	41 6	2 6	26 6	462 0
Herculaneum No. 1	West	60 0	4 0	26 0	758 6
No. 2	Middle	60 0	4 0	26 0	753 0
No. 3	East	60 0	4 0	26 0	768 0
Birkenhead Graving Docks					
West Float No. 1		60 0	4 0	25 0	930 0
No. 2		50 0	7 9	25 0	750 0
No. 3		85 0	7 9	25 0	750 0

* Level may be increased by impounding

table continued overleaf

Name and position	Width of entrance		Sill below datum	Coping at hollow quoins above datum	Length of floor
1917					
Liverpool Graving Docks					
		ft in	ft in	ft in	ft in
Gladstone		120 0	25 0	33 0	1050 0
Langton No. 1 (south)	Outer	60 0	5 6*	27 0	448 0
	Inner	60 0	5 7*	22 0	500 0
No. 2 (north)	Outer	60 0	5 5*	27 0	500 0
	Inner	60 0	5 8*	22 0	448 0
Brocklebank		93 3	12 9*	27 0	799 5
Canada		94 0	12 11*	28 0	925 6
Clarence No. 1 (north)	Outer	44 6	2 5	26 6	461 0
	Inner	45 0	0 1 (above)	18 0	289 0
No. 2 (south)	Outer	44 9	2 9	26 6	454 0
	Inner	32 9	0 1	18 0	286 0
Prince's		44 9	1 11	28 2	283 9
Canning No. 1 (north)		35 3	3 1 (above)	23 3	436 0
No. 2 (south)		35 0	1 0 (above)	23 3	482 0
			Below		
Queen's		80 0	16 2	28 0	634 0
Herculaneum No. 1 (west)		60 0	3 4*	26 0	758 6
No. 2		60 0	3 3*	26 0	930 0
No. 3		59 6	3 5*	26 0	768 0
No. 4 (east)		80 0	7 5*	27 0	754 0
Birkenhead Graving Docks					
West Float No. 1		60 0	4 0*	25 0	930 0
No. 2		50 0	7 9*	25 0	750 0
No. 3		85 0	7 9*	25 0	750 0

* Level may be increased by impounding

Acts of Parliament relating to the development of the Mersey docks

Liverpool Docks Acts

8 Anne, c.12, 1709	For making a convenient dock or basin (Old Dock) at Liverpool.
3 George I, c.1, 1716	For enlarging the time granted by the 1709 Act.
11 George II, c.32, 1737	For making an additional dock (Salthouse Dock).
2 George III, c.86, 1761	For enlarging the harbour and making an additional dock (George's Dock) and erecting lighthouses.
25 George III, c.15, 1785	For making two additional docks (King's and Queen's Docks) and piers.
39 George III, c.59, 1799	To alter and enlarge the powers of previous Acts, and for making two additional wet docks (one of which was Prince's Dock).
51 George III, c.143, 1811	For the improvement of the town and port; for the completion of Prince's Dock; to close the Old Dock and to convert the Dry Dock to a wet dock; to build additional basins (including Brunswick Dock and Brunswick Basin); to borrow money up to £600,000.
53 George III, c.156, 1813	To authorize the advancement of money.
59 George III, c.30, 1819	For improving the lighthouse on the Isle of Anglesea; amending Acts relating to the docks; providing residences for Harbour Master and Dock Masters.
6 George IV, c.187, 1825	For the further improvement of the town, port and harbour; building of Brunswick Dock.
9 George IV, c.55, 1825	To raise a further £200,000, making a total of £1,200,000 to be applied to completion of the several docks.
9 George IV, c.114, 1828	To authorize Trustees of the Liverpool Docks to pay for certain lands purchased under the Acts.
11 George IV, c.14, 1830	To borrow additional sum of £200,000.
4 Victoria, c.30, 1841	To erect transit sheds on the west quays of Prince's Dock; to make a wet dock (Albert Dock) with warehouses on the quays; to borrow a further £884,000.
6 & 7 Victoria, c.98, 1843	To alter and amend certain provisions of the Acts relating to the docks and harbour of Liverpool
7 & 8 Victoria, c.80, 1844	To construct additional wet docks (Salisbury, Collingwood, Stanley, Nelson, Bramley-Moore); to acquire the assets of the Harrington Dock Co.
8 Victoria, c.11, 1845	To amend previous Acts, particularly in view of the opening of the Prince's Dock transit sheds.
9 & 10 Victoria, c.109, 1846	To construct additional wet docks (Wapping Dock and Wapping Basin); to raise another £1,000,000; for extending and amending other Acts.
11 Victoria, c.10, 1848	To build warehouses as necessary on any dock quays; to construct additional wet docks.
14 & 15 Victoria, c.64, 1851	To alter the Constitution of the Committee for the affairs of the estate.
18 & 19 Victoria, c.174, 1855	To construct new works (Canada Dock) and to raise a further sum of money.

Mersey Docks and Harbour Acts

20 & 21 Victoria, c.162, 1857	For consolidating the docks at Liverpool and Birkenhead into one estate.
21 & 22 Victoria, c.90, 1858	To construct certain works at Birkenhead in substitution for and in addition to those already authorized.
21 & 22 Victoria, c.92, 1858	To consolidate and amend provisions of several Acts.
22 Victoria, c.20, 1859	To raise a further sum of money for works at Liverpool.
23 & 24 Victoria, c.150, 1860	To erect floating bridges at Liverpool and Woodside for improving the communication between Liverpool and Birkenhead.
24 & 25 Victoria, c.188, 1861	To purchase lands and complete works at Birkenhead.
26 Victoria, c.54, 1863	To extend the North river wall at Liverpool.
27 & 28 Victoria, c.213, 1864	To raise a further sum of money for the purpose of increasing the accommodation on the Liverpool side of the River Mersey.
29 Victoria, c.84, 1866	To convert the low-water basin and Morpeth Basin (Birkenhead) into wet docks.
29 & 30 Victoria, c.103, 1866	To confirm an agreement for land purchase at Birkenhead.
30 & 31 Victoria, c.206, 1867	To confirm certain expenditure.
34 & 35 Victoria, c.197, 1871	Liverpool River Approaches Act for improving the access to the River Mersey on the Liverpool side.
36 & 37 Victoria, c.143, 1873	Liverpool Dock Extension Act to construct new docks (including Harrington and Toxteth Docks) and to raise further monies.
36 & 37 Victoria, c.144, 1873	To authorize the construction of a new landing stage at Birkenhead.
37 & 38 Victoria, c.30, 1874	For varying the rates and dues leviable.
38 Victoria, c.19, 1875	To purchase from the Corporation land on the riverward side of Queen's Dock.
39 & 40 Victoria, c.69, 1876	To improve the river entrance to the Canada Basin.
40 Victoria, c.2, 1877	For confirming certain awards made with reference to the provisions of the Liverpool Dock Extension Act of 1873.
41 & 42 Victoria, c.198, 1878	Overhead Railways Act.

43 & 44 Victoria, c.14, 1880	To amend provisions of certain Acts regarding bye-laws.
44 Victoria, c.49, 1881	For authorizing the MDHB to acquire and work vessels for the pilotage service.
45 & 46 Victoria, c.204, 1882	To repeal the Overhead Railways Act 1878 and to confer new powers for the erection of overhead railways.
47 Victoria, c.29, 1884	To sanction the purchase of certain lands at Dingle Bank and Parkhill.
50 & 51 Victoria, c.139, 1887	Overhead Railways Act.
52 & 53 Victoria, c.140, 1889	Overhead Railways Act.
54 Victoria, c.8, 1891	To alter, extend and improve docks, basins and works at the north end of the Liverpool dock estate.
56 & 57 Victoria, c.82, 1893	For the purchase of certain lands at Tranmere
56 & 57 Victoria, c.162, 1893	To construct railways and alter and improve dock accommodation and works.
60 & 61 Victoria, c.170, 1897	To confer further powers on the MDHB.
61 Victoria, c.4, 1898	To confer further powers and to enable the MDHB to borrow further money.
61 Victoria, c.28, 1898	To alter, extend and improve the docks, basins and works (including King's, Queen's and Brunswick Docks) on the Liverpool side of the river.
62 & 63 Victoria, c.172, 1899	To make further provision with reference to the employment of pilots.
62 & 63 Victoria, c.198, 1899	To authorize MDHB to create redeemable stock and to enable the Board to raise money temporarily by bills of exchange or promissory notes.
63 & 64 Victoria, c.68, 1900	To amend in certain respects Acts relating to MDHB, with particular reference to the removal of obstructions in the docks.
1 Edward VII, c.21, 1901	To enclose part of the foreshore of the Mersey and adjoining lands in the borough of Birkenhead.
3 Edward VII, c.121, 1903	To construct additional dock works (Canada Branch No 3, Herculaneum Graving Dock No 4) on the Liverpool side of the Mersey and to acquire some 62 acres to the north of existing estate; also to abandon the construction of the Brunswick Graving Dock.
6 Edward VII, c.40, 1906	To construct additional dock and other works (Gladstone Dock site).
2 & 3 George V, c.12, 1912	To borrow monies in connection with the improvement of the port.
9 & 10 George V, c.14, 1919	To increase the rates, dues, rents, tolls and charges authorized to be levied.
10 & 11 George V, c.72, 1920	To construct further works (Dingle and Parkhill oil installations).
10 & 11 George V, c.103, 1920	To confirm certain Pilotage Orders.
13 & 14 George V, c.23, 1923	To confer further powers on the MDHB with reference to their undertaking and to the Liverpool Overhead Railway Company.
18 & 19 George V, c.6, 1928	To increase the borrowing powers of the MDHB.
26 George V & 1 Edward VIII, c.27, 1936	To extend the period for completion of works.
8 & 9 George VI, c.7, 1945	To construct further works (new entrance to Langton Dock).
14 George VI, c.21, 1950	To make further provision with respect to rates and charges leviable by the MDHB.
2 & 3 Elizabeth II, c.45, 1954	To re-enact powers for the removal of wrecks and other obstructions.
4 & 5 Elizabeth II, c.92, 1956	To construct further works.
6 & 7 Elizabeth II, c.7, 1958	To make further provision with respect to rates and charges leviable by the MDHB.
10 Elizabeth II, c.16, 1963	To increase borrowing powers.
13 Elizabeth II, c.11, 1966	To construct further works.
13 Elizabeth II, c.23, 1966	To construct further works.
14 Elizabeth II, c.6, 1967	To amend and extend financial provisions relating to the MDHB.
14 Elizabeth II, c.30, 1968	To increase borrowing powers.
17 Elizabeth II, c.57, 1971	To reconstitute the MDHB as a company and to alter its name; to re-organize the capital of the Board.

Other Acts

3 & 4 Victoria, c.121. 1840	The Harrington Dock Company's Act. To incorporate the Harrington Dock Company and exempt vessels using their docks, and all goods shipped or discharged therein, from payment of certain rates, tolls or duties.
5 & 6 Victoria, c.110, 1842	Act for better preserving the navigation of the River Mersey; establishment of the Commissioners for the Conservancy of the Mersey.
8 & 9 Victoria, c.4, 1845	Birkenhead Docks Trustees Act for constructing docks, walls, warehouses and other works at Birkenhead.
9 & 10 Victoria, c.146, 1846	Herculaneum Dock Company Act for constructing docks, walls, warehouses and other works at Toxteth Park.
9 & 10 Victoria, c.183, 1846	Act to enable the St Helens Canal and Railway Company to make docks at Garston.
11 & 12 Victoria, c.144, 1848	Act to transfer the powers of the Birkenhead Commissioners to a corporate body to be entitled 'The Trustees of the Birkenhead Docks'.
18 & 19 Victoria, c.171, 1855	Act for vesting the undertakings of the Birkenhead Dock Company and the Trustees of the Birkenhead Docks in the Mayor, Alderman and Burgesses of the Borough of Liverpool.

Appendix 4

Officers and Clerks needed to work the south and south-east stacks of the Albert Dock warehouses in 1846

3 Warehouse Keepers at an annual salary of	£150 0 0
2 Wharfingers or Deputies of the Quays at	£120 0 0
3 Foremen Coopers at	£120 0 0
	to
	£150 0 0
1 Superintendent's Clerk at	£150 0 0
1 Warrant Issue Clerk at	£150 0 0
1 Manifester or Ship Ledger Clerk, and	
Examiner of Landing Accounts, at	£150 0 0
3 Ledger Clerks for the Warehouses at	£100 0 0
1 Ledger Clerk for the Vaults at	£100 0 0
3 Warehouse Clerks at	£ 80 0 0
18 Landing or Check Clerks at	£ 80 0 0
3 Managing Foremen 1 for Silk	
1 for Tea	25s to 45s
1 for Spices, Indigo	per week each
6 Delivery Foremen at	25s per week
3 Assistant Foremen at	21s to 25s
	per week
6 Housing Foremen at	23s to 25s
	per week
1 Ship Worker at	24s per week
6 Samplers at	21s per week
6 Markers at	21s per week
1 Foreman of the Hold at	21s per week

Appendix 5

A foreign visitor's impressions of Liverpool docks in 1842

The account which follows is taken from J. G. Kohl's *Ireland, Scotland and England*, published in London by Chapman and Hall in 1844. Nothing seems known of Kohl; he does not appear in the *Neue Deutsche Biographie*, while the volume of *Deutsches Literatur Lexicon* that would contain his name has not, at the time of writing, been published. It seems likely that the description of Ireland (on the eve of the potato famine and including accounts of such topical items as Irish workhouses and the successes of Father Matthew) which occupies at least half the book, is what led the publishers to issue it.

The account of the Liverpool Docks, however, though little known, is perhaps one of the fullest descriptions of their working to be written by a layman, as well as one of the liveliest. Kohl's being a foreigner is in his favour: contemporary Englishmen would not have been amazed by the things that amazed him and which now amaze us, and while a good deal of statistical information – inserted with a mixture of German thoroughness and sheer wonder at the magnitude of the trade carried on – has been omitted here, he has an excellent eye for details such as the bollards to which ships were tied up, and for the dramatic scene such as the night work at Salthouse Dock.

The passages reprinted here are taken from pages 35 to 59 of Part III of Kohl's book.

'I went on that same evening to Liverpool, and at ten o'clock arrived on the "Cheshire shore", on the south side of the Mersey, opposite to the great town itself. This "Cheshire shore" has risen and flourished simultaneously with Liverpool, and rural houses of entertainment, and villages rich in country seats have been gradually scattered along the river side, serving to the townspeople as watering-places, and as places of residence and amusement. The town receives, likewise, a large portion of its supplies from this side of the river. The broad Mersey lies between the Liverpool people and the Cheshire shore, which for that very reason, probably, is a greater favourite with them as a place of recreation. To each little place on the opposite side of the Mersey, a steamboat plies from Liverpool as a ferry. At certain hours of the day, about twelve of these ferry steamers assemble at the same wharf to take in their several cargoes, and at a given signal they all

start, scattering themselves in different directions over the Mersey, like a pack of cards over a table.

We arrived at the chief of these ferries called Birkenhead, where we and our luggage were packed with railroad speed into a steamer, and within view of the widely spreading and brightly illuminated Liverpool, we glided swiftly over the dark waters of the Mersey. Every moment the echo of the noise made by our paddles as they struck the water, announced that we were passing some stately vessel lying at anchor. These echoes increased in number as we proceeded, and traversing a forest of masts, among which lamps and lanterns were glittering like so many glow-worms in a grove, we speedily reached our landing-place, and the neighbouring hotel to which we were consigned. . . .

In 1561, Liverpool contained only 7 streets, 138 Cottages, and 690 inhabitants. Towards the middle of the seventeenth century the town began to grow into importance, and now it may be looked on as the second commercial town in the world. As its growth still continues, there are not wanting prophets who foretell that it will some day rank as the first.

In 1801 Liverpool contained 77,708 Inhabitants

In 1821 Liverpool contained 118,972 Inhabitants

In 1831 Liverpool contained 165,221 Inhabitants

In 1841 Liverpool contained 224,954 Inhabitants

The population has accordingly trebled in forty years, and several places lying in the vicinity, and almost belonging to Liverpool, have, in the meantime, increased in equal proportion. Everton, Kirkdale, West Derby, and Toxteth Park, contained, in 1821, a joint population of 22,103 inhabitants. Now the number is 71,009. If we add these to the population of Liverpool, and the 13,000 seamen belonging to the town, but absent on voyages, and not therefore included in the census, we shall have 309,000 inhabitants.

The revenue derived from the Liverpool custom-house amounts to one-fourth of the entire customs revenue of the United Kingdom. The harbour receives annually 16,000 vessels from the different parts of the world, and these vessels carry away with them 2,400,000 tons, or, 48,000,000cwts of

merchandise. The vessels belonging to the port are in number about 10,000, forming one-twelfth of the entire British mercantile marine – coasters, of course, included; and, notwithstanding the badness of the times, so loudly complained of, I had sufficient proof that the shipping of Liverpool must still be on the increase in the zeal with which the workmen were labouring night and day at the completion of a new dock calculated for the reception of 200 vessels, a dock which of itself, in any German commercial town, would have been looked on as a colossal undertaking, as forming of itself a magnificent harbour, but which here was only one among a dozen . . . .

Liverpool is still a young city, and has probably not yet availed herself of all the advantages of her position. This town may yet rise to an importance far beyond that which it has yet reached. Among the great cities of the world, of first or second rank, there is no other so exclusively devoted to commerce. Every house in Liverpool is either a counting-house, a warehouse, a shop, or a house that in one way or other is either an instrument or the result of trade. The great buildings and institutions of the town are a custom-house, an exchange, a set of docks, a railway station, or something else that is intended, directly or indirectly, to be serviceable to commerce, and the inhabitants are nearly to a man traders or the servants of traders. Not even the authorities of the county reside at Liverpool, for the county town is Lancaster . . . .

Close to the custom-house lie the docks, and these offer to the stranger a spectacle of commercial bustle, and a multitude of splendid harbour and marine works, unequalled, I believe, in the world, not even excepting those of London. Some of the London docks are perhaps larger than any of those of Liverpool, and may therefore afford accommodation to a larger number of vessels; but, in the first place, they are fewer in number, and not being destined for such various branches of trade, offer not the same variegated scenes as those of Liverpool; and secondly, being at a distance from the central part of the town, they do not afford the same convenience to the merchant. London was already a great town before she began to think of her present commercial importance, whereas Liverpool, her trade, and her docks, grew up together. In London, when docks came to be thought of, it was impossible to clear away half a town, so they had to be placed somewhat out of the way; but in Liverpool, a convenient site was from the first left for the docks, and the custom-house, the exchange, and the merchants' counting-houses, grouped themselves about them. In London, a merchant when he wants to send an order to his ship in the docks, must often send his clerk down by the railroad; in Liverpool, a merchant might almost make himself heard in the docks, out of his counting-house window.

The whole length of the river side at Liverpool is filled up with docks. To have an idea of the grandeur of these works, taken as a whole, the reader must imagine a length of three English miles running along the river, and this occupied, in a breadth of from 250 to 500 yards, with all descriptions of harbour works; with basins cut into the rock, and then lined with solid masonry; with admirable quays surrounding these basins; with entrance locks and canals, provided with various kinds of locks, and crossed by handsome iron bridges, or by wooden pathways. He must next imagine the whole length of three miles armed with a lofty wall, whose imposing greatness can be properly admired only at low water; these basins filled with ships, the quays crowded by busy workmen, engaged in loading and unloading merchandise, with the imposing warehouses, and the really elegant residences of the officers of the docks.

It would be difficult to state the precise number of all the basins and other artificial harbours for the reception of large and small vessels, but, including those belonging to the canals, there are certainly more than forty. Of the docks, properly so called, there are about sixteen. When in these docks, the vessels have the advantage of an unvarying depth of water, and great facilities for loading and unloading, and for effecting all necessary repairs. Most of the docks are intended for the use of a particular class of ships. Thus the Brunswick Dock is for vessels laden with timber from America; the Queen's Dock for West Indian, Baltic, and Dutch vessels; the Coburg Dock for the large class of sea-going steamers; the King's Dock for the tobacco vessels from the West Indies and North America; and the Prince's Dock, the most magnificent of all, for ships from India and China, and for the largest class of American vessels. Each dock is differently arranged, with a view to the accommodation of the class of vessels for which it is intended. Thus at the Brunswick Dock the quays are particularly calculated for the unloading of timber, and often one side of the dock is arranged for loading and the other for unloading.

The graving docks are a particular class of small docks, intended for caulking and other repairs.

To each dock is attached what is called a basin, into which, as it is generally in direct communication with the Mersey, vessels may enter at every period of the tide, and through which all vessels must pass before they can enter the docks themselves. These basins are a sort of preliminary docks ready at all times to afford shelter, while the docks themselves, where it is required that the water should always remain at the same level, can be opened only at high water.

Astonishment and admiration are awakened in no ordinary degree, at the contemplation of the bulwarks which man has here erected against ocean; of locks often fifty feet high, with which he regulates ebb and flood in his docks; sea-gates, often seventy feet wide, of the most magnificent and solid workmanship; and the immense reservoirs which he has dug into the rocks, for the reception of his vessels. The Prince's Dock, the largest of all, cost 561,019*l*, and more than half of this sum was expended in wages to the men employed in digging, excavating, &c. The expense of the whole of the works along the Mersey quay is incalculable, but must have amounted to many millions; and it is not merely the extent of these works that deserves our admiration, but also the short time within which they have been completed. Most of the docks have been constructed during the last thirty years. The first ever built in England was begun in 1708, but this great ancestor of all the docks of Great Britain no longer exists, the custom-house having been erected on its site. If all Germany would but consent to expend on the cathedral of Cologne, as much as the single town of Liverpool has expended on her docks, the noble pile would soon stand complete in all its details, to the admiration of centuries, and to the honour of God.

In general, it is impossible to judge the real magnitude of the work expended on one of these docks, as they are mostly filled with ships and water, but it is when we happen to see one of them empty that we are surprised at their depth and capaciousness. I saw the Salthouse Dock empty. It had been found not to be deep enough, and there had been a wish to correct the irregularity of its form. These alterations were proceeding, at the time of my visit, with great rapidity, it being deemed desirable that the whole should be finished before the autumn. To accelerate the works they proceeded night and day, relays of workmen relieving each other every twelve hours. The men who work at night, slept by day, breakfasted at eight in the evening, and had an

hour allowed them, from midnight till one, for their dinner. At eight in the morning they were relieved by the day party. On Saturdays the night party worked only till midnight, and resumed their work on Monday morning at one o'clock, the hour from midnight being, as usual, allowed them for dinner. This night-work presented a spectacle unique in its kind. The entire cavity, in some places at least fifty feet deep, and covering at least five acres of ground, was filled with numberless torches, lights, and fires, and 300 workmen were busily engaged, – hacking, digging, and breaking and exploding the rock. In five weeks, it was hoped, the dock would be ready for the reception of vessels.

On looking more closely into the details of these docks we see how admirably the English have arranged every little matter connected with these great commercial institutions, and how imperfect most of these things continue to be in other countries. At certain distances round all the docks are large, broad-headed, cast iron posts to which the vessels are made fast. Now it seems almost incredible that in so old a commercial city as Bremen there should still be public walks where the trees have continued to be applied to this use for I know not how many centuries. The patient promenaders of the German city, as they stroll along the Neustadtsdeich, have, for centuries, been accustomed to jump over the ropes, in which their legs are in momentary danger of becoming entangled, as in so many snares, and yet, to the present day, it seems never to have suggested itself to these good people, that for so serious an inconvenience so easy a remedy might be found. In the next place, every dock is surrounded by iron cranes, on each of which is marked the weight it is able to lift, as thus: "Not to lift more than two tons". Now certainly, it seems natural that before people make use of a machine intended to raise heavy weights, they should know the weight it is capable of lifting, but I know seaport towns enough where so self-suggesting a precaution is never dreamt of. Close to the edge of the quays are large long sheds, under which the merchandise can be sheltered immediately on leaving the vessel, and from which it can be packed into the waggons that are to carry it away. These sheds have side walls, consisting either of wooden boards or of canvass stretched on iron rollers. These side walls are moveable, and are generally put out of the way when the weather is at all favourable; but they can quickly be restored to their places should a storm or heavy rain come on, when the sheds are, for the time being, converted into small warehouses, sheltered on every side.

It is to the Prince's Dock one must go, to

see all these arrangements in the greatest perfection, or to contemplate the finest among the vessels that visit Liverpool. Among those most admired are the American packet ships, and particularly the British and North American Royal Mail Steamships, the *Acadia*, the *Britannia*, the *Columbia*, &c. – specimens of architecture quite as wonderful as many a temple or custom-house. I visited the *Caledonia*, of which the crew was so numerous, that at a draper's shop I saw the uniform of a *Caledonia* seamen exhibited as a regular article of sale. These vessels are rated at 1200 tuns, and their steam-engines are of 440 horse power. They are all precisely alike, having been built after the same model. They carry the mail to Halifax and Boston, generally performing the voyage to America in fourteen-and-a-half days, and the voyage home in eleven or twelve days. The quickest voyage hitherto performed was that of the *Britannia*, in July, 1841, when she ran from Halifax to Liverpool in nine days and a half. These beautiful vessels lie somewhat out of the way in the Coburg Dock. In the other docks may be seen other steamers, such as the boats of the Glasgow line, those of the Dublin line, the Isle of Man line, the Cork line, &c.

In consequence of this regular and rapid communication with America, Liverpool has become the principal point of departure for the continent, not only for England but for all Europe, the main ferry to unite the old world and the new. The same circumstance has made Liverpool the principal port of embarkation for emigrants, who are certain, at all times, to find opportunities there for Canada and the United States, more so than even in London. In the month of April, 1842, no less than 13,055 persons embarked at Liverpool for the United States, and 1945, to the British North American colonies, making in all 15,000. This is more than emigrate from Germany, by the way of Bremen, in a whole year. From the whole United Kingdom, the emigration amounts, on an average, to about 100,000 individuals a year; in 1841, the number was 118,592, of whom 72,104 were from England, 32,428 from Ireland, and 14,060 from Scotland, but many, no doubt, of those who went from England were Irish and Scotch, who had come to Liverpool as the most convenient port of embarkation. Of these emigrants, 45,017 went to the United States, 38,114 to Canada, 28,724 to Australia, and 3,901 to New Zealand.

A spectacle particularly calculated to awaken interest, is the sight of a noble vessel, which, after bravely struggling with the storm and the other perils of the sea, now, with her broken ribs and limbs, reposes quietly in harbour. In Liverpool, where there are always a thousand or two of vessels in the docks, it can seldom

happen, that one or other of them has not her tale to tell of some imminent danger recently encountered. Such a vessel I saw in the *Laurel*, which I found lying in one of the graving docks. On her way from Canada, and when still a thousand miles from Liverpool, she had encountered an iceberg, that had broken her bowsprit, and knocked in one of her sides. She would infallibly have sunk, but that her cargo (timber) kept her afloat. It struck me as something strange to hear English sailors making use of the German expression "icebergs", but it is the customary word, "ice-mountains" being never used.

Many of the extensive warehouses in which goods are deposited (in bond) till the duty has been paid, receive all descriptions of merchandise, but others are set aside for particular articles. Of these the tobacco warehouse, near the King's Dock, is the largest of all. This building goes on increasing in extent, to make room for the increased masses of this merchandise for which accommodation is required, to the sorrow and vexation of many an English housewife, who would fain keep the atmosphere of her house clear of the poisonous fumes of the tobacco leaf. Behind this warehouse, along the quay, is a promenade, and a similar one exists behind the Prince's Dock. These "marine parades" are genuine Liverpool promenades. Their trees are masts; their flower beds and parterres are groups of tar barrels, tea chests, and tobacco casks; the occasional vistas that open, carry the eye along rows of warehouses, and the view ranges over the broad green meadows of the Mersey, with the blue ocean and its sportive billows melting away in the distant mist.

Such of the tobacco as has been spoiled, or is not considered by the merchant to be worth the duty, together with the "scraps" that are swept together, are burned in a stove constructed for the purpose. . . .

Few of the houses near the docks are inhabited, most of them being either warehouses or counting-houses, and one house often contains many counting-houses, the names of the different firms being painted on the sides of the doors. The streets are constantly filled with long caravans of waggons laden with merchandise, like the narrow streets of that part of London which lies between St Paul's and the Thames; but this warehouse quarter of Liverpool is much more elegant and convenient than that of London, where, on account of the narrowness of the streets, constant stoppages are occurring.

In the vicinity of the docks are situated various establishments for the manufacture of articles required for the equipment of vessels, such as rope-walks and the like. Among others,

a vast machine established by the Liverpool corporation, for the testing of chain cables. I saw a chain tested, whose links were not above two inches in diameter, and this comparatively thin chain was subjected to a pressure of sixty tons.

I also visited the establishment of a sail-maker, but, as it was a Monday, not a very busy day either in Liverpool or in any part of England, I found most of the workmen absent. "They had not time on Saturday evening", observed one of the directors of the concern, in an ironical tone, "to spend the whole of their week's earnings; and as they could do little that way on Sunday, they must have their Monday into the bargain". A great deal of canvass is exported, and, to give it a more attractive look, it is generally bleached. "We Liverpool people, however, prefer bleaching our canvass at sea, as the bleaching on shore always weakens it." The Liverpool people, I found, considered their sails to be very superior to those made at London. In sails also, I here learned, there is such a thing as mutation of fashion; so of late years it has become customary to introduce a narrow blue stripe into the sails, and the innovation has found great favour in the eyes of sailors. I wanted to have some idea of the quantity of canvass required to equip a large vessel, and to gratify my curiosity the books were referred to, when it appeared that a new vessel of 500 tons that had lately been fitted out, had required 4,841 yards of canvass to make her a complete set of sails; and that 3,300 yards had been used up for the sails of a smaller vessel of 340 tons. . . .

Besides the establishments to which I have already alluded, there are large manufactories of steamboats and steam-engines, anchor smiths, chain smiths, oil mills, sugar refineries, large bakehouses for making ships' biscuits and others; but all these are industries immediately connected with commerce and shipping, or with the immediate wants of the town itself. There is but one manufactory, in the common acceptation of the term, namely, a factory for spinning cotton, which is consequently looked upon as a little curiosity in its way. One of the largest and most interesting of the establishments to which I have alluded, is that of Messrs Fawcett and Preston, for the construction of cannon and of large marine steam engines. Some idea may be formed of the importance of the concern, when we are told that the house undertakes the execution of such orders as 300 pieces of heavy ordnance for the King of Holland. Steam-engines are made here of more than 500 horse power. Their largest was of 520, the engines of the steamers on the Boston line of 440, and the largest employed in any manufactory in Manchester of 300 horse-power. I saw a cylinder, eighteen feet in circumference, making for a steam frigate. Sugar-mills for the West Indies and Brazil are also made at these works. . . .

Wales

I cannot tell how many flags were hoisted on the following morning at the different piers of Liverpool, to inform the several passengers where to look for the Glasgow boat, the Isle of Man boat, the Dublin boat, the Cork boat, the Pembroke boat, and all the rest of them. I for my part ranged myself under the flag of Bangor the most frequented place of transit, to those about to visit North Wales. Uninvited assistants, among whom no doubt were some of the thieves of whom I spoke a few pages back, together with beggars, and other importunate solicitors, surrounded us, and took care that our roses on that morning should not be without thorns. Newsmen offered us the news of the same morning. Others had telescopes for those who wished to contemplate the Welsh coast at their ease. Oranges and gingerbread, with other delicacies of the same kind, were hawked about, and altogether the noise and apparent confusion were enough to make a man run away in despair. The steamers, meanwhile, were humming, hissing, and shrieking around us, but with all their noise and well-known vigour, they lay not the less quiet and orderly at their several places, and gradually as the ear and eye became familiarized with it, the noisy bustling scene became a source of amusement and pleasurable excitement.

"The mouth of the Mersey" is armed with light-houses, land marks, beacons, telegraph stations, and private signal poles, as a mouth with teeth. The Rock Lighthouse is the most important, the most solid, and the handsomest of all these erections, so I was not surprised to learn that Mr Foster had contributed the design. It is built of hard granite from the island of Anglesey. The stones are all dovetailed into one another, and the whole has been united into one solid mass by a cement of volcanic origin. The coloured light thrown out at night upon the ocean, is said to be one of the most brilliant along the whole English coast. When we passed the place, the windows were carefully closed, that the powerful reflecting mirrors might not, by concentrating the rays of the sun, act as a burning-glass, and so perhaps give occasion to a fire somewhere or other.

On account of the frequent fogs to which the English coast is liable, peculiar precautionary arrangements have been deemed necessary, that will probably never be thought necessary on the confines of more sunny regions, such as Arabia, Persia, &c. Among these means of precaution, the fog bells deserve to be first mentioned. These bells are fixed upon empty casks or buoys, and as these are tossed to and fro by the waves, the bells toll in single, irregular strokes, to warn the seaman of his proximity to rocks and sandbanks, when the fog makes it impossible for him to see them, or even to distinguish the lighthouses. He is thus enabled, when he can no longer *see* his danger, at least to *hear* it. The steam-boats have likewise adopted precautionary signals to prevent accidents during a fog. They have their "fog-whistles", for instance, which are connected with the steam-engine, and every now and then, in foggy weather, send forth a few shrill piercing notes over the bosom of the ocean.

We were soon out at sea, but even there on the waste of salt water I saw more smoking chimneys at one glance than I had seen altogether on the Steppes of Southern Russia. The chimneys I allude to were those of the various steamers hastening to and from Liverpool. Each observed its line of way, as strictly as if it had been marked out for her by a regular macadamised road. . . .'

Bibliography

In the Department of Archives, Merseyside County Museums

Minutes of the Liverpool Dock Committee, 1793–1857,
class no 1/1–18
Proceedings of the Mersey Docks and Harbour Board, 1858–1946,
class no 9/1–35
Minutes of the Sub-committee on Warehouse Management, 1842–1857,
class no 6/1–7
Minutes of the MDHB Committee on Traffic, 1858–1940,
class no 15/1–36
Minutes of the MDHB Committee on Warehouses, 1858–1947,
class no 16/1–25
Minutes of the Sub-committee of Works, 1840–1857, 4 VOLS,
class no 7
Minutes of the MDHB Committee of Works, 1858–1949,
class no 17/1–35
MDHB Collection of newspaper cuttings arranged by subject, 1880–1971,
in Maritime History store

MDHB Dock Registers for the south end
Dock Engineers' Annual Reports, 1825–1915,
microfiche, Merseyside Docklands History Survey collection
Contracts Book, 1811–1871, 551 items
no class no; also on Merseyside Docklands History Survey microfiche
Brunswick etc. Docks, 1825–1952, 95 VOLS,
class nos H35, H40, H45, H50, H55, H60
Herculaneum etc. Dock, 1842–1960, 19 VOLS,
class nos D65, D70, D75
Canning, 1837–1868,
unclassified

MDHB Worked-up Papers (Bound volumes)
Albert Dock Warehouses, 1882–1925, 2 VOLS,
class no 3
Accommodation for coal in Liverpool, 1877–1923, 2 VOLS,
class no 4
Dock improvements, 1889–1939, 5 VOLS,
class no 17
Dock line of railway, 1856–1931, 2 VOLS,
class no 23
High level coal railway, 1850–1925, 2 VOLS,
class no 34
Manchester Ship Canal, 1882–1952, 4 VOLS,
class no 45
New works at south end, 1875–1890, 1 VOL,
class no 56
Overhead Railway, 1853–1938, 4 VOLS,
class no 59
Petroleum, 1862–1939, 3 VOLS,
class no 61
Pluckington Bank, 1877–1895, 1 VOL,
class no 64
Double-storey sheds, 1882–1895, 1 VOL,
class no 73

Transit sheds, 1854–1900, 1 VOL,
class no 83
George's Dock, 1884–1919, 1 VOL,
class no 106
Hydraulic machinery, 1874–1920, 1 VOL,
class no 116
Brunswick River Entrance, 1897–1929, 1 VOL,
class no 126
Official residences, 1859–1928, 1 vol,
class no 133
Nova Scotia and Mann Island, 1863–1921, 1 VOL,
class no 136
Cold storage accommodation, 1884–1935, 1 VOL,
class no 152
Manchester Basin, 1859–1938, 1 VOL,
class no 155
MSC Bridgewater Navigation Co Ltd, 1850–1933, 1 VOL,
class no 161
Elder Dempster berths, 1856–1949, 1 VOL,
class no 173

A. Holt & Co berths, 1872–1947, 1 VOL,
class no 174
T. & J. Harrison berths, 1864–1951, 1 VOL,
class no 176
Dock gates, 1882–1949, 1 VOL,
class no 186

MDHB Worked-up Papers (Unbound volumes)
Albert Dock Warehouses,
class nos A122, F39, K3, S43, T86, W39
Appropriated berths,
class nos R8, M62, A52, B141
Buoy Store,
class no B119
Casemates, Herculaneum Dock,
class no C129
Chester Basin,
class nos S71, C107
Coburg and Brunswick Docks,
class no B25
Corn trade (accommodation south end),
class no C116
Dock railways,
class no D15
Duke's Dock property,
class no B53
Enclosed docks,
class nos I15, E13, E45, S66
George's Basin,
class no G5
George's Dock,
class nos W14, G82, G83

Harrington Basin,
class nos F5, F38, M18, H40
Herculaneum Dock and Graving Docks,
class nos H3, G23
High level coal railway,
class nos H24, C51, C127
Hydraulic capstans,
class no H35
Hydraulic men,
class no H36
Hydraulic machinery,
class nos H41, H49
Hydraulic Power Co,
class no H67
King's Dock tobacco warehouse,
class no K1
King's Dock sheds,
class no K11
Kirkmabreck Quarry,
class no K6
Manchester Basin,
class nos M26, M38, B57
Master Porterage,
class no M64
Opening Albert Dock Warehouses,
class no V21
Opening Bridges, George's Dock,
class no G50
Overhead Railway,
class no O15
Petroleum,
class no P13

Purchase of Corporation property,
class nos C96, F10, F60
Salaries,
class no P85
Salthouse Dock,
class no L33
Shropshire Union Railway and Canal Co,
class nos S22, S71
Stevedore,
class nos S32, M24
Timber (greenheart),
class no G64
Timber quays south,
class no F3
Tobacco accommodation,
class no F79
Wages,
class no W41
Water Bailiff,
class no W29

Duke's Dock Arbitration Papers, c1899,
class nos K46–52

Report from John Rennie entitled
Plans and Costings of a Combination of Schemes to Extend and Improve the Port of Liverpool, 1810

Surveyor's Report . . . of the Whole of his Expenditure from March 1824 to December 1835

The Accounts of the Trustees of the Liverpool Docks

In the Athenaeum Library, Church Alley, Liverpool
Robert Gladstone Collection No 37

The Report of Mr. Rennie to the Dock Committee, Liverpool, in December, 1809
Extracts from Observations on the River Mersey by Joseph Whidbey, Esq. in May, 1818
The Report of Messrs. Whidbey, Rennie and Giles upon the present encroachments and state of the River Mersey and upon the means of preserving the Port of Liverpool, June, 1826
Report from Francis Giles, C. E., October, 1826 [re river conservancy in the Port of Liverpool]
Report of Robert Stephenson, C. E., January, 1827 [re general survey and inspection of the river]; also Interim report on the Interior Navigation relating to the works of the Mersey and Irwell Canal Co. at and near Runcorn

Report from Jesse and John B. Hartley, November, 1850 entitled
Report of the Surveyor of the Liverpool Docks upon the means for providing increased facilities for shipping coal at the Port of Liverpool

A Year's Work at the Liverpool Docks,
text of speech made to the Mersey Docks and Harbour Board on 11th January, 1906 by Robert Gladstone, Chairman

Liverpool Pamphlets – A collection of pamphlets chiefly relating to Liverpool, its Docks, its Trade, Improvements, etc

In the Record Office and Local History Department, Liverpool City Libraries, William Brown Street, Liverpool

Local newspapers from 1756

Local directories from 1766

The Norris family (merchants) deeds and papers from the fifteenth to the eighteenth centuries

Corporation Minutes from 1550 and other Corporation records including accounts and deeds

A number of general maps of Liverpool and the docks, including

The Mapp of all the streets, lanes and alleys within the town of Liverpool ... by J. Chadwick, 1725;
Plan of Liverpool survey'd in June, 1765 by John Eyes;
Plan of the town of Liverpool, with its docks, streets, lanes and alleys laid down to the 29 September, 1768, by John Eyes;
Plan of the town and township of Liverpool from an actual survey taken by Charles Eyes, 1785;
Plan of the town and township of Liverpool shewing every house by R. Horwood, 1803;
Plan of the town and township of Liverpool with the environs, 1821, published by J. Gore;
Map of the town and port of Liverpool ... from actual survey by Jonathan Bennison, 1835;
Ordnance Survey maps of Liverpool and district, surveyed in 1845–49, scale 6″ to 1 mile;
Plan of the borough of Liverpool from actual survey by James Newlands, 1863, scale 15″ to 1 mile

Printed and published sources

Aitken, J.	1795	*A Description of the Countryside from 30 to 40 miles around Manchester*
Archaeological Survey of Merseyside	1981	*The Changing Face of Liverpool 1207–1727* Liverpool
Baines, Edward	1868	*The History of the County Palatine and Duchy of Lancaster*, 3 VOLS, London
Baines, Thomas	1867	*Lancashire and Cheshire Past and Present*, 2 VOLS, London
Barker, T. C.	1948	*The Sankey Navigation*, Transactions of the Historic Society of Lancashire and Cheshire, VOL 100, pp. 121–55
Beamish, R.	1862	Memoirs of the life of Sir Marc Isambard Brunel
Bird, James	1963	*The Major Seaports of the United Kingdom*, London
Brooke, Richard	1853	*Liverpool as it was during the last quarter of the eighteenth century*, Liverpool
Cave, Francis H.	1927	*The Development of Master Porterage at Liverpool, and some notes on the present practice of Master Porterage*, Mersey Docks and Harbour Board
Chandler, George	1957	*Liverpool*, London
Clemens, Paul G. E.	1976	*The Rise of Liverpool, 1665–1750*, Economic History Review, vol 29, no 2, pp. 211–225
Colson, C.	1894	*Docks and Dock Construction*, London Corporation of Liverpool and Borough Fund Accounts 18th October 1773 to 31st August 1854
Cunningham, B.	1914	*Dock and Harbour Engineer's Reference Book*, London
Davies, P. N.	1973	*The Trade Makers: Elder Dempster in West Africa 1852–1972* London
Donnachie, Ian	1971	*The Industrial Archaeology of Galloway*, Newton Abbot
Du Plat-Taylor, F. M. G.	1928	*Docks, Wharves and Piers*, London

Eames, Aled   1980   *Ship Master: The life and letters of Capt. Robert Thomas of Llandwrog and Liverpool, 1843 to 1903,*
Gwynedd Archives Service, Denbigh

Enfield, William   1773   *An Essay Towards the History of Liverpool,*
Warrington

England, Richard   1981   *Schoonerman*
London

Glyn, Joseph   1854   *An Elementary Treatise on the Construction of Cranes and Machinery circa 1850*
London

Grantham, J.   1853   *Improved Plan for Working Docks,*
Transactions of the Liverpool Polytechnic Society, pp. 25–48

Green, Sydney H.   *The Financial Crisis 1970*
(unpublished note prepared by the Secretary to the Mersey Docks and Harbour Board)

Hadfield, Charles and Biddle, Gordon   1970   *The Canals of North West England,*
Newton Abbot

Hague, Douglas B. and Christie, Rosemary 1975   *Lighthouses: their architecture, history and archaeology,*
Gomer Press

Harris, J. R., ed.,   1969   *Liverpool and Merseyside,*
London

Harris, Stanley A.   1939   *Henry Berry (1720–1812): Liverpool's Second Dock Engineer,*
Transactions of the Historic Society of Lancashire and Cheshire, VOL 89, pp. 90–116

Hayman, A.   1981   *The Mersey and Irwell Navigation to the Manchester Ship Canal,*
Cheadle Hulme

Hughes, Quentin   1964   *Seaport – Architecture and Townscape in Liverpool,*
London

Hyde, Francis E.   1971   *Liverpool and the Mersey,*
Newton Abbot

Hyde, Francis E.   1967   *Shipping Enterprise and Management 1830–1939,*
Liverpool

James, J. C.   1981   *LNWR and the MD & HB – The History of the Dock Lines of Railway from the Records,*
privately printed

Jarvis, Rupert   1954   *Customs Letter Books of the Port of Liverpool 1711 to 1813*
Chetham Society

Jarvis, Rupert C.   1951   *The Head Port of Chester, and Liverpool its Creek and Member,*
Transactions of the Lancashire and Cheshire Historical Society, VOL 102, pp. 69–85

Jones, F. M.   1967   *Liverpool Dock Buildings as Historical Evidence,*
Transactions of the Historic Society of Lancashire and Cheshire, VOL 118, pp. 87–103

Kenyon, George Cecil   1903   *Dock Improvements at Liverpool,*
Transactions of the American Society of Civil Engineers, pp. 36–72

Lacey, L.   1907   *The History of Liverpool from 1207 to 1907,*
Liverpool

Liverpool Heritage Bureau   1978   *Buildings of Liverpool*
Liverpool

Lowndes, T.   1766   *History of Inland Navigations, particularly those of the Duke of Bridgewater in Lancashire and Cheshire*

Lubbock, Basil   1935   *Coolie Ships and Oil Sailers,*
Glasgow

Lyster, George Fosbery   1890   *Dock Extension, Liverpool*
Minutes of the Proceedings of the Institute of Civil Engineers

Lyster, George Fosbery   1896   *The Physical and Engineering Features of the River Mersey and Port of Liverpool,*
British Association for the Advancement of Science,
London

McIntyre, W. R. S.   1972   *The First Scheme for Docks at Birkenhead and the Proposed Canal across Wirral,*
Transactions of the Historic Society of Lancashire and Cheshire, VOL 124, pp. 108–127

MacLeod, Karen   1982   *The Old Dock, Liverpool*
                                                Merseyside County Archives (unpublished)
MacTier, S. and Falconer, W. H.   1955–61   *The Development of Marine Machinery,*
                                                Transactions of the Liverpool Nautical Research Society, VOL 9, pp. 100–109
Malet, Hugh   1977   *Bridgewater, The Canal Duke,*
                                                Manchester University Press
Malley, E.   1929   *The Financial Administration of the Bridgewater Estate 1780–1800,*
                                                Manchester University (unpublished thesis)
Mather, F. C.   1970   *After the Canal Duke,*
                                                London
Ministry of Transport   1962   *Report of the Committee of Inquiry into the Major Ports of Great Britain*
                                                London
Moss, Linda   1980   *Liverpool's South Docks: An archaeological and historical survey,*
                                                Liverpool
Moss, William   1796   *Liverpool Guide*
                                                Liverpool
Mountfield, Stuart   1965   *Western Gateway,*
                                                Liverpool
Muir, J. R. B.   1907   *A History of Liverpool,*
                                                Liverpool

Page, William, ed.   1966   *The Victoria History of the Counties of England: A History of Lancashire,*
                                                London
Parkinson, Cyril Northcote   1952   *The Rise of the Port of Liverpool,*
                                                Liverpool
Peet, Henry   1930   *Thomas Steers,*
                                                Transactions of the Lancashire and Cheshire Historic Society, VOL 82, pp. 163–206
Phillips, N. A.   1983   *Quayside and Warehouse Fixtures in Liverpool's South Docks,*
                                                Merseyside County Museums, Liverpool
Picton, J. A.   1873   *Memorials of Liverpool, 2 VOLS,*
                                                London
Picton, J. A.   1886   *Municipal Archives and Records from 1700 to 1835,*
                                                Liverpool
Platt, E. M.   *Sir Thomas Johnson,*
                                                Transactions of the Lancashire and Cheshire Historical Society, VOL 52, pp. 147–164
Poole, Braithwaite   1854   *The Commerce of Liverpool*
                                                Liverpool
Pope, D. J.   1970   *Shipping and Trade in the Port of Liverpool 1783–1793*
                                                PhD thesis, 1970

Rathbone, E.   1904   *Report of an Inquiry, into the Conditions of Dock Labour at the Liverpool Docks*
                                        1839   Reports of the Committee of Finance of the Town Council of Liverpool on the subject of Docks
                                                and warehouses on the dock quays
                                                Liverpool
Rideout, Eric H.   1930   *The Development of the Liverpool Warehousing System,*
                                                Transactions of the Historic Society of Lancashire and Cheshire, VOL 82, pp. 1–41
Ritchie-Noakes, Nancy   1980   *Jesse Hartley,*
                                                Liverpool

Sale, Robina McNeil   no date   *South Castle Street Excavations,*
                                                Liverpool University Rescue Archaeology Unit (unpublished draft report)
Skempton, A. W.   1978–79   *Engineering in the Port of London 1789–1808*
                                                Transactions of the Newcomen Society, VOL 50, pp. 87–108
Skempton, A. W.   1981–82   *Engineering in the Port of London 1808–1834,*
                                                Transactions of the Newcomen Society, VOL 53, pp. 73–96
Smithers, Henry   1825   *Liverpool, its Commerce, Statistics and Institutions,*
                                                Liverpool
Stephenson, R. A.   1955   *The Development of the Liverpool Dock System,*
                                                Transactions of Liverpool Nautical Research Society, VOLS 7–9, pp. 61–76

Stewart-Brown, R.	1932	*Liverpool Ships in the Eighteenth Century*, London
Stewart-Brown, R.	1930	*The Pool of Liverpool*, Transactions of the Historic Society of Lancashire and Cheshire, VOL 82, pp. 88–135
Taplin, E. L.	1974	*Liverpool Dockers and Seamen 1870–1890* Hull University Press
Tomlinson, V. I.	1061	*Early Warehouses on Manchester Waterways*, Transactions of the Lancashire and Cheshire Antiquarian Society, pp. 129–151
Touzeau, James	1910	*The Rise and Progress of Liverpool*, 2 VOLS, Liverpool
Troughton, T.	1810	*History of Liverpool*, Liverpool
Wardle, A. C.	1942	*The Opening of Liverpool's First Dock*, Transactions of the Historic Society of Lancashire and Cheshire, VOL 93, pp. 128–131
Williams, Gomer	1897	*History of the Liverpool Privateers* Liverpool
Williamson, F.	1936	*George Sorocold of Derby*, Journal of the Derbyshire Archaeological and Natural History Society, VOL 10 (new series), pp. 43–93
Wilson, T. R.	1930	*The Effect of Growth in Size of Cargo Ships on Docks and their Equipment, with especial reference to Liverpool Docks*, Transactions of the Institution of Naval Architects, VOL LXXII, pp. 292–302

Index

References to left and right columns of the text are respectively identified by the letters 'a' and 'b' after the page numbers.

gate keepers' houses, huts, 155b, 157a
gate piers, 58b, 157a
General Manager & Secretary, 28b
George's Basin, 10a
Georges Docks, 3b, 9b, 12a, 19b, 27–30, 37a,
    83b, 96a, 97a, 103b, 104b, 108ab, 113a,
    140b, 163b, 164a
George's Dock Tunnel, 28a
Gilbert, John, 31a
Gladstone dock system, 13b, 14a, 114b
Gladstone Graving Dock, 100a
Glasgow, 178a, 179a
Glasson Dock, 96b
Glynn, John & Son, 29a
Goliath cranes, 70b
Goree, 22b
Goree Piazzas, 155a
    warehouses, 27ab, 28, 97a, 131b, 139b,
    140ab, 155a
Gospel Oak Ironworks, 50b, 51a
grain trade, 31b, 32b, 34b, 40a, 71a, 84b
Grand Junction Railway, 7a
graving docks, 19ab, 21b, 23a, 40a, 42ab, 62a,
    70a, 118a, 119a, 171–172
Grayson, Edward, 25a
Grayson, H & C, 50a, 63b
Great Britain, 40a
Greathead, James Henry, 167b
Great Western Railway, 7a, 34b, 36a, 80a
Great Western shed, 32a, 136
Green, E & Sons, 120b
Greenland, 12a
Grimsby Dock, 123a
Grindrod, Timothy, 27b
Grocers' Warehouse, Manchester, 31b
Grundy, 96a
Guadeloupe, 55b
Guernsey, 99b
Guest & Co., 92a
Guinness, 26a
Gwynne, J & H, 118b, 120a

Hague, John, 54b
Haigh Foundry, 24a, 50b, 164a, 168a
Haighton, Edmund 37a
Halifax (Nova Scotia), 178a
Hall Lane, 40b
Hanover Square, London, 55a
Hanover Street, 17b
Harbour Master, 37a, 82b
Hardwick, Philip, 50a, 52a, 57b, 159, 160
Harrington Basin, 29b
Harrington Dock, 7b, 32b, 44a, 67–73, 99b,
    125a, 127a, 139a
    Co, 67a
    gates, 126ab
    locks, 70a
    transit sheds, 93b, 139a
Harrison, Thomas & John, 55b, 70b
Harrow School, 100a
Hartley, Bernard, 97b, 99a

Hartley, Jesse, 10a, 12ab, 21b, 27b, 32b, 49b,
    50ab, 51b, 52a, 54b, 57a, 57ab, 95a,
    97b–99a, 104, 106a, 108a, 114b, 121b,
    133a, 136ab, 139b, 146b, 152ab, 155ab,
    157ab, 158a, 159, 160, 161a, 163b, 164a,
    165a
Hartley, John, 95a, 99ab
Haselden, 50b
Hastings, 25a
Havre, Le, 48a
Haydock coal, 71b
Hazledine, William, 164a
Head Wrightson Teesdale Ltd, 62b
Hennebique, 47b
Herculaneum Dock, 10b, 12b, 61–66, 106b,
    111b, 117b, 118a, 120a, 126ab, 127b,
    166ab
    Co, 61a
    Master, 66a
    gates, 115ab
    Graving Docks, 115ab, 118b
    —Harrington passage, 127a
    hydraulic power centre, 60a, 125a
    Pottery, 44a, 61a
    Pottery Co, 61a
    river entrance, 59b, 115ab, 120ab, 10b
    superintendent's house, 158, 161a
Hewitt, Peter & Co., 31b
Heyes, Henry, 82a
Hibernia, 47b
Hill Street, 43b
Hodgson, 62b
Holland, King of, 178c
Holme, S & J, 50b
Holt, Alfred & Co., 14b, 70b
Holyhead, 99b
Hope, John, 27a
Hopps, A & Sons, 64a
Horsfall Road, 69b
Howland Dock/Rotherhithe, 3b, 19a
Howston, R. P., 70b
Hoylake lighthouse, 82b
Hughes, John, 104b
    Thomas, 70b
Hull, Kingston upon, 96ab, 99a, 163b
Hull Dock Co, 163b
Humble, 50a
Hurst Street, 23a
Huskisson Dock, 12a, 13a, 73b
Hutchinson, William, 83b
Hydraulic Engineering Co., 70a, 164b, 126a,
    127a
hydraulic machinery, 121–128

impounding of water, 119–120
India, 40b, 55b, 71ab
Inmans, 7a
Inner Ring Road, 24b
Ireland, 26a, 40b, 56b, 97b, 178a
    National Library of, 97b
Irish & Mersey Co, 40b

Ironmonger Lane, 165a
Irwell, river, 12a, 35a
Irwell Street, 35b, 36b
Ismays, 7a
Italy, 6a, 29a

Jackson's Tide Mill, 43a
James Munroe, 14b
James Street, 27a
Jessop, Dance & Walker, 96b
Jessop, William, 9b, 23b, 37b, 81b, 96b
jiggers, 52b, 121a, 122ab, 125b, 126ab
John, 92a
Johnson & Murray, 54a
Johnson, Sir Thomas, 19a, 22a
Jones, Joseph, 27b
    Richard, 82a
    Thomas, 82a
Juggler Street, 18a

Keays, E. C. & J., 69b
Kerosene Co., 64a
Kershaw, Nat, 39a
Kilkeel, 26a
Kilmarnock, 166b
King's Branch Docks, 39a, 59a
King's Dock, 37–40, 9a, 10b, 12ab, 32b, 43a,
    57ab, 59a, 96a, 97a, 100a, 103b, 113a,
    139a, 163b, 165a, 177a
    tobacco warehouse, 12a, 145ab, 155a, 178b
    transit sheds, 125b, 132a, 133, 135a
'Kings Pipe', 39b
King Street, 18a
King's warehouse, 22b
King William's College, 99a
Kirkcudbrightshire, 58a
Kirkdale, 176b
Kirkmabreck, 58a, 87b, 107b
Kohl, J. G., 176–179

Laird, John, 61a
Lamb, E. B., 155b
Lancashire, 3a, 6b, 71a; boilers, 120b
Lancashire & Yorkshire Railway, 7a, 12b, 67b,
    166a
Lancaster, 96a, 176c
Langton Dock, 9a, 10b, 13b, 167b
    river entrance, 13a
Lansing Road Craft, 70b
Larrinaga & Co, 46b
Laurel, 178b
Leasowe lighthouse, 82b
Leeds and Liverpool Canal, 6b, 163a
Leighton, Leopold, 100b
Lete & Sons, 72b
Lever Bros, 40b
Limerick Steamship Co., 40b
Lisbon, 26a, 29a
Lismore Castle, 97b
Littlehampton Harbour, 97b

Ogden & Barnes, 127a
Ogden, W. H., 51a
oil trade, 64–66
Okill, John, 25a
Olau Knud, 70a
Old Church Yard, 30a
Old Dock, The, 3b, 6a, 9b, 12a, 17a, 19–22,
    23ab, 39b, 41a, 43a, 97a, 103a, 113b, 116a,
    163a
Old Dock Sill (ODS), xiib, 22a, 41a, 62b, 68ab,
    106a
Old Haymarket, 17b
Old Ropery Theatre, 95b
Oporto, 29a
Orell, John, 50b
Orford Street, 163b

Pacific Steam Navigation Co., 34b
Palm Line, 40b, 46a
Paradise Street, 17b
Parkhill, 64b, 65b, 66b
Park Lane, 12a
Park Street, 70a
Parkinson, Thomas, 82a
Parliament Street, 67a
Parr, 26a
Parthia, 68b
Peterson Zachonic & Co, 72b
Pearson & Knowles, 69b
Pearson, Samuel, 25a
Pembroke, 179a
Penney, Ellenor, 97b
Perry, John, 27b
Persia, 179c
Phillip, W. L., 45b
Phoenix Foundry, 16
Pickering, Robert, 82a
Picton, J. A., 22b, 35a, 98a, 155b
Piel Island, 107b
Pier Head, 28a, 93b, 117b, 168a
pier masters, 26b, 45a, 83b, 84a, 161b
piling technology, 103–112
Pilotage buildings, 42a, 160, 161a
pitch boilers, 16a, 42b
Plate, river, 46a, 56b
Pluckington Bank, 10b, 13a, 37b, 40b, 47b,
    117b, 118a
Plymouth, 3b
Pontefract, 97b
Pool Bridge, 6b
Pool, The, 3a, 6b, 8, 17–18, 19b, 22a
port development, 9–14
Porter, Adrian B, 100b
Porter, William & Sons, 72b
Portland stone, 103b
Port of Liverpool building, 28a, 77, 93
Portsmouth, 3b
Port Sunlight, 40b
Portugal, 48a
Potter, William, 61a
Potteries, the, 33b

pottery trade, 33b, 61a
pozzolana, 103b
Price, Samuel, 84a
Priestley, J. B., xib
Prince's Dock, 12b, 43a, 87a, 88b, 97a, 113b,
    164a, 177a, 177c, 178b
Prince's Landing Stage, 47b
Principal Clerk, 94a
    Draughtsman, 94a
Puerto Rico, 48a
pumps, 118–120

Queen Anne Street, 43b
    style, 161b
Queen's Basin, 113a
Queen's Branch Docks, 39a
Queen's Dock, 9a, 10b, 37–40, 43a, 57a, 96b,
    97a, 100a, 103b, 118a, 124a, 125a, 138b,
    139c, 163b, 165b, 177a
Queen's Graving Dock(s), 115b, 118ab
Queen's Half-tide Dock, 113b, 127a
Queen's transit sheds, 125b, 134

railways, dock, 12b, 27a, 40a, 57a, 93a, 164–166
    overhead, 167–168
Rathbone, 50a
    James, 25a
Rawlinson, Robert, 106a
Rayner, H. & Co., 72b
Remuera, 14b
Rendel, J. M., 7b, 99a
Rennie, John, 21b, 27b, 30a, 37b, 43b, 57a,
    81b, 97a, 103b, 163b
Rickman, Thomas, 132b
Rideout, E. H., 22b
Ripley, Thomas, 22b
Riverside Cold Storage & Ice Co., 56b
River Craft Dock, 38a
roads and bridges, 163–164
Robinson, Thos & Son, 93a
Rock lighthouse, 179b
Roe, Charles, 61a, 67a
Rolls & Brown, 93a
Rotherhithe, 3b, 95a
Rowson, Mr., 50b
Royal Liver Building, 28a
Royal Naval Reserve, 26b
Royal Seaforth Dock, 13b, 14ab
Runcorn, 41b, 61b, 96b, 103b
Russia, 179c

St. George's church, 95b
St. Helens, 26a, 95b
St. Helens Canal, 26a, 27a
St. Helens & Runcorn Gap Railway, 7a, 66a
St. James' Mount, 19b
St. Katherine's Dock, London, 49b, 50a, 52b,
    160b
St. Luke's church, 97a
St. Michael le Hamlet, 132b
St. Paul's church, Toxteth, 132b

St. Phillip's Head, 26b
Salford, Hundred of, 97b
Salisbury Dock, 126b
salt trade, 25a, 26a, 71b
Salthouse Dock, 23–26, 3b, 9b, 19b, 50a, 55b, 81a,
    83b, 87a, 95a, 103b, 137, 139b, 163b, 177b
Salthouse—Canning passage, 164b
Salthouse—Wapping passage, 115a
Salthouse Lane, 23a, 163b
Sampson, Moor & Co., 69a
Sandon Dock 5, 13a, 61b, 167b
Sandon Graving Docks, 119a
Sandon Half-tide Dock, 10a
Saner, John, D. J., 100b
Sankey Brook Navigation, 6b, 26a
    Canal, 6b, 95b
San Lorenzo, 60b
Sarra Tintore, 48a
Scoresby, William, 40a
Scotland, 26a
Seaforth Dock, 81a
Seaforth grain terminal, 46b
Seaforth Sands, 167b
Sea Mills, 6a
Second World War, 13b, 56b, 60a, 66b, 155a
Secretary to the Docks Trustees, 82a
    to the Mersey Dock and Harbour Board, 82b
Sefton, Earl of, 67a
Sefton Street, 44a, 67b, 69b, 166a
Semac sack-filling machine, 70b
Shannon, river, 99b
Shaw Enquiry, 1920, 86a
sheds, 131–153
ships, names of, *See Acadia, Acanthus,*
    Agamemnon, Alert, America, Aquitania,
    Areadia, Arcaty, Astronomer, Britannia,
    Caledonia, Caroline, Columbia, Crown and
    Anchor, Eem, Eglantine, Elizabeth, Great
    Britain, Hastings, Hodgson, James Munroe,
    John, Laurel, Marco Polo, Novelist, Oak,
    Olau Knud, Parthia, Remuera, San
    Lorenzo, The Brothers, Vigilant
ship building, 24b, 25a, 46a; repair, 42ab, 47b
Sherwood's map, 87a
Shotton, 71a
Shropshire Union Canal, 35b
Shropshire Union Canal & Railway Co., 36a
Sicily, 29a
Simpson, William, 84b
slave trade, 6a, 25a
Sloyne, the, 19a
sluices and culverts, 116a–118a
Smeaton, John, 103b
Smith, Mr., 3a
Solicitor to the Mersey Dock and Harbour
    Board, 82b
Solicitor to the Dock Trustees, 164b
Sorocold, George, 19a
South Dock, 23a
Southern Works Act, 1898, 38ab, 44a, 47a, 56a,
    70a, 93b, 106a, 139a